Y0-BCQ-717

This book is intended for the specialist in biology, biochemistry and biophysics, to provide information on photoreactions in fields with which he is not familiar, and to introduce students, mainly of graduate level, to photobiology.

After discussing the general basic processes, of a physical, chemical and biological nature, the photoreactions of the major photobiological phenomena are considered up to the formation of the "end product" which is fed into the subsequent "dark chain". In this way, the book is of a fundamental and comparative character. For each field, literature enabling ready access to the entire field is cited.

PRIMARY PHOTOPROCESSES IN BIOLOGY

University of Pittsburgh
Bradford Campus Library

12.95

PRIMARY PHOTOPROCESSES IN BIOLOGY

E HBC

J. B. THOMAS
Professor of Biophysics
State University of Utrecht, The Netherlands

9/29/69

1965
NORTH-HOLLAND PUBLISHING COMPANY – AMSTERDAM
JOHN WILEY & SONS, INC. – NEW YORK
(Interscience Publishers Division)

17401

No part of this book may be reproduced in any form by print, photoprint, microfilm or any other means without written permission from the publisher

PUBLISHERS:

NORTH-HOLLAND PUBLISHING CO. – AMSTERDAM

SOLE DISTRIBUTORS FOR U.S.A. AND CANADA:

INTERSCIENCE PUBLISHERS, a division of

JOHN WILEY & SONS, INC. – NEW YORK

PRINTED IN THE NETHERLANDS

Preface

The natures of the various photophenomena in life diverge widely. Due to this fact, the study of these processes has developed along lines which differ considerably between each of the biological photoreactions. All of them start with the same act, namely light absorption. Where then, does the divergency of the subsequent processes enter the picture, and why? When considering such problems an attempt must be made to counterbalance the draw-back of specialization, unavoidable in the various fields of photobiology, and involves the risk of overlooking information on related phenomena. This book aims at a general view of the biological photoprocesses. It does so by discussing the physical, chemical, and biological basic processes in the first part of the book. In the second part, individual consideration is made of the primary photoreactions of several light-dependent life processes, up to the formation of products functioning as initial reactants in the chain of chemical "dark" reactions. The latter reactions are not treated here since they differ from each other too much to render a comparison meaningful. As a consequence, the selection of cited papers deviates from that needed for a comprehensive, overall review of the various topics. It is emphatically stated that the lack of discussion of a paper does not in the least mean to say that such a paper is considered of minor importance. It is only felt that such a study is of interest with regard to a particular field rather than a comparison of the various photoreactions. However, an attempt will be made to cite the literature in such a way that the various fields are rendered readily accessible. This may also serve the purpose of introducing students who are interested in photobiology into the many enchanting aspects of this science.

Selecting literature in a consistent manner is a rather difficult task, particularly in studies in unfamiliar fields. Therefore the author is greatly obliged to specialists on such topics for their indispensable comments, and it is a pleasure to express his sincere gratitude to them here. Professor J. A. Smit and Dr. J. C. Goedheer, Professor V. V. Koningsberger, Professor M. A. Bouman, Dr. P. Halldal, Dr. O. H. Blaauw and Dr. G. Blaauw-Jansen, Professor R. van der Veen and Professor J. C. van de Kamer, and Dr. W. Terpstra critisized and discussed the chapters on physics, chemistry, vision, phototaxis, phototropism, photomorphogenesis, and bioluminescence respectively. Thanks are also due to Dr. D. C. Fork, Dr. P. G. W. J. van Oordt, Dr. C. Bril, Mr. W. Verwer and Ir. M. Sangster for reading parts of the manuscript, and to Miss M. E. Bitter for the type-writing. The author wishes to thank his wife for assistance in checking both manuscript and proofs.

Utrecht,
April 1964

J. B. Thomas

Contents

PART 2. THE BIOLOGICAL PHOTOPHENOMENA

Introduction

Light enters into life in many ways. Light means energy; organic life needs energy in order to maintain itself. It needs energy for driving the complex entity which we call the organism, for growth, multiplication, working, and fighting the increase of entropy. In one sense, this need for energy makes the difference between a zoo and a museum of natural history.

An organism does not necessarily have to convert light to a suitable form of energy by itself. Actually, this task is confined to chlorophyll containing plants and some coloured bacteria. The complex mechanism of this energy conversion is called photosynthesis. Organisms which are lacking the ability to perform this process obtain the required energy by feeding themselves with compounds ultimately derived from the photosynthesizing creatures. There is only a single exception; a group of bacteria is able to thrive using the free energy of labile inorganic systems. Since these so-called "chemo-autotrophic" bacteria do not use light energy for this purpose, they will be left out of further consideration here.

However, light energy fixed by photosynthesis does not entirely cover the energy requirement of various species. To mention a few examples, many plants need energy for transport of their seeds and for this purpose they use wind. Air currents, in their turn, are brought about by solar energy. Wind power is also used by the bird of prey to stay aloft, his wings motionless while looking for a victim. Turtles have their eggs hatched by solar heat radiation. Thermal energy from their environment is required by all cold-blooded animals. Therefore grass-hopper swarms can be fought just after sunrise, before the insects are able to absorb sufficient heat to become mobile.

Mankind, however, consumes much more energy than is necessary for sustaining life. It is used for "luxury" such as industry, transportation, excessive heating and so on. In order to cope with this situation, solar energy is caught in some indirect manner, for example *via* electric generators operated by water power. The availability of this kind of energy requires precipitation as rain, snow or hail at altitudes sufficiently high above sea level. A prerequisite for precipitation is evaporation, and solar energy enters here. Consequently, the radiation conversion can be separated in time and space from the employment of the energy by living organisms. In these cases the energy has been converted from contemporary sunshine. However, most factories and plants are fuel-powered. This means that they use coal, oil or gas which represent solar energy fixed by photosynthesis in by-gone times.

Sooner or later, the energy absorbed by the living world is released as heat, and as such is dissipated into the universe. It cannot be re-used for the synthetic processes in life and so a continuous supply from outside is required to prevent disturbance of the energy balance on earth. This supply is provided by the sun. At the outer layers of the atmosphere, the energy of the incident sun radiation amounts to 1.25×10^{24} cal/annum. About 10% is absorbed by plant pigments (RABINOWITCH [1945]), and 3×10^{21} calories are fixed by photosynthesis annually.

Light energy reaches the earth surface from the moon and the stars as well. The intensity of the moonlight, which of course is reflected sunlight, at this surface is such that about 3×10^{17} cal/annum are fixed by plant pigments. This value is 10^{-4} times smaller than the estimated number of calories stored by photosynthesis annually. It is clear that our next important celestial light source cannot play a significant role in photosynthesis and is of no energetic interest to life.

This conclusion does not mean that the light from moon and stars is of no interest to living creatures. For instance, as VAN DER LEK [1962] stated, the melanophores of the tailfin of the *Xenopus* larva responds to light intensities of about 10^{-2} ergs.cm^{-2} sec.$^{-1}$, or about 20 times weaker than that of full moonlight. Some crustaceans use moonlight as a means for orientation (PARDI and PAPI [1961]). The sexual reproduction of certain organisms is controlled by the intensity of moonlight (CASPERS [1951]). According to KINCAID [1935], a 15 minute exposure to full moonlight stimulates the germination of tobacco seeds.

The illumination of the earth surface by starlight is still much weaker than that by moonlight. Nevertheless this light plays an important role in the life of migratory birds and fishes as they use it for navigation purposes (*cf.* SAUER [1957]).

However not all of the light involved in biology is of astronomical origin. Some of it is emitted by terrestrial sources. This is true of radiation emitted by living organisms themselves, such as deepsea fishes, fireflies, certain crustaceans, fungi, bacteria and green plant tissues. Though the mechanisms may vary considerably in different species, this kind of light production is commonly designated bioluminescence. Whether the bioluminescence of bacteria and fungi has a functional meaning or is only a by-product of metabolic processes is as yet completely unknown. The very weak long-lived luminescence of chlorophyll-containing cells upon illumination can hardly be considered to be of any biological importance. In the case of some animals, however, it is known that emission and absorption of bioluminescence can function as means of recognition and sex attraction.

Apart from serving the purpose of supplying energy for maintaining life, light is also required for quite different phenomena, such as vision and formative effects. By way of drastic simplification, two groups of biological photophenomena can be distinguished:

(1) processes of a prevailing energetic character. These initiate one or more reactions ultimately yielding a high-energy end-product which is directly related to the number of light quanta absorbed. This product, as such, is of importance to the organism.

(2) processes of a predominantly cybernetic character. In these processes the photoproducts control chain reactions – either by trigger reactions or as photocatalysts – which affect or determine the response of the organism to its environment.

As biological photophenomena, many of these two groups of processes have at least two features in common: (1) light absorption, and (2) conversion of the absorbed light into a different kind of energy, which in some way or another affects the living organism. In most cases, this secondary energy sets a sequence of chemical reactions going. The over-all process therefore consists of both physical and chemical phenomena. Understanding of the process depends on insight into the latter phenomena as well as the way they are linked together. The natures of the purely chemical reactions certainly diverge widely for the various photoprocesses. In the following discussions of these processes, the most profitable approach is by first considering their common base and the resulting reaction products. A survey of what is known about the various pigments and photoreceptor structures will be given, and finally the mechanisms of many of the biological photoprocesses will be dealt with as far as possible on a comparative basis.

PART 1

The basic processes

1

Physical processes

1 *Light absorption and its direct consequence*

Light absorption consists of uptake of electromagnetic radiation energy by matter. The increase of the energy content of matter upon the capture of a quantum – in our case a light quantum or photon – is coupled with a change of the nuclear-electronic equilibrium. Consequently, radiation absorption results in a transition from one energy state of a material particle to another. Every particle absorbs somewhere on the wavelength scale. However it never absorbs at all wavelengths; absorption of quanta depends strictly on their energy content and therefore on wavelength. This phenomenon is a consequence of the occurrence of the discrete energy states which may be occupied by the particle. The energy content of a radiation quantum amounts to $E = h\nu$, where E means energy, ν the frequency of the radiation, and h Planck's constant. Radiation absorption is possible only if E equals the energy difference between two of the states in which the particle can occur. However, according to both experimentally and theoretically deduced "selection rules", not all transitions are "allowed"; some of them are "forbidden" in the sense of radiation processes.

For atoms, absorption is a relatively simple phenomenon. If the phenomenon of photoionization and photodissociation is left out of consideration for the present, it can be stated that a radiation quantum of a given frequency can lift an electron to a higher energy level. This frequency exactly equals the difference between the energies of the state to which the electron is raised (excited state) and the lowest energy level (ground state) divided by Planck's constant h. Since $\nu = c/\lambda$, where c stands for the velocity of light and λ for wavelength, it follows that light of only a single wavelength can be absorbed for any electronic transition and thus a single absorption *line* will be observed.

In the case of molecules however, things are much more complicated.

Polyatomic molecules are quite large in comparison with atoms. They can no longer be considered as extremely small rigid particles. Rotation of the molecule as well as vibration of the nuclei are to be taken into account, and the energies of these two phenomena are also quantified. Therefore energies due to rotation and vibration are added to the energies of the electronic transitions as they occur in atoms. As a

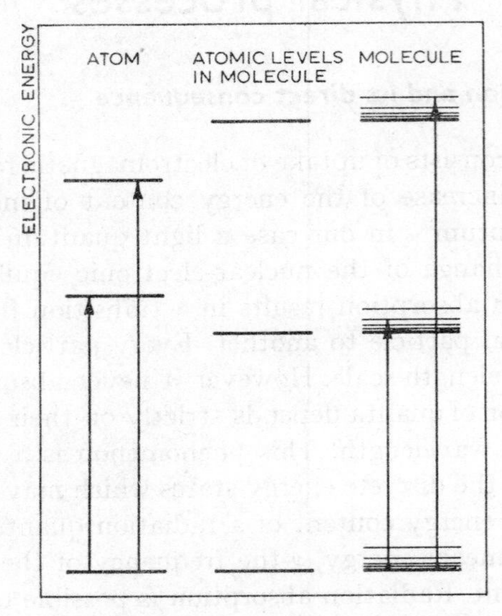

Fig. 1. Comparison of electronic energy states in atoms and molecules

consequence, the energy per photon of the absorbed light need no longer be exactly the same as that for each single electronic transition. It may vary stepwise as far as permitted by the additional energy of vibration and rotation.In other words, no absorption *lines* are observed in polyatomic molecules but the lines are broadened into absorption *bands*. This is demonstrated in fig. 1.

At the left-hand side of the figure, three electronic energy states of a hypothetical atom are depicted. In this particular case two electronic transitions, represented by arrows, are possible upon absorption of adequate quanta. If this atom is supposed to be part of a molecule, the electronic energy levels are changed, for example as shown in the middle of the diagram. This effect is due to interactions between the atom and fellow-constituents of the molecule. The way in which they are changed in the figure is not meant to suggest any particular situation; it is purely that they are unlike those in the free atom. However in the molecule, no transitions occur between the energy levels in the middle of the figure, since quantified vibrational and rotational energy levels are always added as shown at the right-hand side of the figure. The "atomic" levels therefore give rise to families of levels in the molecule, and a single transition in the atom is replaced by a family of transitions.

The additional energies responsible for broadening the absorption lines of molecules originate from the absorption act itself. Since the electronic configuration is changed by an absorbed quantum, the electrostatic field both inside and outside the molecule is also altered. Therefore the nuclei try to readjust themselves in order to attain a new electrostatically balanced position. They do not actually occupy this position, but start vibrating around it in a quantified manner. In this way they give rise to the energies additional to that of the purely electronic transitions. Therefore part of the energy of an absorbed quantum is lost in these additional motions and, for this reason, a 100% efficiency of conversion of the quantum energy in the photochemical processes is not likely to occur.

Since atomic nuclei are much heavier than electrons, the former move considerably slower than the latter. This means that an electron is able to jump to a higher energy level in a period of about 10^{-15} sec. which is too short for the nuclei to move appreciably, and so an electronic transition takes place without effectual change in the nuclear position. This phenomenon is known as the Franck-Condon principle. In other words, the most probable transitions take place so that there is a minimum change of the internuclear distances in the absorbing molecule.

As a molecule vibrates more or less according to an harmonic form, the swinging nuclei will be at their extreme positions, where their motion is slowest, most of the time. Hence the electronic transitions are most likely to occur while the internuclear distances are extreme.

The Franck-Condon principle provides an explanation of the relative intensities of the absorption bands in molecular spectra. For the discussion of this subject in a classical manner, a diatomic molecule will be considered for simplicity's sake. In an undisturbed molecule, the atomic nuclei would maintain a certain distance between themselves. This distance is correlated with the lowest potential energy content of the molecule. The nuclei, however, do not actually occupy such a position but this functions as a centre of gravity for their motion. Thus the distance between the two nuclei varies, and the potential energy content of the molecule will vary with the degree of displacement.

In fig. 2 the potential energy (E) of a diatomic molecule is plotted

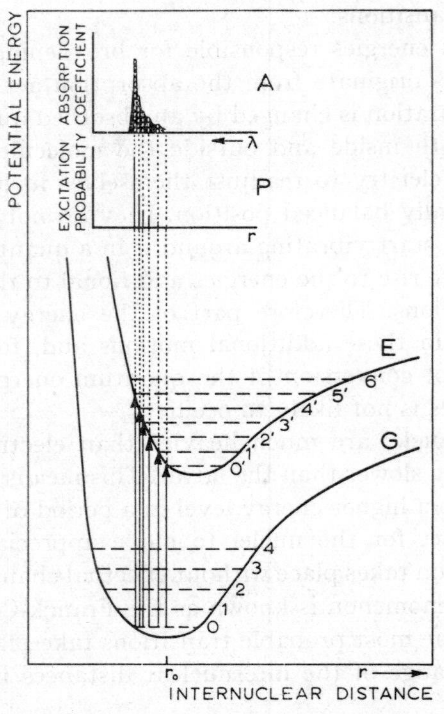

Fig. 2. Potential energy diagram and its relation to the structure of an absorption band

versus the internuclear distance (r). Suppose that one of the nuclei is fixed at the ordinate. Then the other nucleus vibrates around a lowest-energy equilibrium position. At this position, the internuclear distance is r_0, and the vibrational amplitude and the energy content will be represented by the length and the distance from the abscissa of the lowest interrupted line (0) respectively. At higher energy contents of the molecule, for example provoked by raising the temperature, the vibrational amplitude of the nuclei will increase in a quantified manner as indicated by the next interrupted line (1). In this way it is possible for the vibrating nuclei to occupy a number of energy levels. If the extremes of all these levels are connected, a potential energy curve for the ground state of the molecule (G) is obtained. If the molecule is now excited by the absorption of a quantum which results in an electronic transition to a higher energy state, the equilibrium position of the nuclei will be only slightly changed as indicated above. By the same reasoning, a potential energy curve can be drawn for the electronically excited molecule at a larger distance from the abscissa than that for the ground state, as shown by (E). Since, as mentioned earlier, the internuclear distance will be minimal or maximal most of the time, the major part of the light quanta are absorbed while the nuclei are at these positions. As the electrons move much faster than the nuclei do (Franck-Condon principle), the energy level resulting from the electronic transition should correspond with the same internuclear distance in the ground-state molecule. In the figure, this is possible according to the vertical arrow at the left side. The remaining arrows indicate less probable excitations. As previously stated, the more that the swinging nuclei in the ground-state molecule are removed from their extreme positions the smaller the chance that these excitations will occur. The probability of the various excitations, that is the relative number of quanta absorbed per unit time, is indicated in diagram P. Provided no other factor plays a role, this diagram should represent the absorption spectrum. However rotational energy broadens the individual lines in such a way that an "absorption spectrum" results as shown in diagram A.

This consideration of the Franck-Condon principle only deals with the lowest vibrational energy level of the ground state. This level is by far the most populated one. However, at room temperature at least the next level above this should be considered. Therefore the complete absorption spectrum deduced from the data in the figure looks more complex than the one shown here, and will show minor absorption bands at the short-wave side of the absorption maximum.

For polyatomic molecules, things are even more complex, but proceed essentially along the same lines. The Franck-Condon principle also applies in these cases. A complicating factor is that in polyatomic molecules the vibrational and rotational levels are closely packed and also quite a number of electronic levels occur with smaller energy differences between them than in the case of diatomic molecules.

Under certain circumstances these properties may allow radiationless transitions between the excited states and the ground state. If this situation prevails, the absorbed energy fails to excite the molecule to a higher electronic energy state, even though it would be sufficient to do so in a case of a molecule with more pronounced separation of the levels. The only result of such an excitation may be an increase in vibrational and rotational energies of the ground state. In this way the excitation energy becomes "degraded" to heat.

This discussion is applicable to pigments in true solution. However, within living cells pigments often occur in complexes with carrier molecules, such as lipoproteins. The pigment-carrier bond may affect the energy levels of the pigment molecule so much that the absorption bands are shifted up to a thousand Ångstrom units to the long wavelength side of their position in the molecules in the monomolecularly dispersed state. In addition, these bonds may cause the bands to become complex by the absorptions due to a number of different pigment-carrier aggregates, each of them with absorption maxima located so close to the others that overlap occurs between the individual bands. These additional maxima are therefore of quite a different origin than the discussed vibrational bands. Moreover pigment molecules may aggregate with each other. Such aggregates may show the same effects as result from pigment-carrier complex formation.

2 *The formation of excited electronic states*

If an electron is raised to a higher energy level, it will try to release its excess energy and regain its ground state as soon as possible. The average time after which an electron "tumbles down" depends upon whether the electron has been raised to the lowest excitation level or to a higher one.

In fig. 3, three electronic excitation levels, E_1, E_2, E_3, with additional vibration levels are shown. In biological pigments such as chlorophyll, the probability of an excited electron falling back is much higher between E_3, E_2 and E_1 than between E_1 and the ground state, G. This means that it stays in the excited states E_3 and E_2 only for a very short period, about 10^{-12} sec., while this period in E_1 lasts about a thousand times longer. The energy which is released at transitions from E_3 or E_2 to E_1 is dissipated as heat. On the other hand, the time lapse before the electron falls back to its ground level from E_1 is sufficiently long to enable the release of this excitation energy also in the form of light (fluorescence) or chemical energy. Consequently, provided no complications occur, the lowest excitation level is of exclusive interest with regard to photochemistry and emission of fluorescence. This implies that these processes depend on the number of quanta absorbed, but not on the energy content of the quanta.

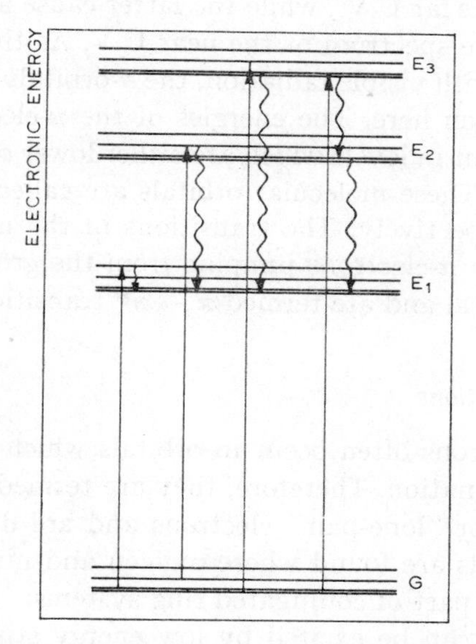

Fig. 3. Formation of excited states in molecules. G: ground state. E_1, E_2, and E_3: excited states. Straight arrows: electronic excitations. Curved arrow: energy losses by internal conversion resulting in filling the lowest excitation band

While the lowest electronic excitation level is of predominant importance with regard to the phenomena under discussion, it is of interest to deal with certain very closely adjoining, possibly interacting, energy levels in this region in more detail.

2.1 $\pi \rightarrow \pi^*$ *transitions*

Expressing the electron configuration in visual terms, the electrons are considered to move in well-separated shells or orbitals. Upon excitation an electron performs a transition from its original orbital to another one corresponding to the energy gained by the excitation act. For example in the carbon atom the only transition to occur in the optical region upon photoexcitation involves an electron from the outer or p-orbital. In carbon-containing molecules, these p-electrons are partially responsible for the chemical stability by encircling, in outer orbitals, two or more nuclei. These molecular orbitals are called σ- and π-orbitals, and the electrons in them are termed σ- and π-electrons.

The σ-orbitals are of higher energy than the π-orbitals and give rise to absorptions in the far U.V., while the latter cause absorption in the visible region of the spectrum or the near U.V. As the phenomena to be discussed deal with visible radiation, the σ-orbitals will be left out of further consideration here. The energies of the π-electron orbitals in molecules may occur in levels which are either lower or higher than the original 2p-levels. These molecular orbitals are called "bonding" and "antibonding" respectively. The transitions in the molecules considered so far concern π-electrons jumping from the ground π-orbital to an excited π^*-orbital and are termed $\pi \rightarrow \pi^*$ transitions.

2.2 *n → π* transitions*

In molecules electrons often occur in orbitals which are not engaged in actual bond formation. Therefore, they are termed "non-bonding", "unshared-pair", or "lone-pair" electrons and are designated n-electrons. Such orbitals are found where oxygen and nitrogen atoms are attached to or are part of conjugated ring systems.

The n-electrons can be excited by low energy stimulation, and so raised into the lowest empty π-orbital. Such transitions are termed $n \rightarrow \pi^*$ transitions. The energy involved in this kind of transition can be quite close to that involved in the lowest $\pi \rightarrow \pi^*$ transition.

Since non-bonding electrons, principally from nitrogen, oxygen, or sulphur, are present in many of the heterocyclic compounds occurring in living cells, and because of the characteristics of the transition of these electrons to the lowest empty π-orbitals, the $n \rightarrow \pi^*$ transition is probably of primary biological importance. Therefore, some of the characteristic $n \rightarrow \pi^*$ transition properties of biological interest are enumerated below.

(1) As already mentioned, the $n \rightarrow \pi^*$ transition energy is often near to the $\pi \rightarrow \pi^*$ transition energy.

(2) $n \rightarrow \pi^*$ bands shift considerably in acid media. If only one pair of n-electrons occurs in a molecule, this shift to shorter wavelengths

can be large enough to cause disappearance of the band from the visible part of the spectrum.

(3) In polar solvents such as water, the n $\rightarrow \pi^*$ transition bands of dissolved pigments or pigments in contact with such media appear at shorter wavelengths ("blue shift") than when dissolved in or in contact with non-polar media, for example, a lipoic medium. In contrast, the $\pi \rightarrow \pi^*$ transitions show a "red shift".

(4) n $\rightarrow \pi^*$ transitions may quench fluorescence. In many molecules absence of fluorescence results from the presence of such transitions.

(5) On an n $\rightarrow \pi^*$ transition one electron is left behind in the n-orbital. Since in this way a single electron becomes rather "isolated" from its partner, the n,π^* excited state may exhibit the character of a radical. If the excited n-electron distribution in the π^*-orbital is heterogeneous, the n,π^* state may be even of a diradical character.

(6) The molar absorption of n $\rightarrow \pi^*$ transitions is of the order of only a few per cent of that of the $\pi \rightarrow \pi^*$ transitions. This implies that the lifetime of the n,π^* excited state is considerably longer than that of the π,π^* excited state.

For detailed information and survey of literature pertaining to this subject which has been extensively studied by Kasha and co-workers, general reference should be made to the publications of KASHA [1950, 1961], PLATT [1956], REID [1957], ROBINSON [1961], and PULLMAN and PULLMAN [1963].

2.3 *The triplet state*

This state is of dual interest in this discussion. Firstly the lowest triplet level is near to the lowest excited level and secondly, it may be a long-lived state. The lifetime of an excited state, as pointed out earlier, is of considerable importance with regard to the possibility of a molecule undergoing chemical changes, and so in our case of performing photochemistry. In order to discuss the relatively long-lived metastable triplet state, it is necessary to consider the electron spin first. Since an electron "spins" while it is also a carrier of electric charge, a circular electric current is produced which in its turn produces a magnetic field. Thus an electron can be considered to be a tiny magnet. Depending on the spinning direction, the sign of the magnetic momentum or "spin" is either positive or negative. Apart from the magnetic momentum due to the electron spin, a second one results from the motion of the electron in its orbital. The number of ways in which both momenta can combine amounts to $2S + 1$, where S stands for the resultant spin of an electron pair. If in a given orbital electrons occur in pairs the electrons have opposite (antiparallel) spins. Consequently the resultant spin, S, of such a pair is zero and both types of momenta can combine only in a single way; the molecule is then in its "singlet state". At excitation, one electron of an electron pair is lifted to an excited level. If nothing else happens, the spins of the individual electrons remain unchanged. Though both of them are in different energy states, the electrons still can be considered to form a pair. The excited molecule thus remains in the singlet state. In this case, excitation has promoted a singlet-singlet transition. If for some reason the spin of the excited electron changes sign, S is no longer zero, but unity.

The combination multiplicity of both types of magnetic momenta then is triple ($2S + 1 = 3$) and the excited molecule is said to be in a "triplet state". The general relationship of singlet and triplet excited states is shown in fig. 4. Triplet levels are usually energetically somewhat lower than the corresponding singlet states (Hund's rule). As a rule, the biologically important molecules are built up of light atoms such as carbon, oxygen, hydrogen and nitrogen. Since the interaction between orbital and spin momenta is relatively weak in light atoms, the probability of changing the spin when an electron is excited is only small. Therefore the singlet-triplet transitions occur relatively infrequently in most of the compounds to be considered in biological light-stimulated processes. Consequently in these cases, triplet states are slowly populated by direct excitation but when they are, they empty slowly as well.

On the other hand, triplet states may be filled relatively easily by "internal conversion" from the corresponding excited singlet level. In other words, their lifetime is long enough to form a short-lived storage of useful energy.

If the energy difference between electronic transitions is only small, there is a considerable probability that transitions between these states can take place. This is true of the three states considered so far, namely the lowest excited singlet state, the n,π* state, and the lowest triplet state. Their mutual position will determine what kind of excitation actually takes place. As interaction of these excited states has been suggested (FRANCK [1958]) to play a role in photosynthesis, it seems

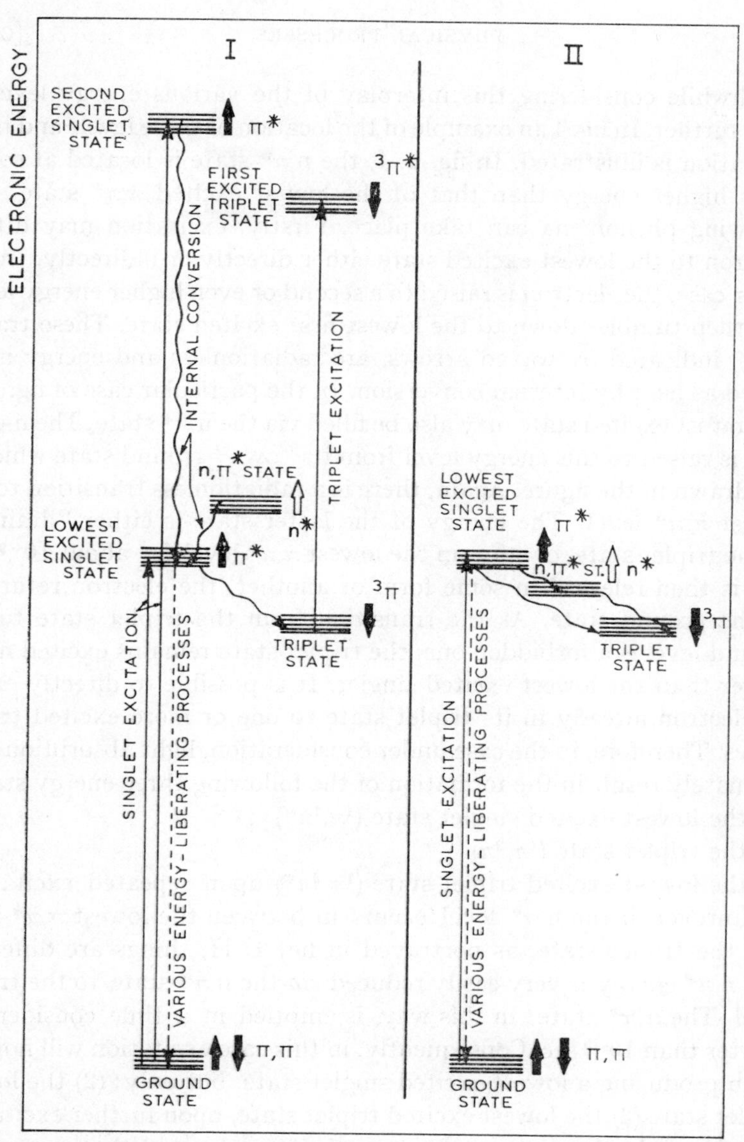

Fig. 4. Relation between singlet, triplet and n,π^* excited states. I. The n,π^* state is of higher energy than the singlet state. The energy of the former state is drained to the singlet excitation level from which the major part is freed as the electron returns to the ground state, though some may be transferred to the triplet state. II. The n,π^* state occurs in between the singlet and triplet states. The energy of the former state is drained to the triplet state where it is stored for a relatively long time, as the triplet-singlet transition is a forbidden one. Since the triplet band is also filled by part of the energy from direct singlet excitation, just as occurs in case I, total triplet excitation in case II surpasses that of case I

worthwhile considering this interplay of the various energy levels a little further. In fig. 4 an example of the location of these levels and their formation is illustrated. In fig. 4, I, the n,π^* state is located at somewhat higher energy than that of the lowest excited π,π^* state. The following phenomena can take place. Firstly, excitation may lift an electron to the lowest excited state either directly or indirectly. In the latter case, the electron is raised to a second or even higher energy level, and then tumbles down to the lowest first excited state. These transitions, indicated by waved arrows, are radiationless and energy is released as heat by internal conversion. In the particular case of fig. 4, I, the lowest excited state may also be filled via the n,π^* state. The n-electron is raised to this energy level from its "own" ground state which is not drawn in the figure. Again, there is a radiationless transition to the lowest π,π^* level. The energy of the latter state is either "drained" to the triplet state, or stays in the lowest π,π^* level for about 10^{-9} sec. and is then released in some form or another, the electron returning to the ground state. As the transition from the triplet state to the ground level is a forbidden one, the triplet state remains excited much longer than the lowest excited singlet. It is possible to directly excite an electron already in its triplet state to one or more excited triplet states. Therefore, in the case under consideration, light absorption may ultimately result in the formation of the following three energy states:

(1) the lowest excited singlet state ($^1\pi,^1\pi^*$)

(2) the triplet state ($^1\pi,^3\pi$)

(3) the lowest excited triplet state ($^1\pi,^3\pi^*$) upon repeated excitation.

However, if the n,π^* level occurs in between the lowest π,π^* level and the triplet state, as portrayed in fig. 4, II, things are different. The π,π^* energy is very easily reduced *via* the n,π^* state to the triplet level. The π,π^* state, in this way, is emptied in a time considerably shorter than 10^{-9} sec. Consequently, in this case excitation will not end up in producing a lowest excited singlet state, but only: (2) the lowest triplet state (3) the lowest excited triplet state, upon further excitation (not drawn in the picture). In general, it can be said that occurrence of an n,π^* state in between a π,π^* level and the corresponding triplet one *may* favor the filling of triplet states.

3 Conversion of energy

The excitations considered so far are supposed to lift the electrons to higher energy states, while leaving the molecules intact. A considerable part of the excitation energy is not released as heat but preserved as high-grade energy in either the lowest excited singlet level or the triplet state configuration. However excitation may also result in fragmentation of the excited species or in intramolecular rearrangement.

Various types of energy conversion are possible. These types are enumerated below.

(I) The excited molecule stays intact, and the lowest excited singlet orbital is filled. Then, after a period of about 10^{-9} sec., the electronic energy is converted to: (a) light, as fluorescence, or (b) heat, by internal conversion (vibrational and rotational energy).

(II) The excited molecule stays intact and the triplet orbital is filled. The energy may be stored for some time, and then released by:

(a) Delayed fluorescence. This kind of fluorescence is emitted if an electron is raised by vibrational quanta from the triplet state to the nearby located lowest singlet excitation level with, of course, simultaneous spin momentum reversal. Next, the electron drops to its ground state, while light is emitted. As this transition is the same as (Ia), the emission spectrum of the delayed fluorescence is identical with that of the normal fluorescence of the same molecule.

(b) Phosphorescence. This light is emitted when the forbidden direct transition from the triplet state to the ground state takes place, again with reversal of the electron spin. Since, according to Hund's rule, the triplet energy level is lower than the lowest singlet excitation level, the emitted quanta are of lower energy content than those resulting from the corresponding singlet-singlet transition. Consequently, the phosphorescence emission spectrum is located at a longer wavelength than the fluorescence spectrum of the same molecule.

(c) Heat (vibrational and rotational energy).

(III) The excited molecule stays intact and remains in the singlet state, but interacts, without collision, with a non-excited molecule. The excitation energy is released in such a way that the second molecule becomes excited, while the former one returns to its ground state. This process is known as "sensitized fluorescence" (CARIO and FRANCK [1923]).

(IV) The excited molecule stays intact and in the singlet state, but interacts with a second molecule which is in the triplet state. The "singlet energy" is released in a way that the latter molecule may become excited to a higher triplet level while the former returns to its ground state.

(V) The excited molecule stays intact, and is in either the singlet or the triplet state but collides with some other molecule. The electronic energy then may be converted to:

(a) Heat (vibrational and rotational energy *plus* collision

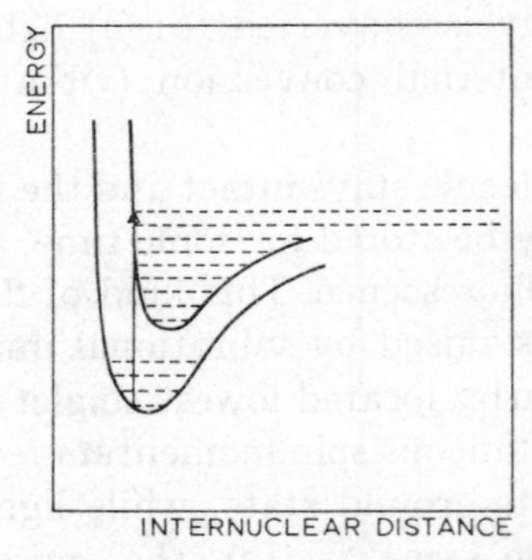

Fig. 5. Potential energy diagram illustrating an excitation resulting in dissocation

(translational) energy). Both molecules remain chemically unchanged after the encounter.

(b) Chemical energy in the form of dissociation energy, if the non-excited colliding molecule dissociates, and the resulting fragments stay apart from each other.

(VI) The excited molecule becomes changed. In this way, the excitation energy may be converted to chemical energy by:

(a) Dissociation. This process can be understood by considering potential energy curves as discussed earlier. The situation which occurs in case of spontaneous dissociation of an excited molecule is shown in this case in fig. 5. The excitation should be sufficiently energetic to raise the energy content of the diatomic molecule to such a degree that the internuclear distance starts to increase from a minimum value to infinity. This means that the nuclei become separated. The energy content of visible quanta, 40–60 kcal/einstein, is rather low compared with the energy required to rupture a chemical bond. Only in cases which entrail a particularly weak bond photodissociation occurs.

(b) Ionization. The same energy problems occur with this process. However a number of cases are known in which the excitation energy of a photon is sufficient to free an electron. The excited molecule is thus brought to an ionized state.

(c) Intramolecular rearrangement, for example of a redox type. Upon electronic excitation an electron may shift within the molecule.

(d) Intramolecular rearrangement, resulting in *cis-trans* isomerization. Electronic excitation may change a double bond into a single bond. Rotation through 180° may follow this if the twisted configuration is more stable.

(VII) The excited molecule becomes chemically changed. The excitation energy is converted to chemical energy by interaction with a colliding species.

(a) Association. The excited molecule may collide with some other non-excited molecule. These may then associate to form a complex. If the non-excited molecule is of the same species as the excited one, polymerization resulting in the formation of a dimer radical may occur.

(b) Association, coupled with dissociation of a non-excited molecule. The excited molecule may collide with a non-excited one resulting in the dissociation of the latter, one of the fragments then associates with the original excited molecule. These possibilities are represented in fig. 6.

In addition it may be remarked that in some cases the presence is required of certain compounds which do not participate in the energy conversion process proper.

4 Electronic energy transfer

An excited molecule need not necessarily convert its excitation energy into chemical energy by itself in order to drive a photochemical reaction. In the previous section it was mentioned that an excited species may excite a ground-state neighbour. This neighbour in its turn may excite a third molecule, and so on. In this way, electronic excitation

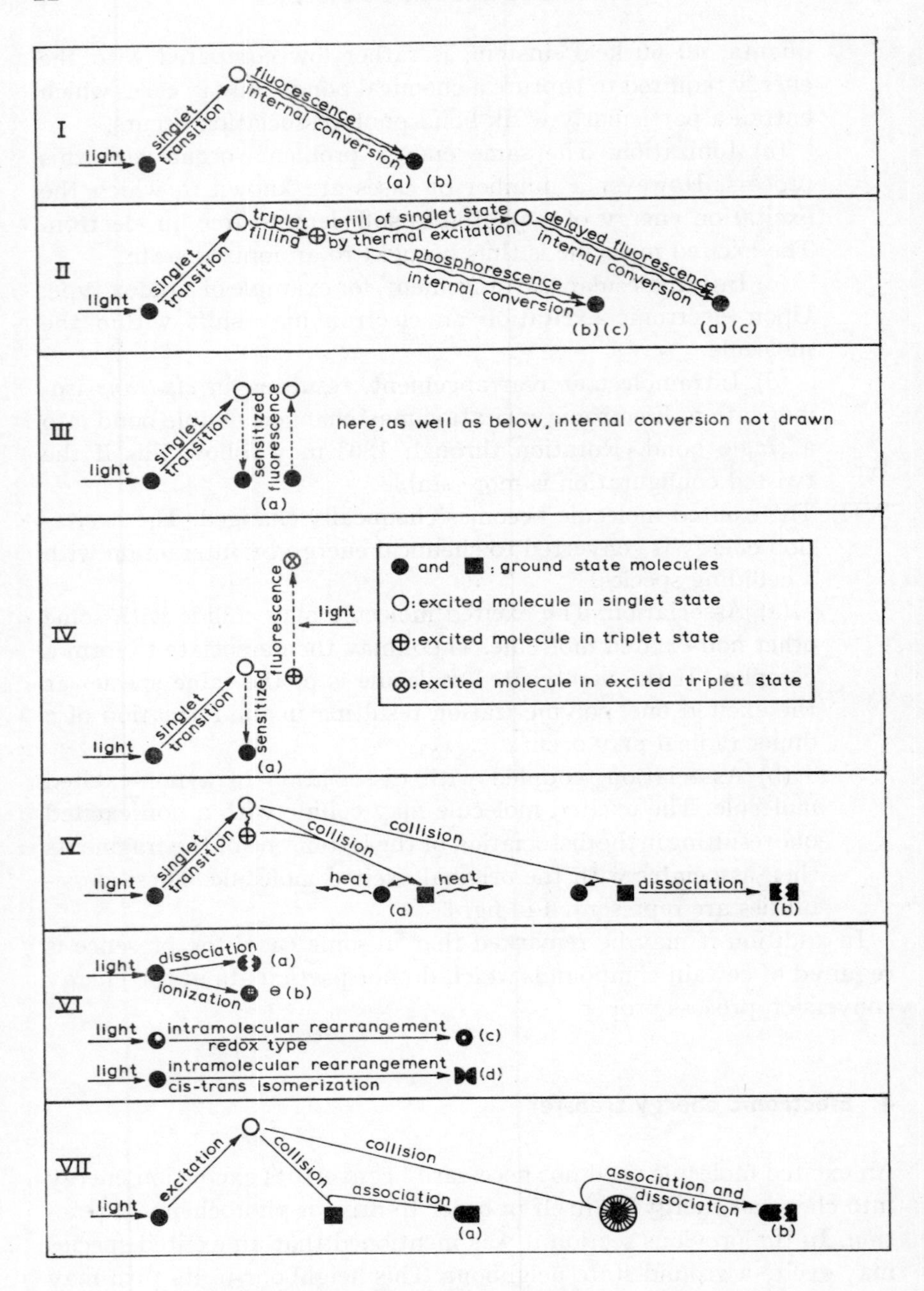

Fig. 6. The principal reactions arising from electronic excitation by light

energy may be transferred through a large number of molecules. A prerequisite for the occurrence of such an energy transfer is that the distance between the transferring molecules should not exceed a certain value and in fact they should be closely packed. Consequently, energy transfer may only take place in highly concentrated solutions. As mentioned earlier, the photopigments in living cells are bound to carrier molecules which, in their turn, are combined to form the photoreceptive structures. Therefore it may well be that properties and rules of solid-state physics also hold for these photoreceptors. It should be noted that KASHA [1959] has pointed out that both the ideas and terminology from the atomic and ionic semiconductor fields of physics should only be applied to the case of biological systems with considerable caution. In semiconductors the binding forces between the particles are strong and rather homogeneous throughout the crystal, while biological photoreceptors usually are quite heterogeneous molecular aggregates.

Basically there are two mechanisms of energy transfer taking place: (1) resonance migration, and (2) charge migration.

4.1 Resonance migration

Suppose that a pigment molecule is excited to a state from which it is able to emit fluorescence. According to the electromagnetic theory of light, this emission gives rise to a "local" vibrating electric field. The frequency of this field is the same as that of the emitted light. If a second molecule is located within the vibrating field of the first excited one and their separation is small compared with the wavelength of light, and if the frequency of the light which can be absorbed by the second molecule is identical with that of the vibrating field around the first molecule, the second molecule may then take over the energy of the first one. Thus by releasing its excitation energy, the excited molecule is able to excite a neighbouring species, provided resonance between the electric fields in question can take place. Whether this requirement is fulfilled can be ascertained by consideration of the locations of both the emission (fluorescence) spectrum of the originally excited species and the excitation (absorption) spectrum of the neighbouring molecule. It follows from what has been said about the frequencies that maximum excitation transfer occurs when there is maximum overlap of these two spectra.

Another requirement has been mentioned already, namely that the energy-receptor molecule should lie in the vibrating electric field of the energy donor. In other words, the concentration of a pigment in solution should exceed a minimum value in order that appreciable energy transfer can occur. If pigment molecules are attached to surfaces such as those of protein macromolecules, they should be located sufficiently close to each other. For example, FÖRSTER [1949] both computed and found experimentally that the distance between the centres of a trypaflavin and a rhodamin molecule in solution should be 60 Å for an energy transfer efficiency of 0.5. According to FÖRSTER [1951] this efficiency is inversely proportional to the 6th power of the intermolecular distance. LAVOREL [1957] found that the average number of transfers of a single excitation in a 0.01 M solution of fluorescein is of the order of 100.

It may be emphasized that other factors such as lifetime, absolute absorption coefficient and the orientation of the molecules relative to each other also play a significant role. These factors will not be considered here. Reference to them will be made in the relevant discussions in the following chapters.

The next case to be considered is that in which a number of pigments in adequate concentrations has been prepared. The pigments are chosen in such a way that the emission spectrum of one species overlaps the absorption spectrum of a second, and similarly those of the second and a third pigment overlap, and so on. Irradiation of this mixture with relatively energy-rich blue quanta may result in the emission of photons of lower energy content which is seen as a red fluorescence. Between each transfer act, on excitation a quantum will stay in a particular molecule for a period sufficiently long for the molecule to reach vibrational equilibrium. The energy "lost" at each step is thus dissipated as heat.

However if the transfer occurs between molecules of one and the same kind, this energy degradation does not occur. At the same time the overlap of absorption and fluorescence spectra is not as large as it may be in the case of dissimilar molecules and as a consequence, the probability that a transfer actually occurs may be smaller.

Such a resonance transfer is a "slow" energy migration. Apart from this type, a "fast" energy migration by resonance is possible which has been described by RABINOWITCH [1956, 1958]. Both cases are extremes and, in fact, a mixture of the two may occur. The difference between the systems depends on whether the duration of the stay of the excitation energy in a molecule is long or short compared with the period of intramolecular vibrations. In the first case, a coupling between electronic excitation and vibration occurs. The excitation energy makes specific "jumps" from molecule to molecule and at a given moment is located on a given molecule. Since it stays there for a time sufficient to allow vibrations of the nuclei, the Franck-Condon principle is applicable. As this principle governs the form of the absorption bands, the bands are not affected by the first kind of energy migration.

In the case of fast migration the excitation energy is already transferred before the nuclei get a chance to carry out any vibrational change. As a consequence, no particular molecule is found in a higher vibrational state. The excitation energy is no longer located at a particular molecule at any given moment but affects the total assembly of identical molecules. Therefore electronic excitation and vibrational energy are uncoupled and so the Franck-Condon principle does not hold in this case. This implies that the fast migration has considerable effect on the absorption spectrum. This phenomenon has been observed by SCHEIBE [1937a and b] with concentrated solutions of isocyanine, pinacyanol and other pigments. In these concentrated solutions micelles of linearly arranged molecules are formed. The absorption spectrum of such a suspension shows very narrow bands at the short-wavelength side of the spectrum which resemble those of a metal vapour, that is a spectrum of isolated atoms while the same molecules in a less concentrated true solution show the normal broad bands. This example is clear proof of the uncoupling of excitation energy and vibration energy in a molecular assembly.

Energy transfer by resonance, it should be emphasized, is a phenomenon entirely different from the trivial process of secondary fluorescence. In the latter process, light is emitted by a molecule, and this fluorescence is subsequently absorbed by a neighbouring species. Both phenomena depend in totally different ways on factors such as concentration.

The theory of electronic excitation energy by resonance, (PERRIN [1925], FÖRSTER [1948] and VAVILOV [1950]) deals with the interactions of two molecules. The process has been termed "sensitized fluorescence". When more than one neighbour of the originally excited molecule lie at roughly the same distances from, and with the same orientation as this molecule, the transfers are no longer restricted to a single pair of molecules but may affect the other neighbours as well. In such a case the resonance transfer theory, elaborately developed by FÖRSTER [1951] does not strictly hold. The greater the number of interacting molecules and at the same time, the greater the degree of order of their arrangement, the more the molecular assembly gains the properties of an aggregate or a crystal. Förster's theory then becomes changed into the excitation theory of FRENKEL [1931a and b], PEIERLS [1932], and FRANCK and TELLER [1938]. The process dealt with in the latter theory is known as "exciton migration". Though, *in extremo*, sensitized fluorescence and exciton migration are different processes, HELLER and MARCUS [1951] pointed out that even theoretically these phenomena are very much alike. In the first process, emphasis is laid mainly upon dipole interaction, while in the second one, consideration is mainly of the influence of a large number of surrounding molecules on the excited species.

An exciton can be defined in three ways. A comparative discussion of these definitions is given by KASHA [1959]. For our purpose the following definition is the most suitable. An exciton consists of two partners; an excited electron, and the positive hole this electron leaves in the ground state. Electron and hole are able to migrate together through the crystal or aggregate lattice. According to Kasha one may say that the exciton is an electrically neutral excitation "particle". An exciton is therefore not able to give rise to electrical conductivity. Since in an aggregate or crystal, the exciton is not restricted to a certain species but may jump from one molecule or atom to another one, such a body can be considered a giant molecule in this respect. Consequently the excitation of one electron of the system brings the whole system up to a higher energy state and the crystal or aggregate is raised from its ground state into an "exciton state". The exciton states are split into exciton bands due to dipole-dipole interactions in the condensed system. The hole is formed and remains in the valence band. Electronic energy may travel *via* these bands through such an atomic or molecular assembly.

4.2 *Charge migration*

The second type of energy transfer, charge migration, will only occur in highly condensed systems. Here the binding energy between both exciton constituents may be so small that due to prevailing electric fields or by thermal energy, the electron and the hole may become separated. In this way, they may migrate independently of each other. If "impurities" occur at the surface or within the lattice system they may function as electron donors or electron acceptors and they may therefore trap either the hole or the electron, or both. In other words, when such a system occurs, free electrons and holes may be formed upon excitation. The excited system thus becomes an electrical conductor. This phenomenon is called "semiconductivity". When "impurities" are introduced in the form of electrodes in contact with the surface of the highly condensed aggregate or crystal, the electrons or holes may be collected at the electrodes and the conductivity can be measured. If the excitation is brought about by light, "photoconductivity" results. By this mechanism, based on charge separation and charge migration, the excitation energy is transferred as electric charges. The energy is released at the moment at which an electron or a hole is trapped and subsequently is used for some other process.

General surveys, on which part of this discussion is based, and which also deal with the possible role of energy transfer in biological systems, are given by FRANCK and LIVINGSTON [1949], DUYSENS [1952], RABINOWITCH [1957, 1959a and b], TOLLIN, SOGO, and CALVIN [1958], LUMRY and SPIKES [1960], and LAVOREL [1961].

Beyond the density and structure of the system, the consequences of energy transfer depend largely upon the nature of the particles which constitute the excited assembly. For example, the compound acting as an energy sink, namely an "impurity" of the lattice or some energy trapping centre in a concentrated pigment solution may either "spoil" the caught energy by degrading it to heat, or "use" the excitation energy in some chemical reaction. New factors, such as reaction constants, may enter the picture in the latter case. The combination of excitation-energy, transfer and energy trapping actually determines the ultimate result of an excitation of such a system, and thus it may be considered as an example of a possible photophysical unit.

5 *The photophysical unit*

Defining a unit is a difficult task. For example, consider the construction of a wall. The Romans solved the problem by piling nicely fitting stones on top and beside each other. Clearly these stones are building units; their meaningful arrangement results in the production of the wall. The wall can be broken down stone by stone, the units become isolated again, and their "wall function" is lost. With a brick wall, however, things are different. The bricks cannot form a proper wall without the presence of cement layers. Are the bricks units? According to the brick manufacturer they certainly are, but the owner of the wall may have a different opinion. Actually for the owner it is a matter of psychology. He may look at the wall, notice the colour difference between cement and brick and thus recognizing the identity of the bricks, call them units. Alternatively he may emphasize the function of the wall. In this case, the individuality of the bricks is of no importance. His first care is that the binding forces between cement and brick are at least as strong as those between the "brick molecules" themselves. He may point to the fact that tearing down the wall will not yield a heap of units, but of non-uniform fragments. These fragments are not of brick, but of a "chemical" compound between brick and cement. In his eyes, the wall itself is the unit.

Such a difficulty is found in defining the photophysical unit. Is the pigment molecule to be taken as the unit or should it be an assembly of molecules between which energy transfer is possible? In the latter case, which factors determine the extension of a unit? Does it depend on the number of theoretically possible transfer acts which is in turn dependent upon the optical properties, the state, arrangement and concentration of the pigment molecules? Conversely, are the dimensions of a unit limited by the presence of "impurities" such as enzyme molecules, in the pigment assembly? In one sense, the term "unit" may apply in each of these cases, depending on the field in question. For instance, a pigment molecule is a chemical entity which may be excited and so become a carrier of excitation energy. As such, it is a physical unit but an organism is unable to do anything with this "loaded" molecule unless the excitation energy can be introduced into a physicochemical process which is part of the metabolic pattern of the cell. Hence for our purposes the conception of a unit must include the possibility of introducing excitation energy into some metabolic process, in order to make sense. A photophysical unit may therefore be tentatively defined as a pigment molecule, or assembly of pigment molecules, able to transfer excitation energy in the form of chemical energy to a substrate molecule which is of a different nature and which subsequently participates in some process within the cell. The following basic possibilities which fit this definition may occur:

5.1 *Single molecule unit*

(a) The pigment molecule is chemically changed by photoexcitation. In the changed form it reacts chemically with a substrate molecule. Energy input and output are quantitatively related to each other.

(i) The substrate molecule is converted to a terminal product.

(ii) The substrate molecule is converted to an active enzyme which promotes a single reaction or a chain reaction.

(b) The excited pigment molecule initiates a trigger reaction. Energy input and output show no quantitative relation.

5.2 *Molecular assembly unit*

(a) A number of pigment molecules occur in combination with an enzymic centre. Input and output of energy are quantitatively related to each other.

(i) The excited pigment molecules form photoproducts which diffuse from their site of origin to an enzyme molecule. Here the energy of this product is introduced into the chemical steps of the overall process. Because the energy transfer is by diffusion, such a unit works relatively slow. For example, WOHL [1937] calculated for one particular case, that in a unit of about 2500 pigment molecules per enzymic centre, the mean time for transfer of energy by diffusion may be of the order of 10^{-3} sec.

(ii) The excited molecules pass their energy by resonance migration to an enzymic centre. As mentioned before, this migration may be "fast" or "slow". Even this slow migration is faster than the migration mentioned in (i) by a factor of 10^5. The fast resonance migration is more rapid still by a factor of at least 10^5.

(iii) The excited molecules pass their energy by charge migration to a single enzymic centre, or to a pair of them. In the first case, an electron or a hole is trapped by an enzyme molecule. In the second case, both electron and hole are trapped by different enzyme molecules more or less simultaneously and so form a redox couple.

(b) An excited assembly of pigment molecules initiates a trigger reaction. Energy input and output are not quantitatively related to each other.

The type of unit involved in each of the specific cases dealt with later in the book will be discussed in the relevant chapters. It should be noted that the "cage effect" of FRANCK and RABINOWITCH [1934] may make the unit appear to have too many constituents.

This phenomenon, which is often termed the Franck-Rabinowitch effect, is found with molecules in a condensed phase. Two molecules, free radicals, ions, or atoms formed upon photochemical excitation in a condensed phase may be prevented from becoming separated by a "cage" formed by surrounding molecules. This "cage" counteracts their separation by diffusion and increases the chance of kinetic encounter of these two particles. Since collision of the products in question readily results in recombination or "back reaction", the quantum efficiency of the photoprocess is decreased; that is a larger number of light quanta will be absorbed than are actually required for the overall chemical process. Thus, a unit may contain a single pigment molecule but this may be excited and undergo a back reaction a number of times and so it will be erroneously implied that a number of pigment molecules cooperate in a molecular assembly unit. These problems do not necessarily pertain to units based on energy transfer by resonance. These remarks are meant to demonstrate that one should be very careful indeed when considering and discussing the occurrence and the type of a photophysical unit.

6 Common fundamentals of photophysics and photochemistry

In the foregoing pages a number of basic phenomena have been discussed. Three of these are of particular interest as they determine the link between photophysical and photochemical processes. They are reviewed here under their current names:

(1) The law of Einstein. The absorption of each photon causes a primary chemical change of the pigment molecule (EINSTEIN [1905]).

(2) The law of Grotthuss-Draper. Only absorbed photons can be photochemically active (DRAPER [1872]).

(3) The rule of E. Warburg. The number of absorbed photons, not their energy content, counts in photochemistry (E. WARBURG [1920]).

With these statements in mind, the general photochemical phenomena are discussed below.

2

Chemical processes

bilisation of photoproducts

T. primary photoproducts may be stable, or at least exhibit a lifetime sufficiently long to store the acquired chemical energy until it can be used in the cell metabolism in its broadest sense. A purely chemical analogue is the process in a silver bromide crystal or more efficiently in a photographic plate, upon illumination. Exposure of such a crystal or plate to light causes photodissociation of the AgBr resulting in the formation of metallic silver. In photography, this deposit of very tiny metallic silver particles is called the "latent image". This latent image will only become visible upon considerable overexposure when all the silver bromide is decomposed, and the film or plate turns black. So far this photoprocess may be of physical or chemical interest, but since the only photoproduct formed is without any effect whatsoever on any subsequent chemical process – the latter being analogous to cell metabolism – the biologist will not feel himself satisfied with this example.

However, he may feel so when considering the processing of a photographic plate or film. The development requires a reaction with certain chemicals, and although in this case it is in an inversely related manner, the amount of these chemicals used depends on the number of quanta absorbed during exposure. In this way the analogy of feeding excitation energy into metabolic processes is completed.

However in many cases the lifetime of the very first photoproduct(s) is only short. If this product is left to itself, there is a considerable probability of a back reaction to occur which will result in a degradation of the excitation energy to heat.

An analogue for such a kind of biological photoprocess can be found when considering the irradiation of a barrier layer photocell. In this type of cell light quanta free electrons. If the excited cell is left to itself, the electrons regain their original distribution within 10^{-8} sec. However, if the electrodes of the barrier layer cell are electrically connected, the electrons flow through the circuit and the resulting current may be used for driving some other process.

In case of fast back reactions of the labile products, the excitation energy must be stored in the form of stable compounds in order to attain a reasonable efficiency of the photoprocess. This means that either the energy absorbed by the pigment should be directly fixed in chemically stable compounds or the primary photoproducts stabilized within the lifetime of the labile compounds. In the first case, the electronically excited pigment molecules are considered the labile products. In the second case, the energy of the excited state is used for the formation of labile products which need stabilization within their lifetime. The possibilities for the occurrence of energy fixation reactions are governed by the following factors:

(1) Lifetime (τ) of the excited complex. The differing natures of these complexes give rise to a wide range of lifetimes. This is evident when considering the various products of excitation:

(i) singlet state excited molecules ($\tau \sim 10^{-9}$ sec.)
(ii) triplet state excited molecules ($\tau \sim 10^{-4}$ sec., in common solvents such as water, hexane, ethanol)
(iii) radicals (τ from 10^{-3} sec. to infinity)
(iv) dissociation products which are stable on their own but may recombine within 10^{-8} sec. if not kept properly separated.
(v) isomers which exhibit widely diverging lifetimes.

(2) Reaction rate of the stabilizing process. The energy fixation reaction should proceed within the lifetime of the excited complex.

The rates of the stabilizing reactions depend on:

1.1 *Reaction mechanisms*

1.1.1 Substitution reactions. At the reaction of two molecules, a new bond is formed. For the substituent which provides the bonding electron pair, the reaction is called nucleophilic (S_N) or anionoid. For the substituent which does not provide an electron pair, the reaction is termed electrophilic (S_E) or cationoid. If a single electron of each of the two molecules under consideration is used for the bond formation, the process is a radical reaction (S_R).

Nucleophilic substitution reactions are either monomolecular (S_N1)

or bimolecular (S_N2). The hydrolysis of tertiary butyl bromide (fig. 7) is an example of an S_N1 reaction. The first step of such a process consists of dissociation of the reacting molecule. This dissociation reaction is followed by the addition of a nucleophilic substituent, in this case OH^-, to the ion. The first process is slow compared with the subsequent one. Consequently the former process is rate-determining with regard to the overall reaction. This means that the reaction rate depends solely upon the concentration of the initial reactant and therefore the process is termed "monomolecular". It should also be noted that the

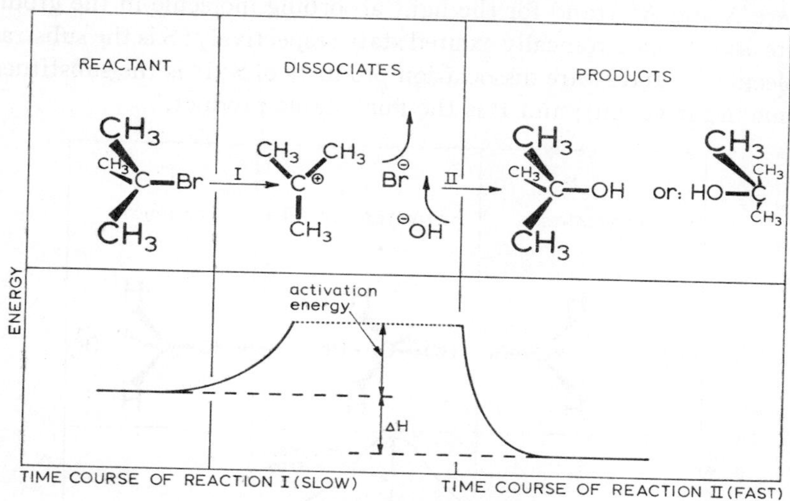

Fig. 7. Example of an S_N1 reaction

reaction is accelerated if the carbonium ion is able to stabilize itself, which, for example, may be by chemical resonance or by being in a solvent of high dielectric constant. It can also be seen in fig. 7 that if the reactant were an optically active compound, the reaction would result in the formation of a racemate.

During the course of the reaction, the potential energy varies as indicated at the bottom of fig. 7. In this particular case, the activation energy required to run the reaction gives rise to the formation of a configuration of lower energy than that of the initial compound. In other words, the structure of the product is of higher stability than that of the reactant. In this process, this energy difference (ΔH) has been ultimately released instead of stored. For energy storage, the potential energy level of the product should be higher than that of the reactant. Such a phenomenon can be accomplished only provided some simultaneous reaction is coupled with the process under consideration. These considerations hold for all the types of reactions discussed below.

The way in which an S_N1 reaction may be involved in the stabilization of the first labile products of a photoprocess is represented by the following scheme:

(I) $A \xrightarrow{h\nu} A^*$

(II) $A^* + S \rightarrow A + s^+ + s^-$

(III) $s^+ + i^- \rightarrow P$

where A and A* stand for the light absorbing molecule in the ground state and the electronically excited state respectively; S is the substrate molecule; s^+ and s^- are dissociation products of S; i^- is the substituent (some negative ion); and P is the final stable product.

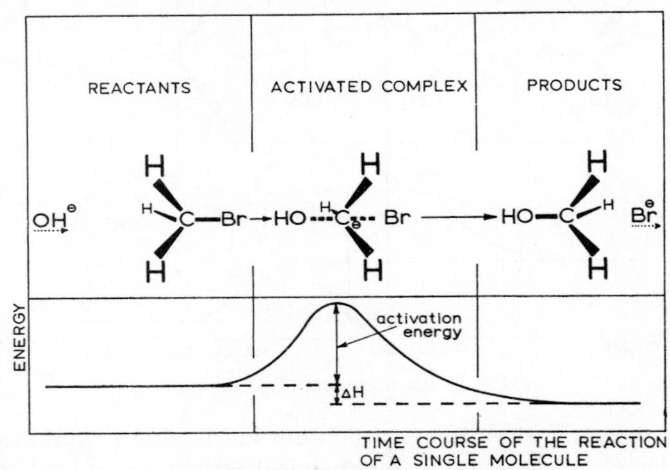

Fig. 8. Example of an S_N2 reaction

S_N2 reactions differ fundamentally from S_N1 reactions because a labile "activated complex", or "transition state" is formed from the two reactants in the first, and from a single reactant in the second case. This activated complex occupies a key position in the theory of rate processes developed by EYRING [1935], WYNNE-JONES and EYRING [1935]. See also KETELAAR [1953], JOHNSON, EYRING and POLISSAR [1954], and LAIDLER [1955]. An example of an S_N2 reaction is presented in fig. 8, depicting the saponification of methyl bromide. As it can be seen, an S_N2 reaction causes inversion of configuration of the reacting molecule (Walden inversion).

S_N2 reactions may be involved in photoprocesses as follows:

(I)	$A \xrightarrow{h\nu} A^*$
(II)	$A^* + S + \ldots \rightarrow A + (L) (+ M)$
(III)	$(L) \rightarrow P (+ N)$

where in addition to the previously defined symbols, (L) is the activated complex, M is some species formed simultaneously with (L), and N is some species formed simultaneously with P.

With this type of reaction, two species with increased energy content participate in the photochemical process, namely: (1) the electronically excited pigment molecule or pigment complex, and (2) the, chemical, activated complex or transition state.

With the exception that the substituent is electrophilic instead of

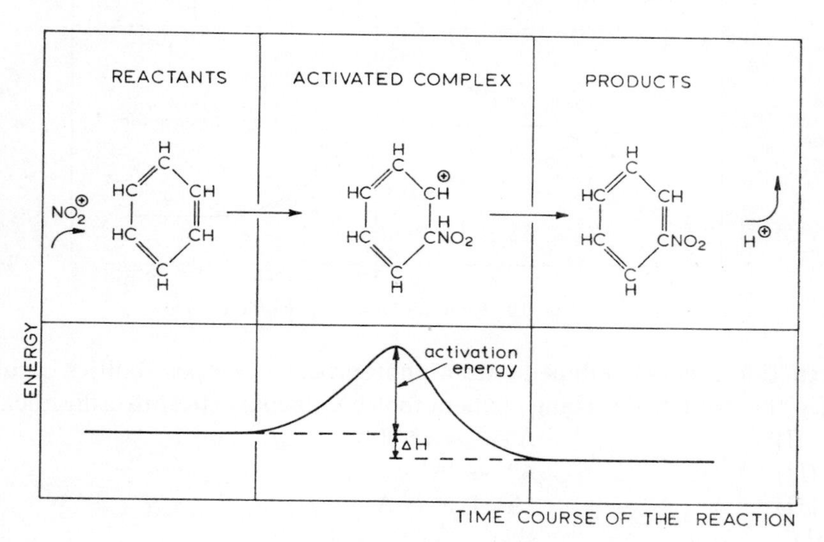

Fig. 9. Example of an S_E2 reaction

nucleophilic, S_E reactions are not substantially different from S_N reactions. The nitronium ion NO_2^+ is a typical electrophilic species. It is able to nitrate a benzene molecule in the S_E2 reaction shown in fig. 9. The reaction schemes for S_E processes which are possibly involved in photochemical reactions, are the same as those for the corresponding S_N processes.

S_R reactions proceed by kinetic encounters exclusively. Basically, radicals are very reactive and as a rule their lifetime is very short.

In some cases, however, the radical configuration is stabilized by resonance which lengthens the lifetime to such an extent that these long-lived radicals are to be considered stable compounds. For this reason, these radicals will not be considered here.

A short-lived radical tries to find a partner for its odd electron and so form an electron pair. For instance, two free ethyl radicals may combine and form an n-butane molecule as shown in fig. 10. If such a

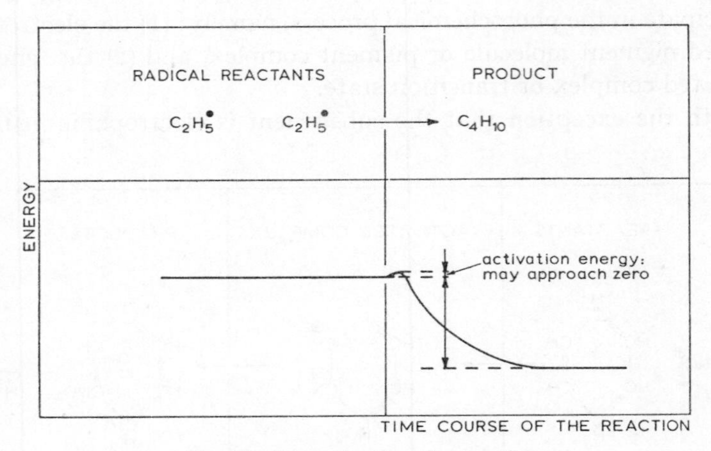

Fig. 10. Example of an S_R reaction

reaction occurs combined with a photoprocess, two possibilities occur:
(i) the excited absorbing pigment molecule is converted into a diradical:

(I) $A \xrightarrow{h\nu} A^*$
(II) $A^* \rightarrow {}^{\bullet}A^{\bullet}$
(III) ${}^{\bullet}A^{\bullet} + S \rightarrow A + s_1^{\bullet} + s_2^{\bullet}$
(IV) $s_1^{\bullet} + s_2^{\bullet} \rightarrow P + M$

where in addition to the previously defined symbols, ${}^{\bullet}A^{\bullet}$ means the diradical of the light absorbing molecule, and $s_1^{\bullet}$ and $s_2^{\bullet}$ stand for radicals formed from S. M is a species which should be formed simultaneously with P. Otherwise, the reaction is a recombination, while the excitation energy is dissipated.
(ii) the excited absorbing molecule causes the direct formation of substrate radicals:

(I) $A \xrightarrow{h\nu} A^*$
(II) $A^* + S \rightarrow A + s_1^{\bullet} + s_2^{\bullet}$
(III) $s_1^{\bullet} + s_2^{\bullet} \rightarrow P + M$

In the above cases, the radical is assumed to succeed in reacting with another compound carrying an odd electron. However, if a radical combines with a molecule, a new radical must be formed, and since the same holds for the resulting radical, a chain reaction may result. An example of a radical chain reaction is the process resulting from the introduction of a chlorine radical, which may be obtained by U.V.-irradiation of chlorine vapor, into a mixture of chlorine and methane:

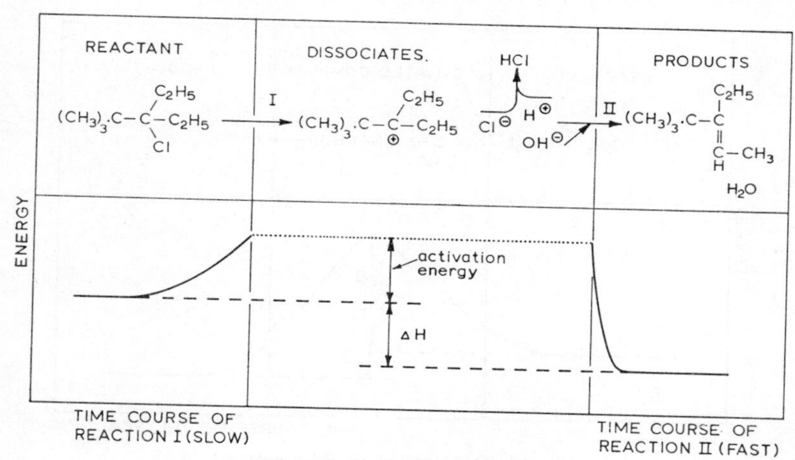

Fig. 11. Example of an E1 reaction

$$Cl^{\cdot} + CH_4 \rightarrow CH_3^{\cdot} + HCl$$
$$CH_3^{\cdot} + Cl_2 \rightarrow CH_3Cl + Cl^{\cdot}$$
$$Cl^{\cdot} + CH_4 \rightarrow CH_3^{\cdot} + HCl$$

and so on.

Actually radicals often initiate chain reactions and such reactions should be considered as possible mechanisms involved in photoprocesses.

1.1.2 Elimination reactions. In elimination reactions, one or more components of the original reactant are split off. These reactions are either monomolecular (E1) or bimolecular (E2). The elimination of hydrogen chloride from 3-chloro, 3-iso-butyl n-pentane, as shown in fig. 11, is an example of an E1 reaction. This kind of reaction is promoted by a solvent of high polarity and by any effect which tends to stabilize the carbonium ion, for example by resonance.

An example of an E2 reaction is the formation of trimethylamine and ethylene out of trimethyl ethyl ammonium, as depicted in fig. 12. Low polarity of the solvent and a high polarizability of the substituent favour the occurrence of such a reaction.

The main difference between elimination reactions and substitution reactions is that in the first type of reaction the product molecule has a smaller number of component parts than the reacting molecule, whereas in substitution reactions this number is the same for both

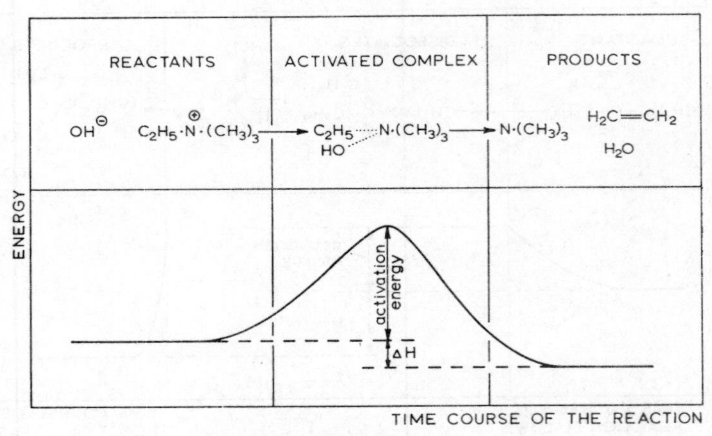

Fig. 12. Example of an E2 reaction

reactant and product. Regardless of this difference, the schemes indicating the way in which S_N1 and S_N2 reactions may be coupled with photochemical processes are also valid for E1 and E2 reactions.

1.1.3 Rearrangement reactions. Two types of rearrangement reactions occur. In the first type, the migrating group does not leave the molecule, the process occurs intramolecularly, and so the reaction is monomolecular. The way in which such a rearrangement may occur is shown in fig. 13. It represents the final steps of the so-called Hoffman reaction. The end product, an isocyanate, is formed *via* a labile intermediate.

The combination of such a reaction with a photoprocess can be written as follows:

(I) $A \xrightarrow{h\nu} A^*$

(II) $A^* + SUB \rightarrow A + UBS'$

(III) $UBS' \rightarrow UBS$

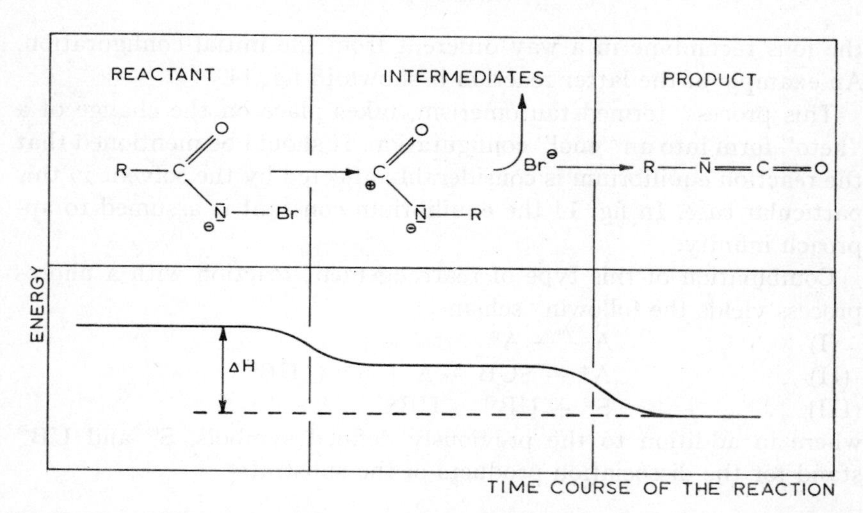

Fig. 13. Example of a rearrangement reaction in which the migrating group does not leave the reacting molecule

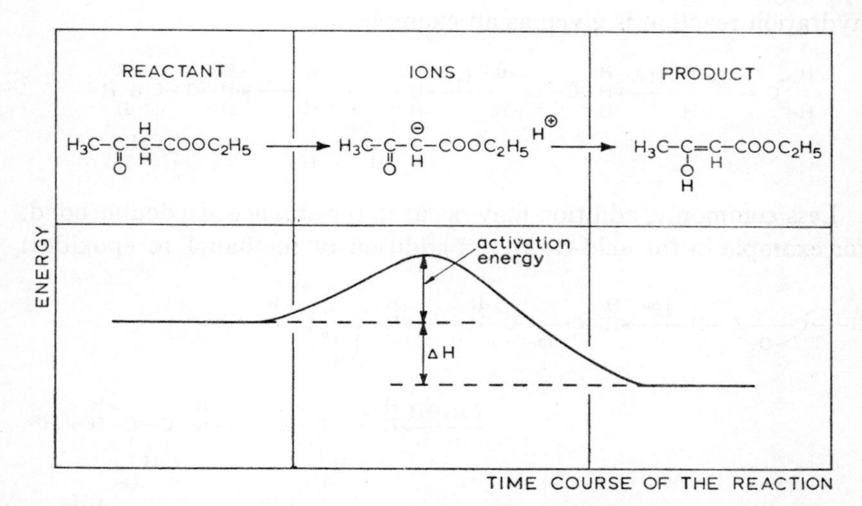

Fig. 14. Example of a rearrangement reaction in which the migrating group leaves the reacting molecule temporarily

where SUB stands for substrate, UBS′ is a labile intermediate, and UBS is the final stable product.

In the second type of rearrangement reaction, the migrating group temporarily leaves the molecule. The parent molecule dissociates and the ions recombine in a way different from the initial configuration. An example of the latter reaction is shown in fig. 14.

This process, termed tautomerism, takes place on the change of a "keto" form into an "enol" configuration. It should be mentioned that the reaction equilibrium is considerably affected by the solvent in this particular case. In fig. 14 the equilibrium constant is assumed to approach infinity.

Combination of this type of rearrangement reaction with a photo-process yields the following scheme:

$$\text{(I)} \qquad A \xrightarrow{h\nu} A^*$$

$$\text{(II)} \qquad A^* + SUB \rightarrow A + S^{\ominus} + UB^{\oplus}$$

$$\text{(III)} \qquad S^{\ominus} + UB^{\oplus} \rightarrow UBS$$

where in addition to the previously defined symbols, $S^{\ominus}$ and $UB^{\oplus}$ stand for the dissociation products of the substrate.

1.1.4 Addition reactions. In general, addition reactions occur upon opening of a double bond such as a C=C or C=O bond. The following hydration reaction is given as an example:

$$H_2C{=}CHR \xrightarrow{H^{\oplus}} H_3C{-}\overset{\oplus}{C}HR \xrightarrow{H_2O} H_3C{-}CHR{-}\overset{\oplus}{O}H_2 \longrightarrow H_3C{-}CHR(OH) + H^{\oplus}$$

Less commonly, addition may occur in the absence of a double bond, for example in the acid-catalyzed addition of methanol to epoxides:

$$H_2C{-}CH{-}H \text{ (O bridge)} \xrightarrow{H^{\oplus}} H_2C{-}CRH \text{ (}\overset{+}{O}H\text{ bridge)} \longrightarrow H_2C(OH){-}\overset{\oplus}{C}RH \longrightarrow$$

$$\xrightarrow{CH_3OH} H_2C(OH){-}CRH{-}\overset{\oplus}{O}(H)CH_3 \longrightarrow H_2C(OH){-}CRH{-}OCH_3 + H^{\oplus}.$$

In both cases, the initial reaction exists of a proton addition which results in the formation of a carbonium ion in the case of C=C addition, and an oxonium ion from epoxides. It is hardly possible to generalise the potential energy variations of these processes; with some solvents the molecule may be more stable than the ionic configuration, while in other media this relation is reversed.

Addition reactions may occur in photoprocesses as follows:

(I) $A \xrightarrow{h\nu} A^*$

(II) $A^* + S + H^{\oplus} \rightarrow A + SH^{\oplus}$

(III) for epoxides: $SH^{\oplus} \rightarrow SH'^{\oplus}$

(IV) $SH^{\oplus}$ (or: $SH'^{\oplus}$) $+ OY \rightarrow SHOY^{\oplus}$

(V) $SHOY^{\oplus} \rightarrow P + H^{\oplus}$

where apart from the previously defined symbols, OY means an oxygen-carrying molecule.

In reactions such as the formation of $FeCl_3$ out of $FeCl_2$ changes of valency may be involved as well. Actually, such reactions are based on oxidation or reduction phenomena and are not true addition processes.

1.2 Rate-determining factors

In general, rates of chemical reactions and the rates of the above processes in particular, depend on the following factors.

1.2.1 Activation energy. Activation energy is needed to overcome the energy barrier which separates the energy contents of reactants and products. The rate of a chemical process, defined as the number of particles which react in unit time, also depends on a probability factor.

According to the theory of absolute reaction rates, this factor may be explained in terms of changes in entropy and in the partition functions occurring during the formation of the activated complex (*cf.* GLASSTONE, LAIDLER and EYRING [1941]).

As a reaction can only occur by "climbing the activation energy hill", it follows that the reaction rate is related to the inverse of the "height" of the energy barrier. It may be stressed that it is this "height" and not the difference between the energy contents of the reactants and the products (ΔH) which is rate-determining. Only the sign of ΔH is of interest with regard to the nature of a reaction. It determines whether it will be endergonic or exergonic, that is, takes up or releases energy. As an oversimplification, considering the overall photoprocess, ΔH is positive for mainly energetic processes, and negative for mainly cybernetic processes.

1.2.2 Temperature. The energy content of a reacting system increases with a rise of temperature and decreases on lowering the temperature.

On raising the temperature the number of active reactant molecules with energies sufficient to pass the "energy hill" increases, and so increases the rate of the reaction.

1.2.3 Catalysis. Without entering into details with regard to the mechanism of action of a catalyst, for instance an enzyme, it is sufficient to mention that catalyst activity results in lowering the energy barrier of a chemical reaction, and so increases the reaction rate. Enzymes may need activation by certain cofactors, for example metal ions. Therefore the presence of these cofactors can be rate-determining in an indirect way.

1.2.4 Concentration. In a reaction mixture only a relatively small number of the particles are active at a given time. A concentration change does not affect the fraction of active particles in such a mixture at constant temperature.

Consequently the absolute number of these active particles is dependent upon the concentration. Since the reaction rate is defined as the number of particles reacting in unit time, concentration is a rate-determining factor.

1.2.5 Diffusion. In heterogeneous systems, the reaction rate is influenced by the diffusion constants of the reacting substances. This is easily understood on consideration of the fact that in the neighbourhood of a reacting "centre" a zone of low substrate concentration is formed. The concentration decrease is counteracted by the supply of fresh substrate molecules by diffusion. Consequently this phenomenon is rate-determining, and in its turn, is affected by temperature and viscosity of the medium.

1.2.6 Inhibition. In general, two kinds of inhibition are known: (1) competitive inhibition, and (2) non-competitive inhibition. In the first case, the inhibitor competes with one of at least two reacting species in such a way that a compound is formed differing from the normal end product of the reaction. If the reaction is enzymic the inhibitor may act by occupying active sites of the enzyme which are not then available for substrate molecules.

If the substrate concentration is sufficiently greater than that of the inhibitor, the reaction rate may not be appreciably changed in the presence of this kind of inhibitor. However, if the concentration of the substrate is lower than this critical level of concentration of the inhibitor, the reaction rate is proportionally decreased. Thus competitive inhibition depends on the concentration ratio of substrate and inhibitor.

The second type of inhibition depends only on the concentration of the inhibitor. Each inhibitor molecule "attacks" one of the reactants rendering it unable to enter the reaction with its "normal" partner. In the case of enzymic processes with non-competitive inhibition, the inhibitor reacts with essential parts of the enzyme molecules resulting in a retardation of the formation of the enzyme-substrate complex. The reaction rate is therefore inversely proportional to the number of inhibitor molecules.

The nature of the inhibitors is widely divergent and they may be specific or non-specific. A discussion on this subject is beyond the scope of this book. It is sufficient to note that in the living cell inhibitors have two origins: (1) they may occur within the cell for some reason which is independent of the inhibited process.

Alternatively (2), the inhibitor is formed by the actual process itself. This may occur upon accumulation of intermediates, by-products, or end products of a reaction chain, if these products are able to inactivate one or more of the relevant enzymes.

1.2.7 Chemical nature of the medium. The chemical properties of the medium may considerably influence the lifetimes of both the excited states and the activated compounds. These properties can be generally classified as follows.

Polarity. If charged complexes are formed, as they are in S_N1 and in some S_N2 reactions, the polarity of the medium affects the reaction rate by influencing their solvation and with it, the activation energy of the reaction.

An increase in polarity means a decrease of activation energy and consequently an increase in reaction rate.

It has already been mentioned that where n,π^* levels are somewhat higher than π,π^* levels in polar media, their relation may be reversed in non-polar solvents. If, in the latter case, n,π^* levels occur in between singlet and triplet π,π^* states, they may favour triplet formation and consequently increase the lifetime of the excited pigment.

The polarity of the medium is thus an important factor with regard to the stabilization of reaction intermediates. The polarity is determined by the dipole moments and the polarizability of the solvent molecules, as well as by the ionic strength of the solution.

Hydrogen ion concentration. The labile compounds formed in the photoprocess can be considered to be intermediates in a chemical reaction. As the cell medium is aqueous and most of the reactions are enzymic, the reaction rate is influenced by the pH of the medium. The effect of pH on enzyme activity depends on (1) the enzyme sensitivity towards extreme pH values which gives rise to denaturation, and (2) the ionization state of generally both the enzyme and the substrate, and consequently, on the formation of the enzyme-substrate complex.

1.2.8 Density of the medium. It was mentioned earlier that molecules surrounding the excited species may form a "cage" which hampers the separation of primary photoproducts. In this way the chance of recombination is increased. This "cage effect" may occur only if the surrounding species are not substrate molecules. Otherwise the "walls" of the "cage" should promote a fast reaction of the photoproduct with substrate molecules and hence the probability of the occurrence of stabilization reactions is enhanced. A "cage" consisting of species not participating in the photoprocess may show another effect in addition to that of preventing the photoproducts from escaping. This second effect works in the opposite direction, the "cage" preventing the substrate molecules from entering and reacting with the excited species. Whether an assembly of molecules surrounding an excited particle actually functions as a "cage" at a given temperature depends on the balance of two factors: (1) the degree of packing of the "wall molecules", which means the density of the medium, and (2) the kinetic energy content of the reaction partners inside and outside of the "cage". At a given temperature, the kinetic energy of the substrate molecules is a constant amount of thermal energy acquired from the environment and for the excited species, part of the excitation energy is added to the "environmental" thermal energy.

1.2.9 Structure. Up to now, a mainly homogeneous distribution of the reactants has been considered. However in the living cell, a number of photoreceptors show an intricate macromolecular structure under the electron microscope. In addition, there is optical evidence that in various cases the pigment molecules occur in very thin layers, which are probably monomolecular. For reasons which will be discussed later, photopigments are likely to be bound to carriers, and the resulting complexes are incorporated in the macromolecular structures referred to above. This means that the photoreceptor is of a highly heterogeneous nature and accordingly the local concentration of the reactants can be considerably higher than cell extracts may make us believe. As a result, a highly efficient energy transfer between the pigment molecules may be possible while if the pigments were homogeneously distributed throughout the photoreceptor the amount of energy transfer might be insignificant.

Another feature of such structures is the possibility that all the reaction participants are close together, for example on the surface of a macromolecule which carries both pigment molecules and prosthetic groups at the same time.

Both aspects in one sense can be considered to be a means of obtaining a maximum local concentration with a minimum number of reactant molecules in the bulk phase.

Apart from this "concentration effect", the more or less rigid structure of the macromolecule surface may enable orientation of the pigment molecules. Such orientation favours efficient energy transfer between these molecules. It may be recalled that efficient energy transfer means an optimum chance that the excitation energy reaches some "enzymic centre" where it can be converted to, and stored as, chemical energy.

Beyond this, structured molecular assemblies may mean that reacting molecules which are close together are effective in different environments. Such may occur in the case of lipoprotein structures. Part of the reactive groups may be embedded in lipid constituents while some of them may be surrounded by water and aqueous solutions. This can give rise to a favourable mixture of excited states of differing lifetimes. This will be more fully discussed later.

Finally, two further points should be made. Firstly, it is emphasized that a number of factors are able to affect the rate of a process or a chain of processes. In the case of a chain reaction, its rate is determined only by one single factor at a time, called the "rate-limiting factor". Which factor is the limiting one depends on the type of process as well as on the conditions, such as temperature or concentration.

Secondly, if stabilization of the photoproducts is inadequate, back reactions will occur. The rate of these back reactions is governed by the same factors as the forward reaction and the overall effect of stabilizing processes will depend upon the balance between the rates of both "forward" and "backward" reactions.

2 Chemical energy transfer

The chemical energy which is initially the conversion of light quanta should be available for running a number of subsequent "dark reactions" at both the right place and time. Therefore, transportation of this kind of energy is vital and in general may take place by two kinds of "chemical" transfer mechanism. In the first the photochemically produced compound travels from its site of origin to the place where it is needed. Such a type of mechanism may be called "migratory transfer". On the other hand, no dislocation of any compound occurs in the second type but the energy in the form of electronic excitation may repeatedly jump from molecule to molecule, even though the molecules are of differing species. This kind of transportation is termed "electron transfer". Actually both types may occur in combination with each other. Both mechanisms will be briefly discussed below.

2.1 Migratory transfer

Chemical compounds may move in two ways, namely by (a) diffusion, and (b) interface activity.

The rate of diffusion depends on temperature, concentration, molecular weight and shape, viscosity of the medium, and charge. Except for the fact that in general the particles move down the concentration gradient, their distribution is random. In our case, this means that the photoproducts or intermediates just leave their site of origin and are dispersed in all directions, provided that nothing else happens. If there is a reactant or enzyme molecule bound to a site near the point of production, the concentration of the intermediates will be reduced at this particular spot. The diffusion "sphere" then becomes deformed by the formation of a preferential, but not complete flow in the direction of the "consuming" centre. Such a deformation may also occur by mechanical hindrance or charge phenomena in structured media such as membranes. As diffusion proceeds relatively slowly as well as randomly, this kind of energy transfer does not seem to be a very profitable one.

A fast transfer by spreading along interfaces is possible in many cases. The phenomenon of spreading is determined by the "spreading coefficient". This coefficient equals the difference between the work of adhesion of the compound onto the surface, and the work of cohesion of the compound. If the spreading coefficient is negative – a case which is of no interest in relation to the present problem – a drop deposited on the surface is only flattened to a lens shape and does not spread. If, however, this coefficient is positive the spreading is spontaneous. A detailed discussion about this is given for instance by ADAMSON [1960]. For our purposes, an example may be of assistance. A droplet of petrol spreads instantly along a water-air interface, the petrol molecules fleeing very quickly from the original droplet. If they meet some petrol-consuming "reaction centre", a much faster and more effective transfer from the droplet to the centre is possible than could ever occur with "spherical" diffusion.

The compounds of particular interest to the present discussion are those which are carriers of energy fixed by the photoprocess. The energy of chemical compounds is released upon rupture of their bonds. Linkages are usually classified as "energy-poor" or "low-energy", and "energy-rich" or "high-energy" bonds, as suggested by LIPMANN [1941]. Among many other excellent reviews are those of FRUTON and SIMMONDS [1953], and PULLMAN and PULLMAN [1960].

Actually, the term "energy-rich bond" is slightly misleading. The energy is not restricted to the linkage proper, but is distributed over the linked configuration. Such configurations are found in such molecules as mixed anhydride-phospho-amide-, phospho-enol-, and certain ester bonds.

These terms are now commonly used in biochemistry to indicate low and high standard free energies of hydrolysis of bonds.

According to LIPMANN [1941], the escaping tendency of groups linked with "energy-rich" bonds is usually high, while it is low for groups linked with "energy-poor" bonds. In a chemical sense, this escaping tendency is of greater importance than the strength of the bond and is called "group potential". Although it may be more correct to use this name, the more commonly occurring terms "energy-rich" and "energy-poor" will be employed here.

Originally a chemical bond within certain organic phosphate compounds was considered energy-rich if the change in standard free energy, ΔF, accompanying its hydrolytic cleavage is between 6 and

10 kcal per mol. The phosphate linkage in adenosine-5′-triphosphate at a pH of about 7.5 is in this range.

Energy-poor phosphate bonds were those yielding a ΔF of about one third of this value upon such a cleavage. This is the case with glucose-6-phosphate.

It was found later, however, that the distinction between energy-poor and energy-rich bonds is not as clear-cut as it was believed at first (GING and STURTEVANT [1954]). NEILANDS and STUMPF [1958] even introduced a third group of "intermediate energy".

A number of substances are "energy-rich", that is, contain "energy-rich" linkages. Among these organic phosphate compounds occupy a most prominent place. These compounds can be classified as follows:

(1) carboxyl phosphates: $R{-}C({=}O){-}O{\sim}P({=}O)(OH)_2$

(2) enol phosphates: $R{-}C({=}CH_2){-}O{\sim}P({=}O)(OH)_2$

(3) pyro- and other poly-phosphates: $R{-}P({=}O)(OH){-}O{\sim}P({=}O)(OH){-}OH$

(4) amine phosphates such as guanidine phosphates: $R_2N{-}C({=}NH){-}NH{\sim}P({=}O)(OH)_2$

Other energy-rich compounds contain thiol ester bonds:

$$R{-}C({=}O){\sim}S{-}R'$$

or acyl imidazole bonds:

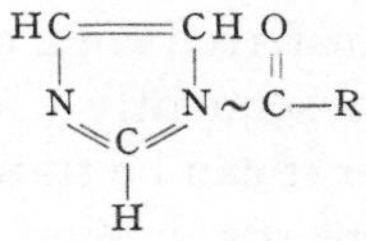

HC═══CH O
| | ‖
N   N ~ C—R
  ╲C╱
   |
   H

where ~ indicates the energy-rich bond.

At first the high energy content of these bonds was believed to be due to the fact that their formation is coupled with the occurrence of a smaller number of resonance configurations than those expected of both parent species. This phenomenon, known as "opposing resonance", was recognized by KALCKAR [1941] and discussed in more detail, be it qualitatively, by OESPER [1950, 1951]. It is partially due to a rather improbable distribution of charges within the molecule. HILL and MORALES [1950] pointed to the role of electrostatic repulsion between the components of such energy-rich compounds. GERSMANN and KETELAAR [1958] and KETELAAR and GERSMANN [1959] concluded from spectroscopic data that in addition to opposing resonance there must be other factors involved in the formation of high-energy bonds. PULLMAN and PULLMAN [1960] discriminate between "primary opposing resonance", which is Kalckar's "opposing resonance", and "complementary opposing resonance".

Of the high-energy compounds, adenosine-tri- and adenosine-diphosphates, usually abbreviated as ATP and ADP respectively, are widely distributed among the living world and play a most prominent role in metabolism.

2.2 Electron transfer

The concept of "chemical" electron transfer is derived from consideration of oxidation-reduction reactions. In many cases such a reaction can be written in two ways. In one instance, it can be described as hydrogen transfer:

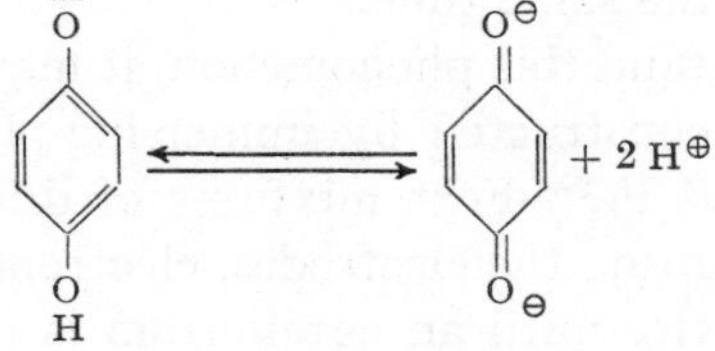

$$\text{p-hydroquinone (HO–C}_6\text{H}_4\text{–OH)} \rightleftharpoons \text{p-quinone (}^{\ominus}\text{O=C}_6\text{H}_4\text{=O}^{\ominus}\text{)} + 2\,\text{H}^{\oplus}$$

p-hydroquinone p-quinone

In this case, energy is transferred *via* a chemical reaction of hydrogen. If the hydrogen reacts subsequently with a number of compounds of increasing oxidizing power it can be transferred along a series of different molecules. In other words, a kind of "migratory transfer" may result.

On the other hand the same reaction can be considered as taking place in the following way:

$$HO-C_6H_4-OH \rightleftharpoons {}^{\ominus}O-C_6H_4-O^{\ominus} + 2\,H^{\oplus} \qquad (a)$$

$$^{\ominus}O-C_6H_4-O^{\ominus} \rightleftharpoons O=C_6H_4=O + 2\,e \qquad (b)$$

The hydrogen ion is taken care of by the aqueous medium resulting in a decrease of the pH. Therefore in this second approach, emphasis is laid upon the transfer of an electron. Obviously electron transfer occurs in the reaction:

$$\underset{\text{(ferrous)}}{Fe^{2+}} \underset{\text{reduction}}{\overset{\text{oxidation}}{\rightleftharpoons}} \underset{\text{(ferric)}}{Fe^{3+}} + e$$

This particular reaction is of considerable biological interest as it occurs in cytochromes upon the oxidation and reduction of these iron-porphyrin proteins. If a number of such compounds with differing electron affinities occur in close combination with each other, electrons may jump from molecule to molecule by reducing one of them and oxidizing the other species at the same time.

In order to understand this phenomenon, it may be recalled that an electric cell can be constructed by immersing platinum electrodes in electrically connected Fe^{2+}–Fe^{3+} mixtures of different concentration ratios. By short-circuiting the electrodes, electrons are allowed to flow *via* the connecting wire until an equilibrium is reached between the mixtures. The e.m.f. of such a cell can be measured. In practice, however, the potential of a redox mixture is expressed relative to that of a standard hydrogen electrode. The former potential depends upon the ratio of the Fe^{2+} and Fe^{3+} concentrations as well as on a constant which is a characteristic of each particular species. Thus if the concentration of both the reduced and the oxidized forms are the same, different potentials will be found with other redox substances. In other words, such a "fifty-fifty" potential is characteristic for a particular substance. It is called the "oxidation-reduction" or "redox" potential. If one constructs a battery out of two compounds with different redox potentials, the electrons flow through a short-circuiting wire from low to high potential. The high-potential compound thus receives electrons and is partially reduced, while electrons are drained from the low-potential species which is partly oxidized. Consequently the higher the redox potential of a substance, the higher its oxidizing capacity or the lower its reducing power. If a number of compounds with successively increasing or decreasing redox potentials are located sufficiently close to each other, an "electron ladder" can be formed along which electrons are able to "ascend" from low to high potential. First, of course, an electron has to be "injected" at the lower end of the "ladder".

This may be done in photoprocesses by the light-induced generation of reducing power. The excited photopigment itself may yield an electron for this purpose. The electron then "climbs" stepwise from lower potential (higher energy) to higher potential (lower energy) along the electron ladder. At each step, some energy of the electron is consumed. Finally the electron is caught by a terminal electron acceptor and is taken up in some stable chemical configuration. The terminal acceptor is therefore ultimately reduced and may tend to neutralize its acquired negative charge by the uptake of a proton from the medium. Thus beyond the fact that the reacting molecules may stay where they are, this type of energy transfer differs from migratory transfer in that the energy is not constant but decreases during transportation. The energy freed upon "climbing a potential step" can be used for driving an endergonic chemical reaction in which part of this energy is fixed in some stable compound. For example, in one step an ATP molecule can be generated out of ADP and inorganic phosphate. This means that the energy derived from the absorption of one light quantum need not be used in one single process. For one einstein of red light this energy amounts to about 40 kcal which could be distributed to generate three molecules of ATP, each of them carrying about 8 kcal.

The free energy of hydrolysis of ATP may subsequently be "injected" at different points of an energy-consuming reaction chain.

3 Chemical light production

An excited particle or body, such as a crystal, may emit light when returning to its ground state. In the preceding chapter excitation by light quanta alone was considered. However, light is by no means the only way to excite a species and make it emit visible radiation. At least 15 ways to induce "cold light" emission are known, (HARVEY [1940]). Molecules excited by the absorption of light may emit quanta in two ways. (1) The light emission is restricted to the period of irradiation and up to about 10^{-8} sec. thereafter, and is called "fluorescence". (2) Light emission continues for an appreciable time after the removal of the exciting source and it is called "phosphorescence". These processes are collected under the term "luminescence", irrespective of whether they occur simultaneously with excitation or as after-effects. If light is chemically generated in living organisms the process is called "bioluminescence", or, less commonly, "organoluminescence".

However, it is not very logical to consider bioluminescence as a distinct type among the other luminescent processes. It is distinguished from what is usually termed "chemiluminescence" merely by the fact that enzymes are involved, whereas they are not in chemiluminescence. Fundamentally, therefore, there is no basic distinction between these two types. Nevertheless, since the term "bioluminescence" is commonly used, it will be used in future chapters, and will serve to emphasize the chemiluminescent character of light production by living cells.

Chemiluminescence is based upon the formation of some emitting species by a chemical reaction. Two mechanisms of chemiluminescence have been distinguished: (1) atom or molecule transfer, and (2) charge transfer. In the first type of mechanism the excited state is produced by conversion of the chemical energy of one system into electronic energy in another. Such a process may occur in the reaction between different species of gas molecules resulting in the production of a hot flame, for example, the blue zone in a gas flame. The excited molecule may then return to a lower energy state by emission of radiation. As this type of chemiluminescence is not likely to occur in biological systems, it will not be considered further.

Charge transfer, the second type of chemiluminescence mechanism seems to play a dominant, if not exclusive, role in bioluminescent systems. Very frequently the chemiluminescence of complex organic molecules is accompanied by decomposition of peroxides. LINSCHITZ [1961] remarks that this phenomenon suggests a general mechanism for the excitation of the systems under consideration. The process may be initiated by removal of an OH-group from a peroxide by an organic molecule, L, perhaps by a specific metallic ion within the latter. In this reaction L yields an electron to the OH-group and thus becomes L^+. Next a charge-transfer complex of the type (L^+–OH^-) may be formed and an electron is then transferred from OH^- back to L^+ resulting in the formation of a neutral, but excited, L^*. In its turn, L^* may fall back to the ground state, L, while emitting a light quantum. This means that one molecule of a peroxide has been decomposed.

Luminescence reactions nearly always require the presence of peroxides or molecular oxygen which is strange since oxygen is known as a quenching agent for fluorescence and it is not clear why it does not quench chemiluminescence. REID [1957] remarks that the function of oxygen in this process implies that it is involved in many highly exothermic processes. It may be added that the presence of oxygen is required for the production of peroxides and that little is known about the oxygen tension within the living cell. It might be that *in vivo*, respiratory enzymes take care of molecular oxygen within the cell in such a way that free oxygen can never reach a luminescent molecule.

3

Biological processes

It has long been recognized that an organism is more than the algebraic sum of its constituents. This means that a living creature consists of an intricate complex of organs or cell components each of which is responsible for its own special function while being closely correlated to the other components. Actually this correlation is an interaction for if one considers a single system, such as some photoprocess, one cannot escape taking into account the influence of other processes upon the reaction that we are considering. While it can not be said that life as a whole is only physics and chemistry, the phenomena to be considered in this book are basically physical or chemical. While other processes of life may have a very complex influence upon the photophenomena, only their overall effect is of interest with regard to the process to be studied, and so they may be considered collectively as "biological processes". The diversity of these processes is such that it is impossible to give an exhaustive summary.

This means that only some of the more obvious biological processes will be enumerated below and their relationship to photobiological reactions will be briefly discussed.

1 *Metabolism in general*

In unicellular organisms, the cell is an independent unit in itself, although the way in which it functions will depend on various external factors, for example oxygen and substrate content of the medium, removal of waste products, pH and temperature. The more that these factors are in harmony, the more efficiently the metabolic machinery will function, resulting in an improved energy balance of the organism. For optimal functioning of the cell it is vital that there is a proper supply of the materials required for the metabolic processes. For example, so long as the enzymes and cofactors are produced satisfactorily there will be no harmful competition for the elements or molecules necessary to their formation and so the correct pH will be maintained since both the supply of substrates to, and the removal of waste products from the cell are undisturbed, and so on. In other words, the general metabolic condition will have a direct influence on any particular special process under examination.

In multicellular organisms things are essentially the same. However the conditions of the "medium" of the individual cells of such a system do not, or not exclusively, depend on factors outside the organism. The functioning of neighbour cells or even remote organs mostly determine the environmental situation of the individual cell and hence its metabolism. As photobiological processes are part of the metabolic pattern they will be affected by such environmental factors.

2 *Growth*

The driving force for the growth processes such as germination, development and increase in size are again part of the metabolism. Nevertheless growth should be mentioned separately. In mature cells metabolism proceeds, more or less, under equilibrium conditions but during growth, this equilibrium may be badly upset. It is even possible that metabolic activities, perhaps recognised by changes in the respiratory quotient switch from one type to another, for example, like the shift occurring during germination of the fat-containing damar seed. In the early phases of germination fat metabolism prevails, but this is gradually superseded by carbohydrate metabolism. Metamorphosis is an extreme example of changing metabolism. As soon as the cell metabolism changes it is expected that a number of photobiological processes will be affected and such changes are actually observed.

3 *Aging*

This phenomenon is also a matter of metabolism. The optimal condition of an organism upon reaching maturity stays constant for some time, but then starts to decline. In multicellular individuals hormones may play a role in this process, although it occurs in monocellular organisms as well. For example, there are obvious changes in the efficiency of a photoprocess throughout the life cycle of purple bacteria. With young cells, the phototactic response is low. It increases to a maximum after a period of three to five days at room temperature, and then starts to decline.

4 *Adaptation*

Neither the amount of enzymes nor their activity is a given constant in biological objects. Protein molecules are steadily broken down and replaced by freshly formed ones. Moreover, enzymes may be in an "inactive" state, their functioning sites requiring activation before being able to function. It is one of the unique features of the living world that the "enzyme household" adapts itself, within limits, according to the requirements at a given moment. Upon a change of conditions not only the rate of existing metabolic processes may change, but at the same time reactions may start up that were previously dormant.

This kind of change is seen upon illumination, when an equilibrium between the individual processes of the reaction chain is established over a relatively short interval resulting in a steady state. This "induction phase" in the case of photosynthesis, is of the order of minutes. One may consider the induction phase to be an adaptation phenomenon although such adaptation phenomena are a consequence of the normal functioning of the photoprocess. They are not caused by changes of concentration or activity of enzymes and are not covered by the definition of biological processes covered by the present chapter. An example of a different type of adaptation by a photoprocess is demonstrated by the experiments of GAFFRON [1940] who succeeded in activating an hydrogenase by anaerobic dark pretreatment which would then bring about the reduction of carbon dioxide by molecular hydrogen in the light. Instead of minutes however, this kind of adaptation requires a few hours.

5 *Regulatory processes*

Apart from fluctuations due to the phenomena listed so far, the overall metabolic condition may change with time as a result of the influence of a number of regulation mechanisms. The natures of these diverge widely, some belonging to the "feed-back" type of process which may be operated by hormonal, humoral or nervous systems. The relation between cause and effect may be an even more direct one, as in the case of membrane phenomena. Biological membranes, as a rule, are semipermeable, allowing certain particles to pass while others are retained. This property is influenced quite considerably by the metabolic condition of the cell and so the metabolism itself may regulate the passage or accumulation of the involved substances.

Quite different types of regulatory processes seem to be responsible for endogenous rhythms encountered in both animals and plants. Such rhythms are observed for a variety of phenomena including photoprocesses, (*cf.* BÜNNING [1956]). The very nature of these rhythms is not yet understood. They can be influenced to some degree by varying external conditions though purely endogenous components are certainly involved in these phenomena. The periods of the rhythms range from less than a second, for example in flagellar movements, to the diurnal rhythm of the leaf movements of many plants, while even seasonal cycles are observed, for instance in bird colours. Despite the variety of these phenomena, one is inclined to look for some common basis for such rhythms. Their complexity as well as the scarcity of experimental evidence make it impossible however to indicate any general cause for the development of endogenous rhythms. When discussing diurnal rhythms in plants Bünning remarked that periods of energy accumulation alternate with periods of energy turnover in a regular manner. He suggested that this phenomenon may be fundamental in the functioning of all living cells, though the cause of these energetic fluctuations is totally unknown.

The above may suffice to demonstrate the complexity of the interaction of bioprocesses. There is always a risk in studying a process *in vitro* or with fragments of an organism and extrapolating the results towards an explanation of *in vivo* phenomena. One is forced to do so sometimes by the nature of either the object or the experiment, and it is most important to be cautious when generalizing the results. Moreover one should be aware of the fact that the observed reactions or features might be artifacts of the experimental technique rather than natural processes.

PART 2

The biological photophenomena

The various biological photoprocesses which are to be discussed in the following chapters will be considered in a comparative way as far as possible. Emphasis will thus be laid upon the phenomena which these processes have in common. This means that some aspects, for example the study of the active pigments, will be dealt with in greater detail than the features of an individual photoprocess, such as a number of chemical reactions. This treatment necessarily leads to a certain unbalance but may be justified since it facitilates making comparisons.

4

Photosynthesis

1 *Introduction*

Photosynthesis – the production of chemical compounds by light – is a general physico-chemical term which is commonly reserved for the special process by which "green" plants are able to convert light into chemical energy.

Photosynthesis is defined in a less sketchy way as the process of assimilation of carbon by chlorophyll-containing organisms with the aid of light. As we know by now, the overall process in green plants can be described as a reduction of carbon dioxide upon illumination resulting in the production of organic matter and oxygen which may be represented:

$$n\mathrm{CO}_2 + n\mathrm{H}_2\mathrm{O} \xrightarrow{\text{green plants + light}} (\mathrm{CH}_2\mathrm{O})_n + n\mathrm{O}_2.$$

Because of the differing natures of the components – gas, liquid and solid, and the "factors" – function of the plant and energy – it is quite understandable that the pioneers in this field met with a considerable number of difficulties. This was particularly true at the time when research on photosynthesis was just beginning since the nature of "air" was then unknown. Yet the study of photosynthesis was retarded for quite a different reason as well. This reason, demonstrating the risk of being a scientific genius far ahead of one's time refers to an idea of Aristotle (257–180 B.C.) that plants absorb all compounds required for their life and growth from the soil. It lasted from the second century B.C. until the seventeenth century when the validity of this statement was challenged by Van Helmont (1577–1644) who suggested that plants grow by uptake of water. Though this hypothesis is an erroneous one, it opened up the way towards the study of photosynthesis. Malpighi (1628–1694) discovered that leaves produce substances required for plant growth and Hales (1677–1761) concluded that plants most probably take up part of their "nourishment" from the air. Moreover he wondered whether light might play a role upon entering leaves and flowers. Bonnet (1754) observed the formation of gas bubbles from leaves submerged in water upon illumination, which ceased in the dark. These scattered observations laid the basis for research leading to the overall photosynthesis equation given above. Figure 15 gives a survey of the pioneer names and dates pertaining to this research. A more elaborate history of photosynthesis is beyond the scope of this book but is excellently carried out by RABINOWITCH [1945].

Before leaving the story of the elucidation of the overall equation of photosynthesis in green plants, it should be mentioned that VAN NIEL [1941] studied the photosyntheses of green and purple bacteria and compared them with that of the green plants. On consideration of the above equation for "green plant" photosynthesis it is obvious that carbon dioxide is reduced by hydrogen derived from the splitting of water which also causes oxygen to be evolved. In other words, the water molecule functions as a hydrogen donor. On the other hand, in bacterial photosyntheses no oxygen is liberated and the presence of hydrogen sulphide or other oxidizable substances is required. For example, the green sulphur bacteria photosynthesis can be written:

$$n\mathrm{CO_2} + 2n\mathrm{H_2S} \xrightarrow{h\nu} (\mathrm{CH_2O})_n + n\mathrm{H_2O} + 2n\mathrm{S}.$$

Van Niel pointed out that such equations are basically the same as the overall photosynthesis equation for green plants. The only difference between these reactions lies in the fact that the nature of the hydrogen donor varies; for green plants it is water, while for green bacteria it is hydrogen sulphide. Consequently if the hydrogen-carrying substance is designated "A", it is possible to write the following general photosynthesis equation:

$$n\mathrm{CO_2} + 2n\mathrm{H_2A} \xrightarrow{h\nu} (\mathrm{CH_2O})_n + n\mathrm{H_2O} + 2n\mathrm{A}.$$

It should be mentioned at once that this general equation only describes the overall effect, and the reaction is a multi-stage process which will be discussed later. Still these equations do serve as a concise description of the photosynthetic process.

General information on photosynthesis is available in many textbooks and reviews and a number of these are listed below. STILES [1925] and SPOEHR [1926] dealt with the earlier literature. RABINOWITCH [1945, 1951, 1956] compiled and discussed the literature espe-

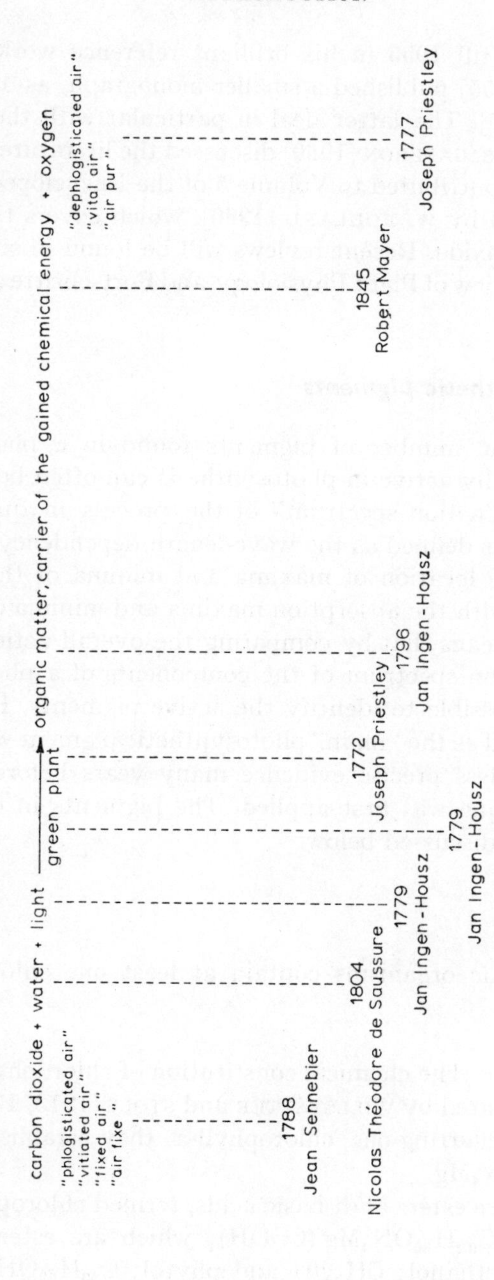

Fig. 15. Survey of the early history of photosynthesis research

cially from 1925 till 1955 in his brilliant reference work. HILL and WHITTINGHAM [1955] published a smaller monograph, as did BASSHAM and CALVIN [1957]. The latter deal in particular with the photosynthetic carbon cycle. GAFFRON [1960] discussed the literature up to 1958. Several authors contributed to Volume 5 of the Encyclopedia of Plant Physiology edited by W. RUHLAND [1960], which covers the assimilation of carbon dioxide. Recent reviews will be found in such journals as the Annual Review of Plant Physiology, and Fortschritte der Botanik.

2 The photosynthetic pigments

Which out of the number of pigments found in a photosynthetic organism is actually active in photosynthesis can often be decided by establishing the "action spectrum" of the process in question. The action spectrum is defined as the wave-length dependency of a photoreaction, and the location of maxima and minima of this spectrum should coincide with the absorption maxima and minima of the active pigments. This means that by comparing the overall action spectrum and the absorption spectrum of the components of a photosynthetic organism it is possible to identify the active pigments. However the role of chlorophyll as the "main" photosynthetic pigment was proposed on the basis of less precise evidence many years before the action spectrum technique was first applied. The pigments in question are enumerated and discussed below.

2.1 Chlorophylls

All photosynthetic organisms contain at least one chlorophyll-type pigment.

2.1.1 Chemistry. The chemical constitution of chlorophylls of higher plants was elucidated by WILLSTÄTTER and STOLL [1913, 1918]. For the most generally occurring one, chlorophyll-a, they established the formula: $C_{55}H_{72}O_5N_4Mg$.

Chlorophylls are esters of di-basic acids, termed chlorophyllins, *e.g.*: chlorophyllin-a: $C_{32}H_{30}ON_4Mg\,(COOH)_2$ which are esterified by the two alcohols: methanol: CH_3OH and phytol: $C_{20}H_{39}OH$ and so the chlorophylls are phytyl-methyl chlorophillides, *e.g.*:

chlorophyll-a: $\begin{matrix} CH_3OOC \\ C_{20}H_{39}OOC \end{matrix} \Big> C_{32}H_{30}ON_4Mg.$

Willstätter and Stoll concluded that chlorophyllins contain four pyrrole nuclei, and the non-ionizable magnesium atom which is probably centrally located. The structural formula was definitely established by FISCHER [1940], (see also FISCHER and STERN [1940]). Fig. 16 shows the formula for chlorophyll-a. The four pyrrole nuclei are arranged in a porphyrin ring. Apart from the pyrrole nuclei, indicated I–IV, there is a fifth ring, the isocyclic or cyclopentanone ring. The magnesium atom is located in the centre of the porphyrin ring.

As the ring structure of chlorophyll is derived from porphin, it is called a porphyrin. The structure of porphin is shown in fig. 17. For such compounds a number of conjugated double bond systems can be drawn. The most simple case in which it is possible to draw various configurations of aromatic double bond systems is encountered with benzene. However, as calculations of the energy content of these possible constructions show, this energy content is higher than the experimentally obtained one. This means that the theoretical configurations do not cover the actually occurring form. This phenomenon is termed chemical resonance. The true structure cannot be depicted: it is indicated as a "resonance hybrid" towards which a number of theoretical forms or "resonating structures" contribute. In this terminology, benzene is a resonance hybrid with two forms:

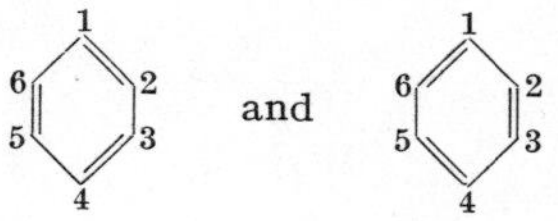

1 2 3 4 5 6 and 1 2 3 4 5 6

as the main contributors. According to ARONOFF [1960], chlorophyll is a resonance hybrid with major contributions from three forms.

Chlorophyll may be regarded as a derivative of *dihydroporphin* since it will form the latter if the double bond between positions 7 and 8 is opened up by the addition of an hydrogen atom to the pertaining carbon atoms. Derivatives of dihydroporphin are called *chlorins* if the cyclopentanone ring is absent. If these compounds belong to the series based on chlorophyll-b, they sometimes are designated *rhodins*. When the cyclopentanone ring is present, dihydroporphin derivatives are termed *phorbins*. If, in addition, they contain magnesium they are

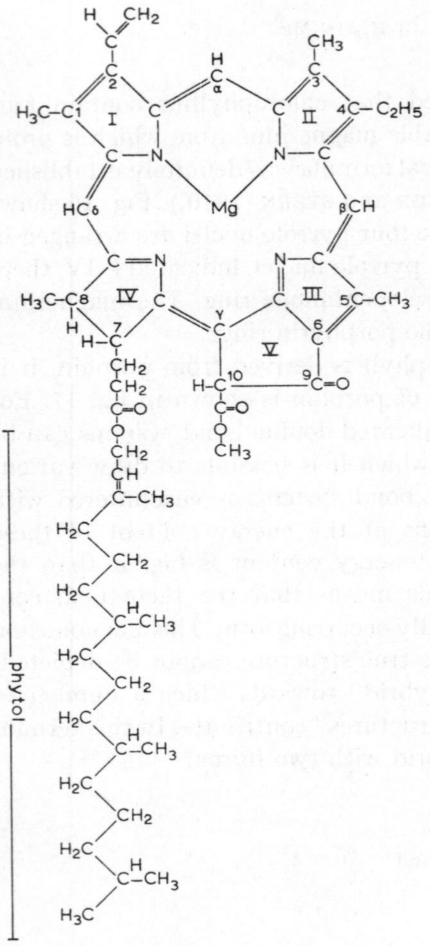

Fig. 16. Chlorophyll-a

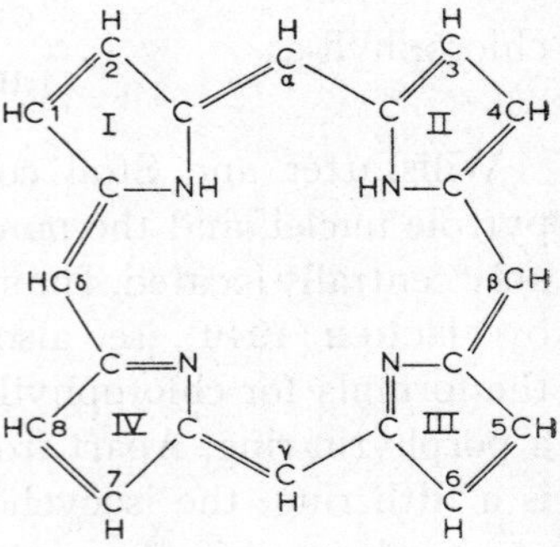

Fig. 17. Porphin

called *phyllins,* while these compounds are termed *phytins,* if one of the esterifying alcohols is phytol. Porphin derivatives carrying the same constituents as chlorophyll but lacking magnesium are indicated by the prefix *pheo-*. Compounds in which the $-CO_2CH_3$ group at position 10 is replaced by hydrogen are indicated by the prefix "*pyro-*", while the prefix "*meso-*" is used if the vinyl group at position 2 is replaced by $-C_2H_5$. Without suggesting that this represents any kind of chemical synthesis, a survey of the nomenclature is given below.

```
porphin
   ↓ + 2H
dihydroporphin
   ↓ + substituent at C–3
chlorin
   ↓ + cyclopentanone ring
phorbin
   ↓ + phytol
phytin
   ↓ + Mg and other substituents
chlorophyll
  ├─ − Mg → pheophytin
  │           − phytol
  │           − methanol
  ├─ → chlorophyllin
  └─ − phytol, + methanol → (di)methyl chlorophyllide
                                ↓ − Mg
                             methyl pheophorbide
```

When considering the substituents at the porphin system, one's attention is focussed on the central magnesium atom first since it seems to be most important to the functioning of chlorophyll. Evidence of the role of Mg is mainly derived from studies of "allomerization" and the "phase test" reaction. Allomerization was first described by WILLSTÄTTER and STOLL [1913] who observed changes of chlorophyll in alcoholic solutions upon standing under air. CONNANT, DIETZ, BAILEY and KAMERLING [1931] showed that on allomerization one mole of oxygen is taken up per mole of chlorophyll and FISCHER and RIEDMAIR [1933] demonstrated that this oxygen uptake occurs only with phyllins, phorbins being inactive in this respect.

The cyclopentanone ring was chosen as the site of the allomerization process which consists of a peroxidation at C–10 resulting in fixation of the H–atom attached to C–10, as shown below.

```
          N—                                   N—
          ||                                   ||
       γ  C   6                             γ  C   6
     =C       C=                          =C       C=
      |       |                            |       |
      |10    9|                            |10    9|
  H—C ——— C = O + O₂ ⟶ HO—O—C ——— C=O
      |                                    |
     C=O                                  C=O
      |                                    |
     OCH₃                                 OCH₃
```

The Mg atom of chlorophyll is readily removed by hydrolysis, even by weak acids. After removal it is no longer possible to perform the allomerization reaction.

Allomerized chlorophyll is not an homogeneous product, but contains at least three fractions. HOLT and JACOBS [1954a, b] observed that, although the structure of these products is different, the chemical change in all of them had taken place in the isocyclic ring as evidenced by their inability to yield the brown compound in the "phase test". In this test, described by MOLISCH [1896], a 30% methanolic KOH solution is layered under a chlorophyll solution in ether. If the cyclopentanone ring is unchanged and the carbomethoxy group at C–10 is present, a yellow-brown ring develops at the interface of the solutions. The appearance of this brownish phase, which according to WELLER [1954] is stable only in the absence of oxygen, is believed to be due to the enolization of the carbonyl group at C–9 (FISCHER and STERN [1940]) in the following way:

```
        N—                           N—                              N—
        ‖                            ‖                               ‖
     γ╱ C ╲6                      γ╱ C ╲6                         γ╱ C ╲6
   =C       C=                  =C       C=         +KOH        =C       C=
    |10     9|       ⇌           |10     9|          ⇌           |10     9|
 H—C————————C=O                 C════════C—OH                   C════════C—OK
    |                            |                               |
   C=O                          C=O                             C=O
    |                            |                               |
   OCH₃                         OCH₃                            OCH₃

 green (chlorophyll)            brown (phase test intermediate)
```

Due to the oxidative fixation of the H-atom at position 10, this enolization is not possible with allomerized chlorophyll.

The double bond which is formed between C–9 and C–10 places the cyclopentanone ring under strain, which means that it can be readily disrupted by oxidation, and more slowly by alcoholysis to give a chlorin as the product.

According to WELLER [1954], the energy of the bond triplet state in the brown phase is lower than that of its singlet state. He therefore suggests that the intermediate compound is an ionized molecule in a triplet or diradical state which is stabilized by resonance. The formation of the brown intermediate is a reversible process although if the reaction is allowed to proceed until the green colour of chlorin appears, it is no longer reversible.

Upon consideration of the facts that (1) allomerization requires the presence of a central magnesium atom, (2) allomerization means oxidation of the H-atom at C–10, (3) allomerized chlorophyll does not yield the brown phase test intermediate in alcoholic alkali, and (4) the initial reaction of the phase test consists of a displacement of the H-atom at position 10 to the oxygen atom at position 9, it seems likely that the central magnesium atom determines the mobility of the H-atom in question. In addition, WEIGL and LIVINGSTON [1953], HOLT and JACOBS [1955] and HOLT [1958] (see also RABINOWITCH [1956]) studied the infrared spectra of the chlorophylls and the relevant derivatives. Among others, Holt suggested that the presence of the central magnesium atom induces a negative charge on the keto oxygen at position 9, thus facilitating enolization.

The "lability" of the H-atom at C-10 might make one expect that it is easily replaced. This supposition however, is not supported by the experiments of WEIGL and LIVINGSTON [1952a] on hydrogen-deuterium exchange between chlorophyll and deuterated water. No such exchange could be detected in neutral solutions of either chlorophyll-a, or pheophytin-a. Moreover, WEIGL and LIVINGSTON [1952b] studied the chlorophyll-sensitized reduction of the azo dye "butter yellow" by deuterated ascorbic acid. In order to avoid proton-deuteron exchange between chlorophyll and solvent, the reaction was studied in dry dioxane. Though the yield of this reduction was very low, it was possible to conclude that no deuterium had entered the chlorophyll molecules after two hours. The authors therefore stated that this particular reaction does not involve a primary hydrogen removal from the chlorophyll. Nevertheless they emphasized that their conclusion does not mean that such a primary hydrogen transfer is excluded for other processes sensitized by chlorophyll.

KUTYRIN [1960] observed a small amount of hydrogen exchange with chlorophyll in aqueous acetone after three hours, while KATZ, THOMAS, CRESPI and STRAIN [1961] using deuterated methanol in a carbon tetrachloride solution of chlorophylls a and b, found a slow but unmistakable, hydrogen exchange at C-10. Complete exchange was obtained after more than 40 hours. The latter authors concluded that both chlorophyll-a and b contain at least one exchangeable hydrogen atom. They suggested that the slowness of this exchange was due to the fact that both chlorophylls occur mainly in the keto form in carbon tetrachloride. KATZ, THOMAS and STRAIN [1962], continuing their expe riments, studied the slow hydrogen exchange in fully deuterated chlorophyll-a by means of the proton magnetic resonance technique. They demonstrated that hydrogen exchange occurred at the δ-carbon atom exclusively. Consequently, the hydrogen atom at C-δ is more "labile" than that at C-10 under their experimental conditions. However, as the authors remarked, it remains to be seen whether such an exchange is of importance with regard to the photosynthetic function of chlorophyll. It should be noted that the exchange was only slow. Moreover, external exchange is a phenomenon quite different from the intramolecular exchange of a hydrogen atom between C-10 and the oxygen atom at C-9 particularly as this involves a change of the electron configuration of the pigment molecule.

Another aspect of the magnesium effect has been studied by HANSON [1937, 1938] who spread ethyl chlorophyllide in monomolecular films on water in a Langmuir trough. By measuring the area occupied by a chlorophyllide molecule, he concluded that this pigment can be hydrated to a considerable extent depending on the pH of the water phase. The degree of hydration of the porphyrin system increased with pH and at the same time its area increased up to a pH of 8.5 when it was about 22% greater than the original area. At pH 4.4., chlorophyll is in its least hydrated state. If the pH is lowered slightly below this value, there is a sudden jump in the molecular surface area of about 17%. This coincides with the loss of the central magnesium atom and its replacement by two hydrogen atoms. Upon subsequently increasing the pH, this area stays constant which means that the pH-dependent hydratation capacity has been lost at the same time as the Mg atom.

By comparing the spreading properties of various chlorophyll derivatives over a broad pH range, Hanson concluded that the cyclopentanone ring is the site of hydratation in chlorophyll. By considering both phenomena together, Hanson furthermore concluded that the central magnesium atom controls the hydratation capacity of the cyclopentanone ring.

This leads to the conclusion that the isocyclic ring shows two features which are of major interest in photosynthesis: it may (1) act in redox reactions, and (2) form complexes with water. It should be emphasized that the information in question has been gained with chlorophyll *in vitro*. Whether this pigment *in vivo* actually functions in the way suggested by these results remains to be confirmed.

Other substituents which might play a role in redox reactions are the vinyl group at position 2, as well as the two extra hydrogen atoms at positions 7 and 8. With regard to these atoms, FICKEN, JOHNS and LINSTEAD [1956] assigned a *trans*-dihydro structure to the chlorophylls.

One substituent which can be reversibly exchanged by enzymic activity is the esterifying alcohol phytol. Chlorophyllase is the active enzyme and was discovered by WILLSTÄTTER and STOLL [1913] who observed the exchange in alcoholic extracts of leaves. Whether this enzyme plays a role in chlorophyll synthesis or destruction, has not yet been experimentally established (see EGLE [1960]). The presence of a long-chain alcohol might be of interest with regard to the *in vivo* arrangement of the chlorophyll molecules. *In vitro*, the long phytol tail prevents crystallization of the chlorophyll and is responsible for its waxy appearance. Crystallization of such a chlorophyllide is possible as soon as the phytol is replaced by a short-chain alcohol.

The phytol tail is hydrophobic while the porphin nucleus, and in particular the cyclopentanone ring are hydrophylic, and so chlorophyll may tend to associate itself with both polar and non-polar compounds, for example both proteins and lipids.

From X-ray analyses of methyl chlorophyllide, HANSON [1938] calculated the dimensions of the porphyrin plate to be 3.87, 15.48, and 15.62 Å. Consequently, the surface area of this plate amounts to 242 Å^2. The thickness of chlorophyll is somewhat larger, namely 4.2 Å (the length of the phytyl group is about 20 Å). The phytol does not appreciably contribute to the colour of chlorophyll since the optical properties in the visible part of the spectrum originate from excitations of the π-electrons of the porphyrin system.

2.1.2 Individual chlorophylls. The following chlorophylls are known:

Chlorophyll-a. It occurs in all autotrophic plants except for bacteria. It will be recalled that the formula is: $C_{55}H_{72}O_5N_4Mg$.

It will dissolve in organic solvents of both polar and non-polar character.

Chlorophyll-b. It accompanies chlorophyll-a in higher plants, ferns, mosses, euglenas and green algae. The abundance ratio chlorophyll-b/chlorophyll-a may vary, but as a rule is not far from 1/3. The formula elucidated by WILLSTÄTTER and STOLL [1913, 1918] is: $C_{55}H_{70}O_6N_4Mg$ and FISCHER [1940] established the molecular structure. It is the same as that of chlorophyll-a, (fig. 16), except for the fact that the methyl ($-CH_3$) group at position 3 is replaced by a formyl ($-CHO$) group.

Chorophyll-b is soluble in both polar and non-polar organic solvents.

Chorophyll-c. Synonyms: *chorophyll γ* and *chlorofucine*, accompanies chlorophyll-a in diatoms and other brown algae, dinoflagellates, cryptomonads, and chrysomonads. The abundance ratio chlorophyll-c/chlorophyll-a is 1/10 at the most according to RABINOWITCH [1945]. It was recognized as a naturally occurring pigment, rather than an artifact, by STRAIN and MANNING [1942a]. The formula is still unknown. According to GRANICK [1949], chlorophyll-c contains magnesium, while JEFFREY [1963] stated that the magnesium content is $2.31 \pm 0.045\%$. The cyclopentanone ring is present but there is no phytol group. It is soluble in aqueous alcohol but insoluble in non-polar solvents.

Chlorophyll-d. It was first observed by MANNING and STRAIN [1943] together with chlorophyll-a in most, but not all of the red algae, though in very small amounts. However in the red alga *Rhodochorton rothii* (STRAIN [1949]) the ratio of chlorophyll-d to chlorophyll-a is as high as 1/3. According to HOLT [1961], some thalli within the single species, *Gigartina papillata* contain this chlorophyll while others do not. This author and HOLT and MORLEY [1959] obtained an oxidation product of chlorophyll-a upon the addition of potassium permanganate which was not the allomerized form of chlorophyll, the cyclopentanone ring being preserved intact. In fact, the vinyl group at position 2 had been oxidised to give a formyl group. The absorption spectrum of this derivative was found to be identical with that of chlorophyll-d and the phase-test intermediates of both compounds showed the same red colour. The reduced forms of both pigments had the same spectrum and chromatography of the purified compounds gave only a single band. Consequently it seems most likely that chlorophyll-d is 2-disvinyl-2-formyl-chlorophyll-a. It is soluble in both polar and non-polar organic solvents.

Chlorophyll-e. Found by STRAIN [1949, 1951] in the yellow-green alga *Tribonema bombycinum* together with chlorophyll-a. This pigment is found only in very small amounts and is soluble in methanol.

Chlorophyll species of a Datura mutant. It was observed spectroscopically by INMAN and BLAKESLEE [1938] who extracted it from the cells with acetone and then transferred the pigment to ether. The corresponding pheophytins were also found to be different from any known ones.

Bacteriochlorophyll. It is found unaccompanied by other chlorophylls in photosynthetic purple bacteria, both Thiorhodaceae and Athiorhodaceae. SEYBOLD and EGLE [1938] isolated three forms by the chromatography of bacterial extracts – according to the authors, two forms may be artifacts – though Fischer and coworkers (see FISCHER and STERN [1940]) noticed only a single form, and established both its

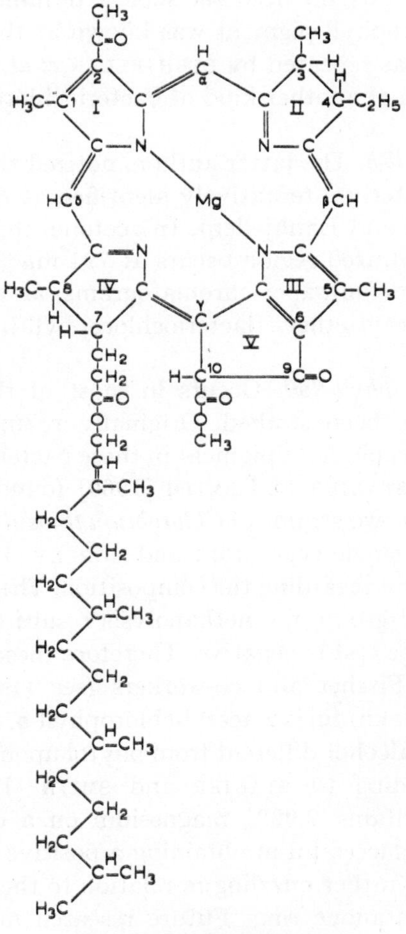

Fig. 18. Bacteriochlorophyll

formula $C_{55}H_{74}O_6N_4Mg$ and its structure as depicted in fig. 18. Bacteriochlorophyll contains two extra H-atoms at positions 3 and 4 and so this pigment is a derivative of tetrahydro-porphin. In addition, it differs from chlorophyll-a in that the vinyl group at position 2 is replaced by an acetyl group. Bacteriochlorophyll is soluble in both polar and non-polar organic solvents.

It was proposed on two occasions that this pigment should be named "bacteriochlorophyll-a". This suggestion did not meet with much approval since there was no need for such a terminology as only one single bacteriochlorophyll pigment was known at that time. The suggestion however, was repeated by EIMHJELLEN *et al.* [1963] as a result of their observation of another kind of bacteriochlorophyll which they termed:

Bacteriochlorophyll-b. The latter authors noticed this pigment in the photosynthetic bacterium tentatively identified as *Rhodopseudomonas* spec. (Aasmundrud and Eimhjellen). In acetone, the main absorption band in the near-infrared region occurs at 794 mμ. The pigment is of a bluish-green colour on paper chromatograms, as well as in solution in acetone and diethyl ether. Bacteriochlorophyll-b is soluble in methanol.

Chlorobium chlorophyll-660. Occurs in most of the green sulphur bacteria which have been studied. Originally P. METZNER [1922] observed a single chlorophyllous pigment in these bacteria which he called "bacterioviridin". STANIER and SMITH [1960] found two chlorophyll species, however, in two strains of *Chlorobium thiosulphatophilum,* each strain containing a single type. HOLT and MORLEY [1960] obtained the following information regarding the composition. The pigment does not contain a methoxyl group, no methanolysis resulting in ring opening occurs and the phase test is negative. Therefore these authors rejected the suggestion of Fischer and co-workers (see FISCHER and STERN [1940]), that bacterioviridin is 2-acetyl-chlorophyll-a. HOLT and HUGHES [1961] obtained an alcohol different from phytol upon hydrolysis of this chlorophyll. According to STANIER and SMITH [1960], chlorobium chlorophyll-660 contains 2.92% magnesium on a dry weight basis. They too were not successful in obtaining a positive phase test.

This result seems rather puzzling in relation to the normal functioning of the cyclopentanone ring. Future research may elucidate this problem but only after the establishment of the molecular structure will it be possible to draw any conclusions about this matter. The pigment is soluble in ether, acetone and methanol, but insoluble in petroleum ether.

Chlorobium chlorophyll-650. Is also found in green bacteria, though probably in not so many cases. It has been isolated from *Chlorobium thiosulphatophilum*, strain L, by STANIER and SMITH [1960]. The magnesium content is 2.59% on a dry weight basis and the phase test is negative. According to HOLT and HUGHES [1961] there is no methoxyl group at position 10. Hydrolysis does not yield phytol but gives an alcohol which is identical with that from the 660-form. It is also similar to the 660-form in being soluble in ether, acetone and methanol, but insoluble in petroleum ether.

HUGHES and HOLT [1961] succeeded in demonstrating by means of liquid-liquid partition chromatography the occurrence of six components of chlorobium chlorophyll-650, though they did not discover whether these components occur simultaneously in one and the same cell.

Chlorobium chlorophyll-770. Was observed in "warm-methanol" extracts from *Chlorobium thiosulphatophilum* and *Chloropseudomonas ethylicum* by OLSON and ROMANO [1962]. It is suggested by the authors that this chlorophyll acts as the terminal excitation energy acceptor, rather than chlorophyl-650 or -660. It has not been established whether chlorophyll-770 is identical with the bacteriochlorophyll from purple bacteria, though this possibility has gained support by the results of EIMHJELLEN *et al.* [1963].

Apart from the photosynthetically active chlorophylls, a number of precursor pigments have been isolated. As the biosynthesis of chlorophylls and related compounds does not fit directly into the present discussion, it may suffice to quote pertinent reviews by GRANICK [1951] and BOGORAD [1960]. An exception will be made for the following two compounds from the biosynthesis chain.

Protoporphyrin-9. The parent species of both hemes (iron porphyrins) and chlorophylls (magnesium porphyrins). This protoporphyrin has been found by GRANICK [1948a, b] in a dark brown, X-ray-induced *Chlorella* mutant devoid of chlorophyll. Its formula is $C_{34}H_{34}O_4N_4$. Fig. 19 shows the molecular structure.

Protochlorophyll. Is of interest here as in most cases, its conversion to chlorophyll-a is evoked by light. This kind of conversion will be discussed later. However chlorophyll formation in conifer seedlings and algae is exceptional in that it occurs in darkness. GODNEV and TERENTJEVA [1953] infiltrated etiolated corn seedlings with an extract of pine seedlings and observed the subsequent protochlorophyll-chlorophyll conversion in the dark.

Protochlorophyll occurs in etiolated seedlings and, in relatively large

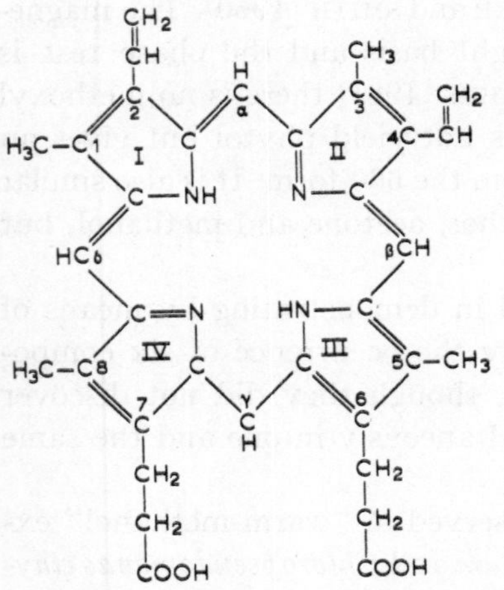

Fig. 19. Protoporphyrin-9

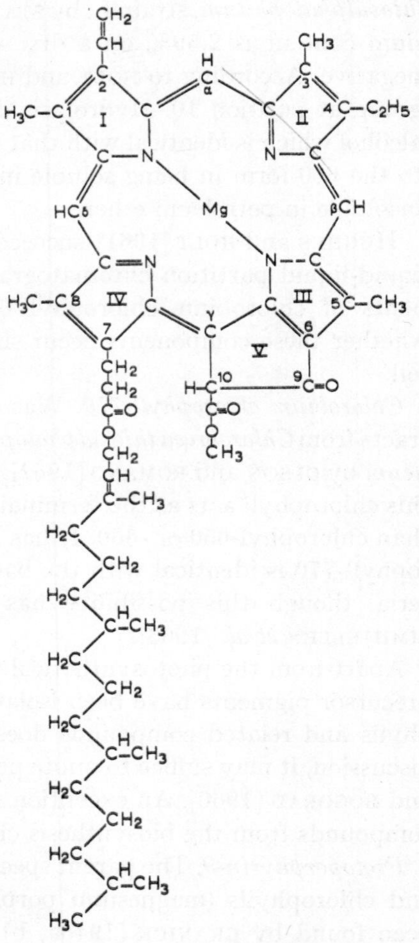

Fig. 20. Protochlorophyll

quantities, in the inner seed coats of squash. In the latter tissues it is in a form which cannot be converted into chlorophyll. Presumably this kind of protochlorophyll is a storage form. It is also formed in green leaves but, as a consequence of its slow formation and the immediate conversion into chlorophyll-a by light, its concentration remains extremely low. Both formula and structure have been elucidated by Fischer and coworkers (see FISCHER and STERN [1940]). The formula is $C_{55}H_{70}O_5N_4Mg$. The structure is shown in fig. 20. It is similar to that of chlorophyll-a, except for the absence of the extra H-atoms at positions 7 and 8.

It has been clearly established by SMITH and YOUNG [1956] that protochlorophyll yields only chlorophyll-a upon conversion. The formation of chlorophyll-b is still a problem. According to SMITH [1960], chlorophyll-b is not likely to originate from either chlorophyll-a or protochlorophyll. Protochlorophyll b has never been unambiguously observed. STANIER and SMITH [1959] isolated a protochlorophyll-like pigment from a *Rhodopseudomonas spheroides* mutant. Normally this bacterium contains bacteriochlorophyll.

According to STRAIN [1949], chlorophylls are very labile compounds and may exist in a number of isomeric forms. In the living cell, only one single isomer of each pigment occurs though upon extraction with organic solvents other forms readily appear. The following have been isolated and studied by STRAIN and MANNING [1942]: chlorophyll-a′ and chlorophyll-b′, and, by MANNING and STRAIN [1943], chlorophyll-d′, isochlorophyll-d, and isochlorophyll-d′.

2.1.3 Optical properties. In general, chlorophyll spectra are characterized by the four independent electronic transitions lying between 350 and 900 mμ. As a rule, two major absorption bands are observed. The main low-energy band is located in the red (chlorophyll) or near infrared (bacteriochlorophyll), and is accompanied by at least one vibrational band. A second transition gives rise to a minor band in the yellow, while in the blue-violet a doublet band originating from two separate electronic transitions occurs. Spectra of chlorophylls and derivatives are shown in fig. 21.

The spectra are those of solutions in ether. The solvent exerts some influence on the spectra in the sense of Hundt's rule: the higher the refractive index of the solvent, the more the absorption maxima are shifted in the long-wave direction. In this respect, polar and non-polar solvents act as different series. A thorough discussion of these effects as well as the interpretation of porphyrin spectra has been presented by RABINOWITCH [1951, 1956].

When considering fig. 21 more closely, it is apparent that the height of the "red" absorption band varies considerably relative to the blue-violet band. In order to compare the relative heights of the red and blue bands in the various compounds, the spectra have been plotted so that the blue band is of the same height in all of the compounds. Where the blue band is not a single peak but appears as a "doublet", the average height of the two peaks has been adjusted to be equal to

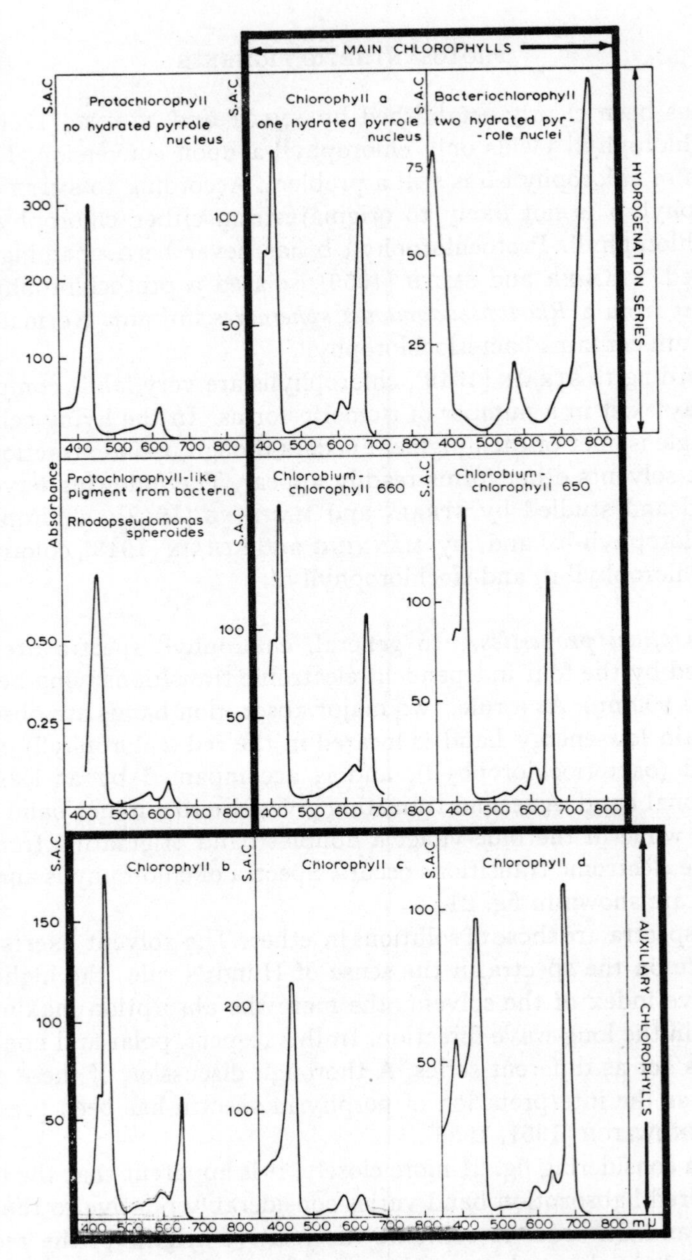

Fig. 21. Survey of absorption spectra of chlorophylls and derivatives. The spectra are replotted on a different scale from KOSKI and SMITH [1948] (protochlorophyll), by permission of the American Chemical Society, SMITH and BENITEZ [1954] (chlorophylls a-d, bacteriochlorophyll), SMITH [1960] (bacterial protochlorophyll), and STANIER [1960] (chlorobium chlorophyll). S. A. C.: specific absorption coefficient

the others. This method of plotting, it is emphatically stated, is only approximative and is done purely to facilitate a comparison of the heights of the red absorption bands. The three upper spectra show that the height of the red band increases considerably and its location shifts to the long-wave side with an increasing number of hydrogenated pyrrole

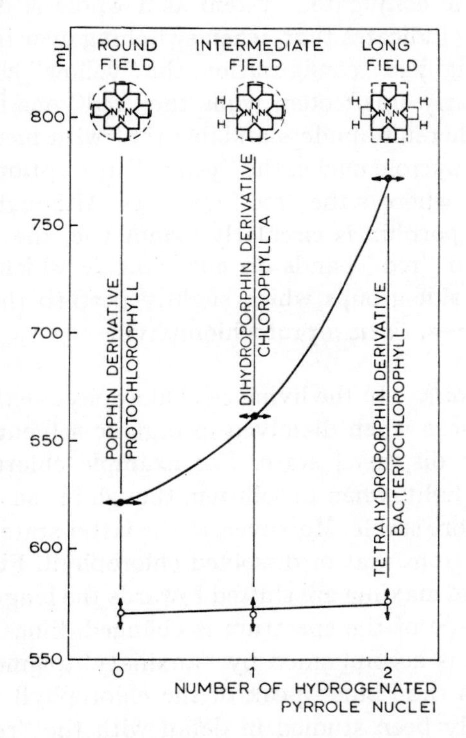

Fig. 22. Relation between electronic structure and location of yellow and red absorption maxima of porphin, dihydroprophin, and tetrahydroporphin derivatives. The direction of the arrows indicates the "vibration direction" of the two absorbing oscillators

nuclei. On the other hand, the yellow band at around 570 mμ which is due to a different electronic transition, is less affected by the hydrogenation of the pyrrole nuclei as far as height is concerned and its location remains nearly unchanged. These phenomena are discussed by GOEDHEER [1957] on the basis of the LCAO (Linear Combination of Atomic Orbitals) method of LONGUETT-HIGGINS, RECTOR and PLATT [1950]. This method is a means of calculating the spectrum of a molecule from its electronic structure. As mentioned earlier the porphyrin molecules are resonance hybrids and so it is incorrect to depict the conjugated bond system as a definite succession of single and double bonds. However it is possible to indicate which part of the molecule belongs to a conjugated bond system. This is shown in fig. 22. Instead of alternating single and double bonds, the conjugated system as a whole is drawn in heavy lines. The picture indicates that, when switching over from the "round field" to the "long field" configuration, the "yellow" electronic transition remains nearly unaffected, while the "red" one is changed considerably. It is therefore understandable that with increasing number of hydrogenated pyrrole nuclei, the "yellow" absorption band does not shift appreciably whereas the "red" one does. Although the electronic configuration of porphin is circularly symmetric, the wavelengths of the "yellow" and "red" bands do not coincide which is due to the influence of the side-groups which slightly perturb the symmetry in porphin derivatives, *in casu* protochlorophyll.

2.1.4 Physical state. In the living cell chlorophylls exhibit properties different from those when dissolved in organic solvents, that is, in a monomolecularly dispersed state. For example chlorophylls readily bleach in strong light, when in solution, though in the "natural" state they are much more stable. Moreover, in the latter state the absorption spectrum differs from that of dissolved chlorophyll. Firstly, the locations of the *in vivo* maxima are shifted towards the long-wave side, and secondly, the shape of the spectrum is changed. Since chlorophyll in the *in vivo* state is accompanied by "auxiliary" pigments whose absorption overlaps the "blue" peak of the chlorophyll the latter phenomenon has only been studied in detail with the "red" absorption bands. The simple long-wave band seen in dissolved chlorophylls is broadened by the occurrence of shoulders in the *in vivo* state, and in the case of bacteriochlorophyll there are even additional peaks. This phenomenon is demonstrated in fig. 23.

As the chlorophylls *in vivo* and in the dissolved state are chemically the same (see KOMEN [1956]), the obvious conclusion is that the chlorophylls *in vivo* do not occur in the monomolecularly dispersed state but are in some complex state.

The nature of this may be: (1) chlorophyll-chlorophyll complexes or aggregates, (2) chlorophyll-auxiliary pigment complexes, (3) chlorophyll-(lipo)protein complexes, or a combination of these.

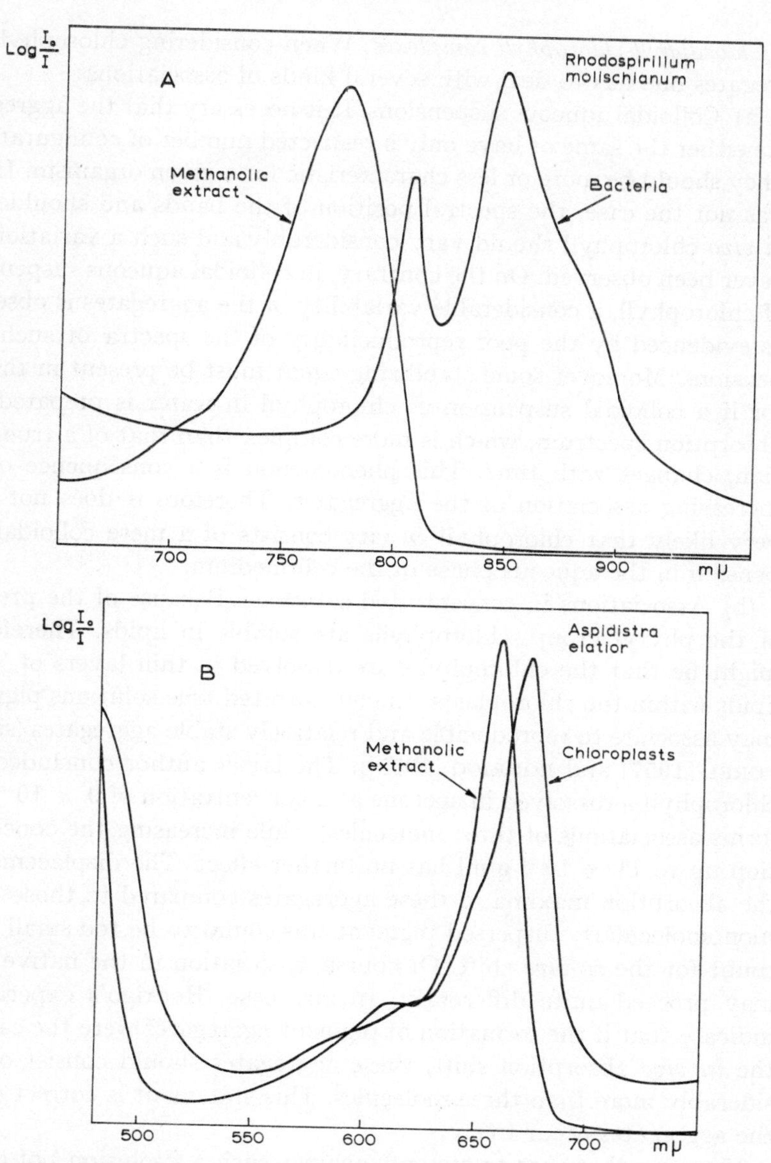

Fig. 23. Comparison of the long-wave absorption band of (A) bacteriochlorophyll and (B) chlorophyll in both the *in vivo* and monomolecularly dispersed states

Chlorophyll-chlorophyll complexes. When considering chlorophyll aggregates one has to deal with several kinds of associations:

(a) Colloidal aqueous suspensions. It is necessary that the aggregates are either the same or have only a restricted number of configurations. They should be more or less characteristic for a given organism. If this was not the case, the spectral position of the bands and shoulders of *in vivo* chlorophyll should vary considerably and such a variation has never been observed. On the contrary, in colloidal aqueous suspensions of chlorophyll, a considerable variability of the aggregates is observed as evidenced by the poor reproducibility of the spectra of such suspensions. Moreover some stabilizing agent must be present in the cell for if a colloidal suspension of chlorophyll in water is prepared, the absorption spectrum, which is more complex than that of a true solution, changes with time. This phenomenon is a consequence of the increasing association of the aggregates. Therefore it does not seem very likely that chlorophyll *in vivo* consists of a mere colloidal suspension in the aqueous phase of the cell medium.

(b) Associations in concentrated solutions. Because of the presence of the phytyl group, chlorophylls are soluble in lipids. Therefore it might be that the chlorophylls are dissolved in thin layers of "free" lipids within the chloroplasts. In concentrated true solutions pigments may associate to reproducible and relatively stable aggregates (see LAVOREL [1957] and RODRIGO [1955]). The latter author concluded that chlorophyll-a dissolved in acetone at a concentration of 9×10^{-4} g/ml forms associations of three molecules, while increasing the concentration up to 11×10^{-4} g/ml has no further effect. The displacement of the absorption maxima of these aggregates compared to those of the monomolecularly dispersed pigment was found to be too small to account for the *in vivo* shift. Of course, association in the native lipids may proceed quite differently. In any case, Rodrigo's experiments indicate that if the formation of pigment aggregates were the cause of the *in vivo* absorption shift, these aggregates should consist of considerably more than three molecules. This statement is correct only if the aggregates occur freely.

However there are arguments against such a "solution" of chlorophyll in the free-lipid layers. One is that the thickness of such layers is of the order of 50 Å while according to GOEDHEER [1957] that of the pigment layers is only of the order of 5 Å.

(c) Crystals. Extensive study on this field has been done in Rabinowitch's group by JACOBS *et al.* [1954, 1957]. The absorption of micro-crystals of chlorophyll-a and bacteriochlorophyll show long-wave shifts of 80 and 90 mμ respectively from that of the monomolecular state. This shift falls to as much as 40% of this amount in crystals smaller than 0.5 μ in diameter. The fact that these shifts are much larger than those of *in vivo* chlorophyll and the absence of crystal fluorescence (at least, at wavelengths up to 1 μ) means that the occurrence of crystalline chlorophyll in the living cell is rather unlikely.

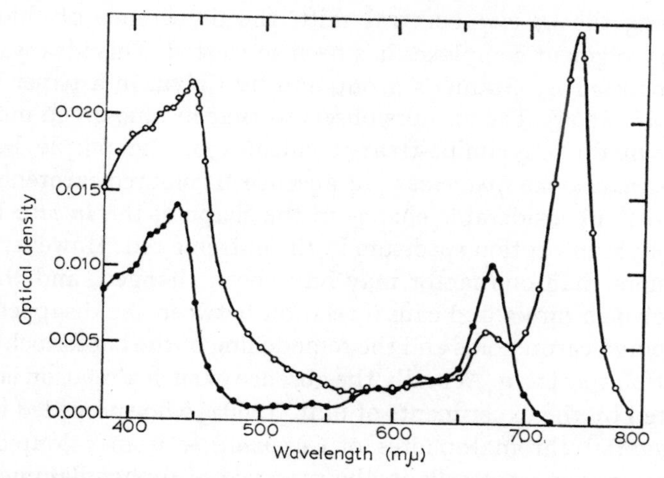

Fig. 24. Comparison of absorption spectra of crystalline chlorophyll-a film (open circles) and non-crystalline chlorophyll-a film (filled circles). From: JACOBS, VATTER and HOLT [1954]

(d) Monolayers. Chlorophyll monolayers on water were prepared and studied by the same authors. It proved possible to obtain both monolayers of a "compressed gas" character as well as monolayers of a "crystalline" character by adding Ca^{++} ions. The absorption spectra of both kinds of monolayers are shown in fig. 24. The difference is considerable since "crystalline" monolayers absorb maximally in the long-wave region around 735 mμ, whereas "compressed gas" monolayers show the red absorption band around 675 mμ. As the red chlorophyll band occurs in between 673 and 683 mμ *in vivo*, these results are incompatible with the conception that chlorophyll occurs in crystalline monolayers in living cells. On the other hand they do not rule out the possibility that chlorophyll *in vivo* is arranged in "compressed gas" monolayers. The experiments of TRURNIT and COLMANO [1958] who studied chlorophyll films at water-air and water-oil interfaces, support the hypothesis that chlorophyll *in vivo* does occur in monolayers.

Monolayers, of course, need interfaces. The electron microscope revealed that in chlorophyll-carrying organelles, layered structures occur as a rule. These structures most probably consist of alternating layers of lipids and lipoproteins.

Chlorophyll-auxiliary pigment complexes. As a second possibility of explaining the *in vivo* spectral shift, the occurrence of chlorophyll-auxiliary pigment complexes has been suggested. This idea was originally promoted by Stanier's group and by Calvin in a paper by GRIFFITH *et al.* [1955]. The authors observed that in blue-green mutants as well as in diphenylamine-treated cultures of the purple bacterium *Rhodopseudomonas spheroides*, the absence of coloured carotenoids coincided with a considerable change in the shape of the *in vivo* bacteriochlorophyll absorption spectrum in the extreme red. However, in both cases more than one factor may have been changed, and thus there need not be a direct and causal relation between the disappearance of the coloured carotenoids and the remodelling of the bacteriochlorophyll absorption spectrum. Actually the absence of such a relation is strongly suggested by the experiments of BRIL [1960a] who succeeded in freeing the bacterial chromatophores of *Chromatium* from coloured carotenoids by growing the cells in the presence of diphenylamine without any change in the shape of the bacteriochlorophyll absorption spectrum. This is contradictory to the conception that the shape of the *in vivo* bacteriochlorophyll absorption spectrum depends on complex formation between carotenoids and bacteriochlorophyll. The same conclusion was arrived at by WASSINK and KRONENBERG [1962].

It may be added that FULLER *et al.* [1961] noticed a decrease in height of the 850 mμ absorption maximum in chromatophore suspensions from the purple sulphur bacterium *Chromatium*, when isolated in buffered media containing various concentrations of glucose, compared with those of such suspensions in 0.5 M sucrose. The spectra of the latter preparations were similar to those of the live bacteria. They suggested that this may be due to partial uncoupling of carotenoids and bacteriochlorophyll based on osmotic or permeability effects, though the mechanism is not yet clear. This again suggests that some carotenoid-bacteriochlorophyll complex is responsible for the shape of the absorption spectrum *in vivo*. BRIL [1960b] showed, however, that swelling of bacterial chromatophores results in inhibition of electronic energy transfer from the types of bacteriochlorophyll complexes with absorption maxima around 800 and 850 mμ, called B800 and B850 respectively, to the type absorbing around 890 mμ (B890). BRIL [1962] observed that as soon as this energy transfer is blocked, B850 becomes extremely sensitive towards light and oxygen as shown by its being readily bleached. It may well be that this phenomenon underlies the results of Fuller *et al.* Moreover, one may expect that carotenoid absorption should also change on the uncoupling of the complex with bacteriochlorophyll as suggested by the latter authors. According to the published spectra, such a shift is small, if it occurs at all.

Still, carotenoids do exert some influence on chlorophylls. FUJIMORI and LIVINGSTON [1957] found that carotenes are able to quench the triplet state of chlorophyll in organic solutions. FULLER *et al.* [1961] observed that bacteriochlorophyll is protected from photodestruction in air by the presence of carotenoids. This also is true for chlorophyll *in vivo*. CLAES [1961] stated that only carotenoids with at least 9 conjugated double bonds show this effect and so in this sense a close correlation between chlorophylls and carotenoids seems to occur. The present author's opinion on the basis of the foregoing discussion, is that this correlation is not likely to be responsible for the shape of the *in vivo* chlorophyll spectrum.

Carotenoids are not the only pigments which are thought to form complexes with chlorophyll. BUTLER [1961] suggested that a far-red absorbing form of chlorophyll-a with its maximum around 705 mμ may represent a chlorophyll-cytochrome complex.

Chlorophyll-carrier complexes. The third possibility of explaining the *in vivo* shift depends upon the formation of chlorophyll-carrier complexes, the "carrier" being some colourless cell constituent. There are a number of observations which favour this idea. For example, in aqueous extracts of green cells – obtained by rupturing cells or tissues by grinding, sonication or other means – the absorption spectrum remains identical with that of the intact cell. The acid-resistance as well as the photostability of suspensions of such native chlorophyll are much higher than those of dissolved chlorophyll.

According to WILLSTÄTTER and STOLL [1918] the complexes are sensitive to heat. The spectrum changes on boiling the suspension to resemble those of chlorophyll solutions in organic solvents and the stability of the complex is lost. LUBIMENKO [1927] prepared "stable" and fairly clear aqueous extracts from certain leaves, such as *Aspidistra elatior.* Upon adding acetone or alcohol the pigment-carrier complex was precipitated and the pigment dissolved away from its carrier. This author also found that carotenoids always accompany the chlorophyll-carrier complexes.

STOLL and WIEDEMANN [1938] succeeded in purifying the pigment complex by several cycles of salting it out with ammonium sulfate and then resuspending the precipitate. These properties of the complex suggest that the carrier is of a proteinaceous nature and could be either a protein or a lipoprotein. Analysis showed that the complexes from a number of higher plants consist of about $\frac{4}{5}$ parts of protein, of $\frac{1}{10}$–$\frac{1}{5}$ parts of lipoids and of $\frac{1}{20}$ parts of pigments. These pigments are chlorophylls -a and -b, "carotene" and "xanthophyll". The ratio of their concentrations was found to be the same as that in the green leaf. The complex was termed by these authors "chloroplastin". The isoelectric point of a number of complexes from different species varies between 3.7 in *Chlorella* (KATZ and WASSINK [1939]) to 5.06 in *Melilotus alba* (MOYER and FISHMAN [1943]). PRICE and WYCKOFF [1938] obtained a particle weight of the pigment complex of about 5 500 000, whereas SMITH and PICKELS [1941] determined this weight in digitonin-clarified suspensions and found a "molecular weight" of about 265 000. The latter weight is that of the protein carrier deprived of its pigments. The difference in "molecular weight" from both studies is too large to be due to the loss of pigments. It also seems from other investigations that there is no constant ratio of chlorophyll and protein. According to RABINOWITCH [1945], this ratio is at least four times greater than that in the pigment-carrier complexes of hemoglobin or cytochromes.

Quite a number of studies on the pigment-carrier complexes have been made and although only a few have been mentioned above these may suffice to show the likelihood of the occurrence of chlorophyll-(lipo)protein complexes in the living cell. The fact that chlorophyll is readily detached from its natural carrier, for example by organic solvents, suggests that the binding forces between pigment and carrier are relatively weak.

If now we summarize the possible explanations of the *in vivo* spectral shift, it does not seem very probable that crystalline and highly aggregated states of chlorophyll, or chlorophyll-carotenoid complexes are responsible. On the other hand, in "compressed gas" monolayers of chlorophyll, the absorption spectrum changes are comparable to those *in vivo,* while complex formation between chlorophyll and protein in the natural state seems very likely.

As mentioned earlier, GOEDHEER [1957] concluded from optical evidence that pigmented layers occur in the cell with a thickness of the order of 5 Å. Since the thickness of the porphyrin plate of the chlorophyll molecule is about 4 Å it appears that chlorophyll exists as mono-

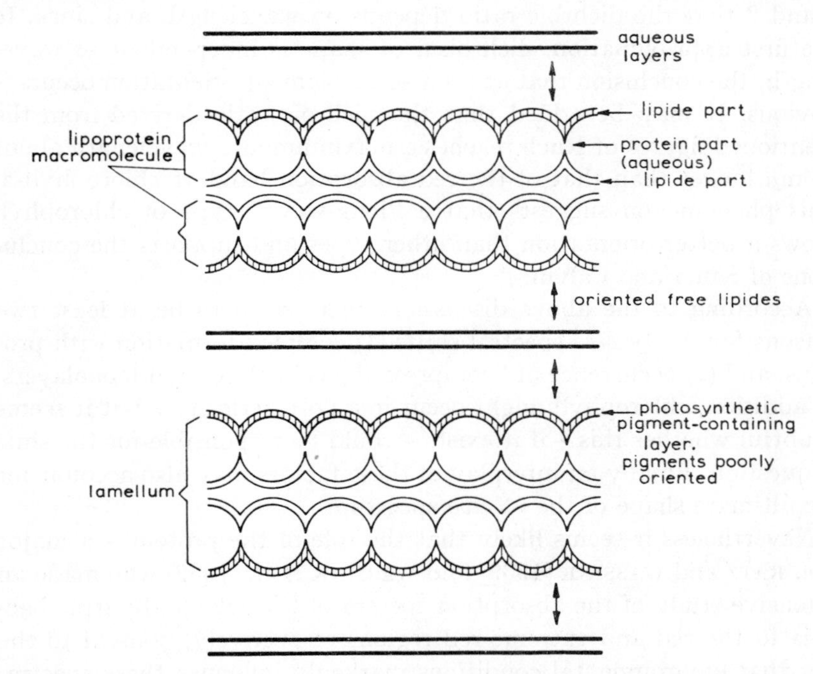

Fig. 25. Location of chlorophyll molecules in *Mougeotia* chloroplasts as suggested by GOEDHEER [1957]

layers in the living cell. Moreover, from fluorescence depolarization and dichroism measurements, Goedheer concluded that chlorophyll molecules are oriented *in vivo* though only to a small extent. Since the electron microscope shows thin proteinaceous lamellae in nearly all chlorophyll-carrying structures, he suggested that the chlorophyll-carrier complexes may be arranged in flat lamellae, as indicated in fig. 25. In this figure the pigments are supposed to occur only at the outer boundaries of the lamellae. This is supported by a paper of THOMAS *et al.* [1958] on the basis of considerations of energy transfer. SAUER and CALVIN [1962] concluded from electric dichroism measurements that only a small fraction (about 5%) of the chlorophyll is orientated in the lamellar subunits of spinach chloroplasts. The authors suggested that this fraction occurs at a particular site in the subunit.

RUCH [1957] stated that dichroism of *Mougeotia* chloroplasts is dichroism *of shape* exclusively. This statement implies that the pigment molecules are not oriented at all. However, it appears from his figures 1 and 2 that the dichroic ratio depends on wavelength and since, to the first approximation, dichroism of shape is independent of wavelength, the conclusion that at least some pigment orientation occurs is obvious. It may be added that the dichroic ratio derived from the mentioned figures of Ruch reaches a maximum at a wavelength about 10 mμ longer than that of the red absorption band of chlorophyll-a. This phenomenon suggests that a "long-wave" type of chlorophyll shows a better orientation than other types and supports the conclusions of Sauer and Calvin.

According to the above discussion, there seem to be at least two reasons for the *in vivo* spectral shift: (1) complex formation with proteins, and (2) occurrence of "compressed gas" chlorophyll monolayers. In addition, chlorophyll might occur in a polymeric state but it seems doubtful whether this – if it exists – could be responsible for the shift in question. Finally an interplay of these factors may also account for the ultimate shape of the *in vivo* spectrum.

Nevertheless it seems likely that the role of the protein is a major one. KATZ and WASSINK [1939] and WASSINK *et al.* [1939] who made an extensive study of the absorption spectra of *Chlorella* and purple bacteria in the red and extreme-red regions respectively, pointed to the fact that environmental conditions markedly influence these spectra, in particular those of the purple bacteria. Furthermore these authors suggest that in purple bacteria the three extreme-red absorption maxima may represent complex formation between bacteriochlorophyll and three different proteins. This hypothesis seems to be supported at least partly by a study by BRIL [1958] who succeeded in separating the major part – if not all – of the bacteriochlorophyll complex B890 from the remainder of the types responsible for the absorption at 800 and 850 mμ in *Rhodopseudomonas spheroides* homogenates by treatment with a non-ionic detergent.

Originally different "types" were observed exclusively in *in vivo* bacteriochlorophyll by the well marked shift and splitting-up of the *in vivo* band relative to that in solution. Improvement of the resolving power of monochromators as well as increased sensitivity of the detector systems enabled more detailed studies of the red band of chlorophyll in its natural state. However before such types had been demonstrated by spectrophotometry, indirect evidence of the occurrence of at least two "forms" of *in vivo* chlorophyll-a had been obtained. HAXO and BLINKS [1950] as well as DUYSENS [1951], concluded from photosynthesis action spectra and fluorescence measurements respectively that at least two "modifications" or "types" of chlorophyll-a must exist *in vivo*. VISHNIAC [1960] also noted a difference in the case of acetone extraction of two fractions of chlorophyll-a from chloroplast fragments.

FRENCH and YOUNG [1956] concluded from calculations of the data on red algae from HAXO and BLINKS [1950], that chlorophyll-a in these organisms occurs in a photosynthetically active form with maximum absorption in the red around 670 mμ, as well as in an "inactive" one with its red maximum around 680 mμ. From experiments on the bleaching of chlorophyll in bright light, KRASNOVSKY and KOSOBUTSKAJA [1955], VOROB'EVA and KRASNOVSKY [1956] and KRASNOVSKY, VOROB'EVA and PAKASHINA [1957] also obtained evidence for the presence of two forms absorbing at the wavelengths 670 and 682 mμ respectively. The occurrence of absorption maxima at these wavelengths was directly demonstrated by HALLDAL [1958a] in the blue-green alga *Anacystis*. As alcoholic extracts showed only a single peak, he suggested that the two forms, termed C_a670 and C_a680, represent complexes with different proteins. In aged *Euglena* cells, FRENCH and ELLIOT [1958] observed a third chlorophyll-a type, absorbing around 695 mμ. KOK [1956] noticed absorption changes upon illumination around 705 mμ due to a pigment present in small amount and called P700 by KOK and HOCH [1961]. Purification experiments made KOK [1961] suggest that P700 is a chlorophyll-a complex. BROWN [1960] observed a weak "shoulder" at 707 mμ in *Euglena*.

The absorption shoulders on the red absorption band of *in vivo* chlorophyll-a are weak and their occurrence seems to depend on certain conditions such as age of the cell and light intensity and temperature during culturing. Therefore certain shoulders might have been only very weak if not unobservable in some preparations. Because of this weakness and a failure to observe them in a reproducible manner, some shoulders might have escaped attention. For this reason, THOMAS [1962] studied the shape of the red absorption band of a large number of chloroplast preparations from *Aspidistra elatior* leaves and plotted the frequency of occurrence of shoulders and maxima *versus* wavelength. It seemed that five shoulders may occur apart from the main absorption maximum, and since no correlation was found between the occurrence of any particular shoulder, it was suggested that each shoulder represents a different chlorophyll form. These types or complexes were designated according to the wavelengths of their main location: C_a664, C_a667, C_a673, C_a678 (main maximum), C_a697, and C_a703. The same author [1963] demonstrated that the shorter wavelength bands are not due to chlorophyll-b by a study of the red absorption band of the blue-green alga *Anacystis nidulans* which do not contain chlorophyll-b. The same frequency distribution of shoulders was found although at slightly different wavelengths. In addition, a sixth shoulder around 660 mμ was observed and it seems likely that at least 7 chlorophyll-a complexes may occur *in vivo*. For a more detailed review concerning the chlorophyll-a types, reference should be made to SMITH and FRENCH [1963].

Beyond the fact that different complexing proteins most probably contribute considerably to the *in vivo* shifts, various other factors may contribute to this shift as well. For instance the group of Krasnovsky (KRASNOVSKY and KOSOBUTSKAJA [1952]), as well as the group of J.H.C. Smith (see SMITH and BENITEZ [1953]) and SHIBATA [1957] noticed a shift of the red absorption band of chlorophyll-a upon its transformation from protochlorophyll. According to Krasnovsky *et al.*, the maximum of the freshly formed chlorophyll shifts from 670 to 678 mμ. Shibata, however, found that prior to this shift an opposite one takes place. Immediately upon conversion of protochlorophyll in etiolated bean leaves, chlorophyll-a displays its red maximum at 684 mμ. Within 10–20 minutes this maximum shifts to 673 mμ and then the previously noted long-wave shift to 677 mμ commences.

A few words should be said about the interpretation of the chlorophyll transformation phenomena. Krasnovsky *et al.* explained the long-wave shift in question by assuming that chlorophyll-a passes from the monomeric state responsible for the 670 mμ absorption maximum into some polymeric configuration with a 677 mμ absorption peak. Much more experimental evidence is needed before this is verified. SMITH [1960] enumerated the possibilities which may underly the conversion phenomena and in particular, the shift from 684 to 673 mμ. These are: (1) rearrangement of the pigment on the carrier molecule, (2) transfer of the pigment from one carrier to another, and (3) phytylation resulting in a realignment of the chlorophyll molecules at the carrier surface. According to SMITH *et al.* [1959], this last possibility seems to be the most probable.

In nature, chlorophyll may occur in equilibrium conditions between formation and destruction. DURANTON *et al.* [1958] obtained evidence of such a chlorophyll turnover in tobacco leaves though there may be considerable differences in this respect between different species (SHLYK [1956]). This may explain why ROBERTS and PERKINS [1962] who labelled chlorophylls in wheat leaves found that the chlorophyll turnover in fully grown leaves is extremely slow, if it occurs at all.

In any case, it might be that some of the seven chlorophyll forms mentioned above are intermediates of the chlorophyll formation and degradation processes.

The conception of chlorophyll *in vivo* occurring in both the monomeric and polymeric, supposedly dimeric, state has also been suggested by BRODY and BRODY [1961]. This suggestion is mainly based on measurements of fluorescence and absorption at room temperature as well as in liquid nitrogen. The "dimer" absorption was localized around 700 mμ, whereas the monomer was supposed to absorb around 680 mμ.

Hence the *in vivo* state may be composed of two, may be more, kinds of states, one of them due to the complex formation with a carrier and another due to the "aggregation" configurations of the chlorophyll itself.

On the basis of considerations of energy transfer and the declining quantum yield of photosynthesis and fluorescence in the region of the long-wave side of the red absorption band of chlorophyll, FRANCK [1958] suggested that part of this pigment in the living cell is in contact with water while part of it is prevented from such a contact by surrounding lipide groups. These chlorophyll portions are named "exposed chlorophyll" and "protected chlorophyll" respectively. The consequences of this situation may be important to the energy content of the n-π^* levels of the chlorophylls though not to the complex formation and state of aggregation. In protected chlorophyll this energy state may lie between the first excited singlet state and the triplet state thus favouring the formation of triplet states upon irradiation while the exposed chlorophylls may exhibit mainly singlet excitation (see fig. 4). These hypothetical states of chlorophyll may therefore be functionally different in that the protected chlorophylls are able to store the absorbed energy for a considerably longer time than is possible for the exposed chlorophylls. These states, consequently, may be different only at the intramolecular level.

A more detailed discussion on the elaborate work on the *in vivo* states of chlorophyll does not fit into the scope of this book. The cited papers, as well as reviews, *e.g.* RABINOWITCH [1945, 1951, 1956], FRENCH [1960] and KUPKE and FRENCH [1960] may serve to make the relevant literature easily accessible.

2.1.5 Photochemistry and photophysics of chlorophyll in vitro and in vivo. Chlorophyll may act in two ways upon excitation by light. When excited, it may pass on the converted light energy to another molecule without taking part in a chemical reaction. In this case, chlorophyll would answer the definition of a photocatalyst in its strictest sense. Excited chlorophyll may also be chemically changed and this new compound initiate a chemical reaction chain. In the latter case the photochemistry of this pigment will form the basic process underlying photosynthesis.

If a pigment is chemically changed by light excitation, the electronic configuration is changed and so its optical properties are affected. *In vivo* and under natural conditions, such changes should be reversible. Otherwise one would observe photodestruction of chlorophyll in the cell at normal light intensities. Consequently the study of the reversible spectral changes of this pigment is of primary interest in the understanding of its function.

Apart from examinations of absorption transients, investigations of light emission may provide further information about the role of chlorophyll. Two kinds of light emission by chlorophyll-a have been observed. These are: (1) fluorescence and (2) delayed fluorescence. Phosphorescence of this pigment has never been detected. The term "delayed fluorescence" is somewhat misleading. It is used for light emission upon thermal emptying of the triplet state which was described under "Physical processes", as well as chemiluminescence. The latter emission in the case of chlorophyll is also termed "afterglow" or generally "luminescence". Both fluorescence and afterglow are emitted by a direct electronic transition from the first excited singlet state to the ground level. As the emission of quanta is a chance process, the fluorescence intensity will be a function of the quantity of excited chlorophyll in the absence of any complications. In other words, under given steady state conditions, a certain constant fluorescence intensity is observed. In organic solutions, where the fluorescence yield is high, about 30% of the light absorbed is re-emitted, while in the natural state it is only a few per cent. However fluorescence both *in vivo* and *in vitro*, is affected by many parameters. These effects resulting in either stimulation ("activation") or quenching may provide further information about the condition of chlorophyll and its way of functioning.

The delayed fluorescence indicates the presence of a long-lived electronic state though metastable activated states, it will be recalled, need not be of such an electronic nature. They may be formed as a result of, for example, photodissociation, photooxidation, photoreduction and light-induced radical production as well.

The most obvious spectral change of chlorophyll is its "bleaching". This process therefore will be discussed first. In the absence of oxygen, a reversible photobleaching of a solution of chlorophyll-a in methanol was observed by PORRET and RABINOWITCH [1937] as well as LIVINGSTON [1941]. At high light intensity a decrease of the red absorption band of about 1% was noticed. This value can be raised to about 10% by the addition of formic acid. In a few experiments with no added compounds, a reversible bleaching of 50% was obtained, probably due to the presence of impurities. A trace of oxygen inhibits this process, as does the addition of ferrous chloride.

RABINOWITCH and WEISS [1937] were able to obtain a fast chemical bleaching of chlorophyll-a in methanolic solution in the "dark" by adding ferric chloride. Immediate addition of ferrous chloride restored the original absorption spectrum. This reversible phenomenon could be repeatedly produced. The authors therefore suggested that the reversible chemical bleaching consists of a reversible oxidation of chlorophyll according to:

$$\underset{\text{(green)}}{\text{chlorophyll}} + Fe^{+++} \rightleftharpoons \underset{\text{(yellow)}}{\text{oxychlorophyll}} + Fe^{++}$$

RABINOWITCH [1945] observed that chlorophyll in methanol to which ferric and ferrous chloride have been added simultaneously in such proportions that just no chemical bleaching occurs in the dark, is bleached in the light. In this case, the photobleaching is not inhibited by oxygen. Its magnitude is comparable with photobleaching of chlorophyll in methanol without any other compounds added to it.

For bacteriochlorophyll, these reactions have been studied by GOED-

HEER [1958]. His results agree with those of Rabinowitch and Weiss. The spectrum of photobleached bacteriochlorophyll in methanol proved to be similar to that of the chemically bleached pigment upon addition of ferric chloride. As the reversible reactions will take place in a number of organic solvents, it seems likely that instead of being due to interaction of pigment and solvent molecules, the absorption changes are essentially a property of the pigment itself. In contrast with chlorophyll-a, bacteriochlorophyll in ether is bleached by iodine as well as by ferric chloride although this salt is barely soluble in ether. The fact that bacteriochlorophyll is bleached nevertheless suggests that the redox potential of this pigment is lower than that of chlorophyll-a. GOEDHEER, HORREUS DE HAAS and SCHULLER [1958] measured a redox potential of 645 $\pm$ 20 mV for chlorophyll-a in methanol, whereas this value was found to be 550 $\pm$ 2 mV for bacteriochlorophyll.

The same authors found an oxygen uptake concurrently with photobleaching under air, and so the bleaching is a photooxidation under these conditions.

Earlier KRASNOVSKY and VOYNOVSKAJA [1951] stated that photobleached bacteriochlorophyll in alcohol or pyridine solution is reduced to its original state by addition of ascorbic acid or hydrogen sulfide. Indication that the photobleached product is an oxidized compound resulted from the fact that the photobleached alcoholic solution of bacteriochlorophyll displays a strong peroxide test in the presence of ferrous thiocyanate.

The above phenomena are but a few examples of processes which are likely to be photooxidation of chlorophyllous pigments. Photoreduction of chlorophyll has also been observed. KRASNOVSKY [1948] observed photobleaching of chlorophyll-a dissolved in air-free pyridine in the presence of ascorbic acid or phenylhydrazine. Instead of a yellow product, as occurs with photooxidation, an unstable pink compound was formed which is presumably a radical. EVSTIGNEEV and GAVRILOVA [1953] determined its absorption spectrum and BANNISTER [1960] showed that water must be present in the pyridine for the reversible photoreductive bleaching to take place.

The fact that chlorophylls can be reversibly bleached by light as well as by chemical means may be significant in photosynthesis only if such reactions are coupled with chemical processes of the photosynthetic chain. The very first step in trying to obtain evidence of such a possibility must be a study of whether chlorophyll is only able to catalyze reactions when excited by the absorption of light. Actually a large number of reactions which are photosensitized by chlorophyll have been observed (see RABINOWITCH [1945, 1956]). A single example may suffice here. GAFFRON [1933] was the first to show that chlorophyll in acetone is able to catalyze the oxidation of allyl-thiourea in the light

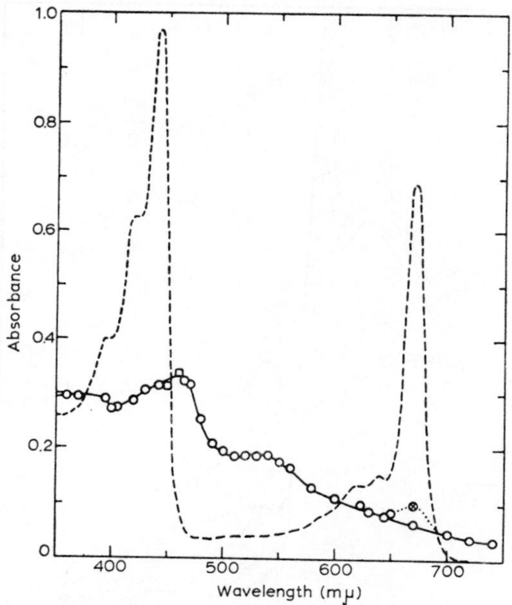

Fig. 26. Spectra of green and bleached chlorophyll-a in pyridine. ○, corrected spectrum using relative calibration of oscillograph deflection; □, corrected spectrum using absolute (neutral screen) calibration; ⊗, original uncorrected absorbance immediately after flash. From: LINSCHITZ and SARKANEN [1958]. By permission of the American Chemical Society

with a quantum yield of about unity. The oxidizing agent in this reaction is molecular oxygen.

In air and in the light irreversible bleaching of chlorophyll can occur. This type of bleaching requires much more time than the instantaneous reversible type, and can take a matter of hours. As this reaction is not likely to be of importance with regard to photosynthesis it will not be discussed any further here. It should be reiterated that dissolved chlorophylls are much more readily irreversibly photobleached than chlorophylls in the *in vivo* state.

What is actually happening to chlorophyll dissolved in an organic solvent and under nitrogen when it is reversibly bleached? In order to study this problem, LIVINGSTON [1954] irradiated chlorophylls and derivatives in organic solvents with very high light intensities using three 1000-watt incandescent lamps for continuous illumination and

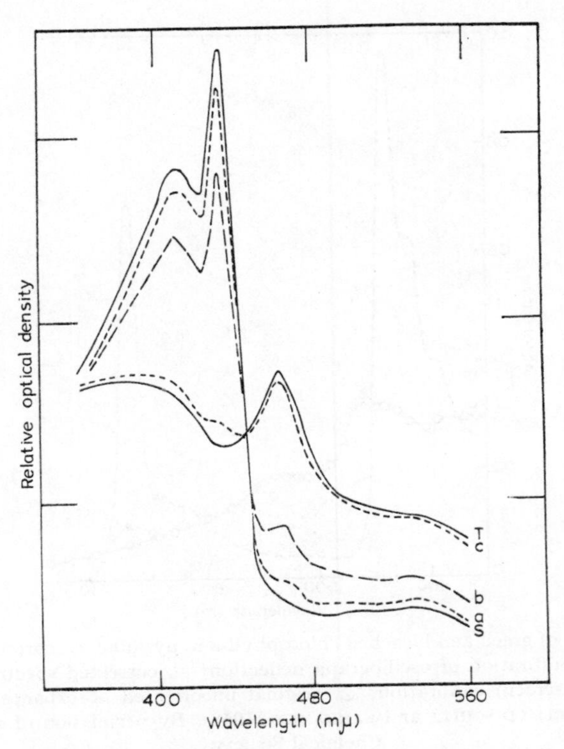

Fig. 27. Absorption spectra of chlorophyll-a in cyclohexanol. S, ground state; c, b, and a, spectra at increasing times after flash; T, excited, bleached, chlorophyll. From: LIVINGSTON [1954]. By permission of the American Chemical Society

three high-power flash-tubes giving 390 watt-seconds for kinetic studies. A "weak" beam from a 100-watt incandescent lamp was passed through the solution in a direction perpendicular to that of the actinic light, and was analyzed by means of a monochromator and photocell. An oscillograph with a resolving power of about 10^{-4} sec. enabled the author to study the kinetics of the "discoloration" of the chlorophyll. Later LINSCHITZ and SARKANEN [1958] established the transient absorption spectrum from chlorophyll-a over a wider spectral range than Livingston, and their spectra are reproduced in fig. 26.

The dotted curve is the absorption spectrum of the green pigment in solution in pyridine. The other spectrum is that of the bleached form which lacks the red band of the chlorophyll singlet state. Absorption

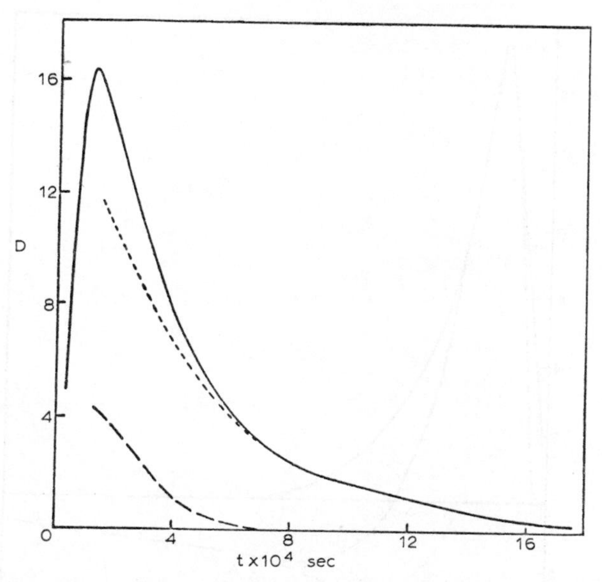

Fig. 28. Averaged oscilloscope traces corresponding to the decay of excited chlorophyll a at 4680 Å. Solid curve, air-free solution; dashed curve, air-saturated solution; dotted curve, air-free solution corrected for scattered flash light. From: LIVINGSTON and RYAN [1953]. By permission of the American Chemical Society

is enhanced in the green region and instead of the blue peak, two minor maxima appear. The spectral changes, (a) "immediately", (b) 900 μ sec., and (c) 2600 μ sec. after the flash are shown in fig. 27. The ground state spectrum is represented by S and that of the excited form generated during the flash is denoted by T. The nature of this excited compound was studied by LIVINGSTON and RYAN [1953] in flash experiments. The transient absorption is not seen in the presence of oxygen, and so the contribution to the oscilloscope traces by scattered light from the photolytic flash could be corrected for by also measuring a solution under air. If only one single metastable product is formed, decay kinetics are the same over the spectral range in which it absorbs.

However, if more than one photoproduct is produced, different decay characteristics should be envisaged at various wavelengths.

The results obtained at two wavelengths by these authors are depicted in the next two figures. Fig. 28 demonstrates what happens to

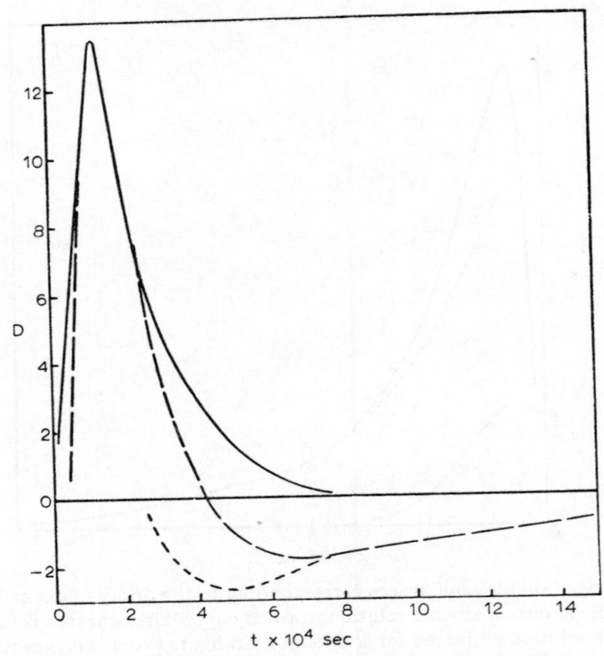

Fig. 29. Averaged oscilloscope traces corresponding to $\lambda = 5245$ Å for the decay of excited chlorophyll-a: dashed curve, air-free solution; solid curve, air-saturated solution; dotted curve, air-free solution corrected for scattered flash light. From: LIVINGSTON and RYAN [1953]. By permission of the American Chemical Society

the chlorophyll absorption at 4680 Å upon excitation by three photographic flash lamps. The displacement of the corrected oscilloscope trace is a function of the concentration of the excited species. From the figure it is evident that this concentration is highest at near the moment of maximum intensity of the flash and then decreases. This is consistent with the occurrence of only a single photoproduct. However if the decay is measured at 5245 Å, as shown in fig. 29, the situation is quite different.

In this case the decay consists of both a negative and a positive part, indicating that at least two photoproducts are present. At 3680 Å the extinction coefficients of the two photoproducts are either about equal or one of these products does not absorb appreciably at this wavelength. On the contrary, at 5245 Å these coefficients are different. The shorter-lived form absorbs less than chlorophyll at this wavelength, while the extinction coefficient of the longer-lived one is higher than that of chlorophyll. From data at steady state illumination it was concluded that the longer-lived product is most probably a radical or possibly an ion. The half-life of the shorter-lived compound is about 5×10^{-4} sec. This is much longer than the life of the first excited singlet state which is about 7×10^{-9} sec. and so it appears that the "shorter-lived" form cannot be due to a singlet excitation, but is some metastable form, presumably the triplet state. The radical then, may be formed by a reaction of this metastable product with a solvent molecule or an impurity. In "moderate" light intensities only the radical and ground-state chlorophyll can be detected. For observation of both radical and metastable state, high-energy flashes are required. The triplet state molecules which do not react to form radicals release their excitation energy by a first-order decay or by reaction with ground-state molecules. The radicals are transformed into non-excited chlorophyll molecules by a second-order reaction.

It should be stressed that these experiments refer to chlorophyll in solution and that the same phenomena do not necessarily take place *in vivo*. Only the possibility of the occurrence of such reactions in the living cell has been demonstrated. The converse may also be true. A reaction which does not occur *in vitro* may occur *in vivo*. For example, this could be the case in the photoreduction of chlorophyll. According to LIVINGSTON and PUGH [1960], though, the photoreduction of chlorophyll does not represent an essential step in efficient photochemical reactions sensitized by excited chlorophyll *in vitro*, it may be essential *in vivo*.

The metastable character of the bleached photoproducts has also been demonstrated with a different technique by LINSCHITZ and RENNERT [1952]. They observed a reversible photobleaching of chlorophyll in organic solvents in the presence of quinone and in the absence of oxygen. After cooling with liquid air, irradiation of the mixture causes a bleaching which is irreversible at -190 °C; for this temperature the metastable state is "frozen". As soon as the temperature is raised to the melting point of the solvent the bleaching is reversed.

The effect of quinones is of particular interest since such compounds are likely to act as cofactors in photosynthesis. KRASNOVSKY and BRIN [1949] discovered an *in vitro* chlorophyll-sensitized reversible reduction of NAD (nicotinamide adenine dinucleotide, coenzyme I) by ascorbic acid upon illumination. BANNISTER and BERNARDINI [1962], however, were not able to confirm such a conclusion and could not observe accumulation of $NADH_2$ in appreciable amounts, at least, not exceeding 4.0×10^{-6} M in the light. Nevertheless, they felt that a cyclic oxidation reductionof NAD under their experimental conditions could not be ruled out.

Fluorescence was mentioned earlier as a possible technique in the investigation of the photochemistry of chlorophylls. The fluorescence quantum yield in various solvents as well as in the presence of different quenching substances has been determined by many workers, but it seems that the results, as far as the function of chlorophyll is concerned, are scarcely in proportion to the effort expended. This statement is illustrated by the conclusions of EVSTIGNEEV, GAVRILOVA and KRASNOVSKY [1950] who studied the quenching effect of various organic compounds on the fluorescence of chlorophyll solutions in pyridine or ethanol, as well as the influence of these substances on the photobleaching of this pigment. No correlation between the two effects could be observed. Therefore they concluded that the fluorescent chlorophyll molecules do not contribute to the bleaching and so this process only involves the metastable state.

These studies represent only a fraction of the work which has been done on the photochemistry of chlorophyll *in vitro*. Further information may be gained from many detailed reviews, for example RABINOWITCH [1945, 1956], LUMRY, SPIKES and EYRING [1954], ROSENBERG [1957], KRASNOVSKY [1960], and LIVINGSTON [1960].

Summarizing, it can be stated that under adequate conditions, excited chlorophyll is capable of oxidation and reduction *in vitro*. The metastable state may be of a biradical character.

The different photobleached chlorophyll configurations can be identified by their absorption characteristics, (see COLEMAN *et al.* [1957]). The major absorption bands are located in the blue region of the spectrum: for metastable chlorophyll-a at 475 mμ; for ionized chlorophyll-a at 486 and 534 mμ; for reversibly reduced chlorophyll-a at 525 and 585 mμ; for reversibly oxidized chlorophyll-a: no sharp bands; increased absorption in the region from 450 to 530 mμ. In all cases, the absorption in the red region is considerably reduced.

University of Pittsburgh
Bradford Campus Library

The photochemistry of chlorophylls *in vitro* may lead to an understanding of what happens in photosynthesis only if there is indication of the occurrence of such photochemical events with these pigments in the undamaged living cell. Actually, characteristic changes have been observed upon illumination of photosynthesizing cells though these changes are far smaller than those observed *in vitro* and are of the order of one per cent or lower. This phenomenon could arise from a more efficient energy transfer than occurs *in vitro*, due to a close packing of the pigment molecules. In this way, singlet excitation can be transferred rather quickly, that is well within 10^{-9} sec., and ultimately reach the one or two chlorophyll molecules which are able to feed the electronic energy *via* a "reaction centre", into the chemical reaction chain. The conditions for the formation of metastable states may be favoured by the association of the chlorophyll molecules to form such units and as a result, only a small number of the chlorophyll molecules in the photosynthetic apparatus may undergo reversible bleaching.

As a consequence of the smallness of the *in vivo* absorption changes, they cannot be detected with conventional spectroscopy and it was believed for a long time that the chlorophylls in the living cell do not change spectroscopically upon illumination. DUYSENS [1952] constructed a sensitive split-beam apparatus which enabled him to establish "difference spectra". In this apparatus a cuvette containing the cell suspension was placed in one of the chopped beams and the intensity of the reference beam, which did not pass through the suspension, was adjusted to compensate the measuring beam. By illuminating the cuvette with continuous actinic light of much higher intensity than that of the analyzing beam, the signals became out of balance when an absorption change occurred. By adequate amplification of the difference signal, Duysens succeeded in observing distinct changes of absorption in purple bacteria. By determining the changes at various wavelengths, a "difference spectrum" was established from which he concluded that bacteriochlorophyll itself is involved. Later DUYSENS [1954a, 1955] obtained light-dark difference spectra for algae covering the ranges from 580 to 370 mμ and from 430 to 320 mμ. From these data it was concluded that both cytochrome and pyridine nucleotide contribute to the difference spectrum. The interpretation of such changes will be discussed later.

The light-dark difference spectra of photosynthesizing cells are rather complicated as may be seen in the case of the green alga *Chlorella pyrenoidosa*, given by COLEMAN and RABINOWITCH [1960] and illustrated in fig. 30. According to these authors, the change around 520 mμ is composed of two effects. Part of this change seems to take place completely at lower incident light intensities while, at higher intensities, the band in the difference spectrum rises again and shifts slightly

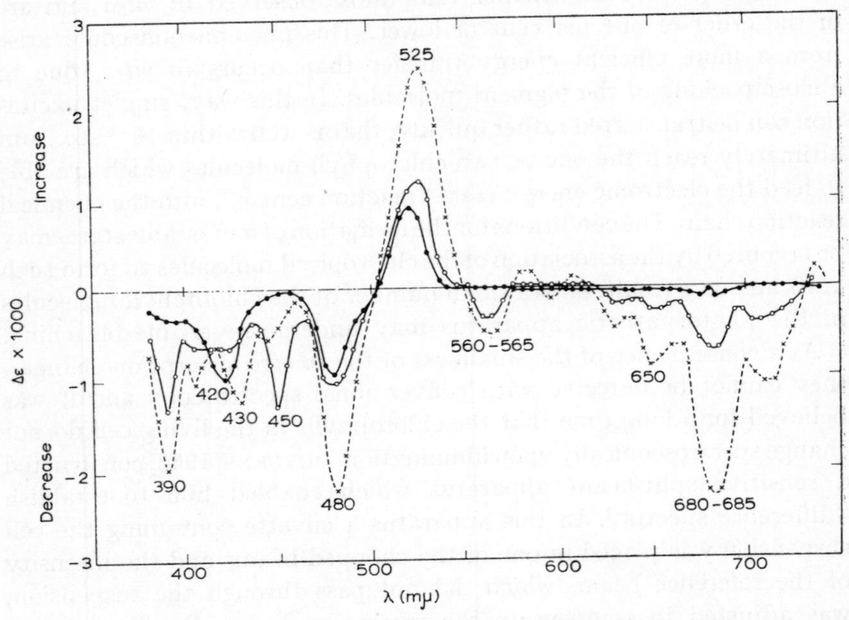

Fig. 30. Difference spectra of thin suspensions of *Chlorella pyrenoidosa* in carbonate buffer in white light of the following intensities: dots, 3.4×10^{14} $h\nu \cdot sec.^{-1} \cdot cm^{-2}$; circles, 12.0×10^{14} $h\nu \cdot sec.^{-1} \cdot cm^{-2}$; crosses, 31.4×10^{14} $h\nu \cdot sec.^{-1} \cdot cm^{-2}$. From: COLEMAN and RABINOWITCH [1960]. By permission of John Wiley and Sons, Inc.

to the long-wave side (525 mμ). Therefore it was concluded that this change probably is brought about by changes in different pigments. The high-intensity change was reported to be correlated with the decrease of absorption around 680 mμ as well as with an absorption decrease at about 430 mμ. These changes coincide with those described by Krasnovsky *et al.*, (see KRASNOVSKY and VOYNOVSKAYA [1951]) upon photoreduction of chlorophyll *in vitro*, provided that the proper correction for the *in vivo* long-wave shift is taken into account. This coincidence made Coleman and Rabinowitch suggest that the maximum and minima of the light-dark difference spectrum indicate a reversible photoreduction of chlorophyll-a *in vivo*.

An elaborate study of the changes upon illumination was made by WITT *et al.* [1959a, b, c, 1960, 1961a, b] and MORAW and WITT [1961a, b). In flash experiments, these authors were able to observe absorption changes with lifetimes down to 10^{-5} sec. They classify the changes as follows:

Type 0: an absorption decrease with its maximum at 430 mμ combined with a flat absorption increase at wavelengths longer than 450 mμ and measured up to 570 mμ. The lifetime of this phenomenon is shorter than 10^{-5} sec. The changes were suggested to be due to triplet excitation of chlorophyll. The effect was not observed in intact cells. If however, chloroplasts were extracted with acetone the authors claim that about 1% of the chlorophyll molecules remain thoroughly attached to the protein and show the type-0 reaction. The same was found with chloroplasts treated with the detergent digitonin, which presumably disintegrates the chlorophyll-protein complexes into rather small units, as well as in a *Chlorella* mutant containing about 1% of the normal amount of chlorophyll and unable to perform photosynthesis.

Type 1: a negative absorption change showing its maximum at 430 mμ together with a positive absorption change located at 520 mμ. The lifetime of these effects is about 5×10^{-5} sec. The duration of the lifetime is independent of temperature and is the same at -160 °C as at room temperature. The authors explained the absence of a temperature effect by suggesting that an electron exchange occurs between chlorophyll-a and some reaction partner in close proximity. The absorption changes are assumed to be due to the presence of changed chlorophyll molecules.

The type-1 phenomena are independent of gas pressure up to one atmosphere, provided the gases are diamagnetic. However, paramagnetic gases such as O_2 and NO were found to decrease these effects in proportion to the gas pressure. As paramagnetic gases are quenchers of the triplet state, the results suggest that this state is the precursor of the type-1 chlorophyll product.

Type 2: a decrease of absorption with maxima at 420 and 475 mμ and a simultaneous absorption increase at 515 mμ. The lifetime of this effect is much greater than that of the previous ones, namely about 10^{-2} sec. Using long flashes or continuous illumination, types 0 and 1 reach their steady state instantaneously. On the contrary, type 2 first shows a spike with a duration of 10^{-2} sec. and then after 10^{-1} sec., the absorption change continues to increase but at a much slower rate. In contrast to the first phase, the second is dependent on both temperature and pre-illumination. Type 2 is therefore of a complex character and indicative of two processes, type 2a showing a negative peak of absorption change at 420 mμ und type 2b with a negative minimum at 475 mμ and a positive one at 515 mμ. At -150 °C only type 2a occurs. Because of its spectral location, this type was attributed to the oxidation of a cytochrome, presumably cytochrome-f (MULLER and WITT [1961]). This oxidation takes about 10^{-3} sec. A second product is formed in the same light reaction, together with the oxidized cytochrome. It could be trapped at -150 °C and was identified as oxidized chlorophyll. The decay time of this compound is also about 10^{-3} sec. The corresponding spectral changes appear as decreases in absorption at 430 and 703 mμ. These changes, together with those listed under types 0 and 1, were ascribed by Witt *et al.* to three reactions involving the chlorophyll molecule: (a) triplet excitation of chlorophyll, (b) the type-1 photochemical reaction at the chlorophyll molecule, and (c) the photooxidation of chlorophyll.

Beyond the absorption changes described so far and interpreted by Witt *et al.*, other changes are also seen which are less generally characteristic. These may vary between species with different composition of the pigment system such as the green, blue-green, red, or brown algae. It may be that there are other common absorption changes which only show up unambiguously at sufficiently high intensities of the actinic light. This may well be the case with the 680 mμ negative change, shown in fig. 30 which was observed by Rabinowitch and coworkers under adequate illumination conditions, and ascribed to the photoreduction of chlorophyll. Later RUBINSTEIN and RABINOWITCH [1963] showed that this change was in fact due to an increase of the fluorescence yield rather than a fall in absorption. In general, the shape of the difference spectrum can be expected to vary at different intensities of the incident light as a consequence of different saturating intensities for the process giving rise to the various absorption changes.

Type 2b is caused by the reduction of some pigment called X_0. Irradiation with different wavelengths provided an indication that the excited chlorophyll type C_a680 is responsible for the oxidation of cytochrome, whereas the excited chlorophyll type C_a670 causes the reduction of X_0. Absorption changes of pigments other than chlorophylls will be discussed later.

KOK [1956], who was the first to observe absorption changes in the region of 700–705 mμ, ascribed these changes to a pigment which he designated "P700". He later obtained an indication [1961] that this pigment probably is a chlorophyll fraction. KOK and HOCH [1961] as well as BUTLER [1961], suggested that the electronic excitation energy of the photosynthetic pigments ultimately flows towards this chlorophyll fraction which is about $\frac{1}{400}$ of the total chlorophyll.

Photosynthesis requires more than one light step and more than one type of chlorophyll need to be excited. Before entering into this matter, the pigments accompanying the chlorophylls will be discussed.

2.2 Carotenoids

Chlorophylls are always accompanied by carotenoids and so the latter pigments occur in all photosynthetic organisms.

2.2.1 Chemistry. Carotenoids are classified as (1) polyene hydrocarbons, called carotenes, and (2) oxygen derivatives of polyene hydrocarbons, termed xanthophylls (see STRAIN [1949]). The names of xanthophyll species end with *-in*. Apart from "xanthophylls", the name "carotenols" is also encountered. According to the latter nomenclature the members of this species are indicated by the ending *-ol*, which normally suggests an alcohol and so it is preferable to use the xanthophyll terminology (see GOODWIN [1952]).

All of these pigments are soluble in fats and lipids and accordingly they are also termed "lipochromes". A further classification is based on their partition between two immiscible liquids such as petroleum ether and methanol 90%. Carotenoids without hydroxyl or carbonyl groups are "epiphasic", whereas those with two such groups are "hypophasic". If a single oxygen-carrying group is present, the pigment distributes equally in both phases. The number of these groups in any known carotenoid is too small to render them soluble in water.

As a rule, carotenoids occur in the all-*trans* configuration. In exceptional cases *cis* isomers have been observed in leaf extracts. They are indicated by the prefix *neo-* and a suffix of a letter relating to their position when separated on the chromatographic column, *e.g.* neo-β-carotene U. Carotenoids are composed of isoprene units as shown in fig. 31. These units are connected to form "rods" which carry an ionone ring at one or both ends. The rings may be closed (β) or open (ψ). The length of a carotenoid molecule is about 20 Å and the linear arrangement of the isoprene units means that a relatively long chain

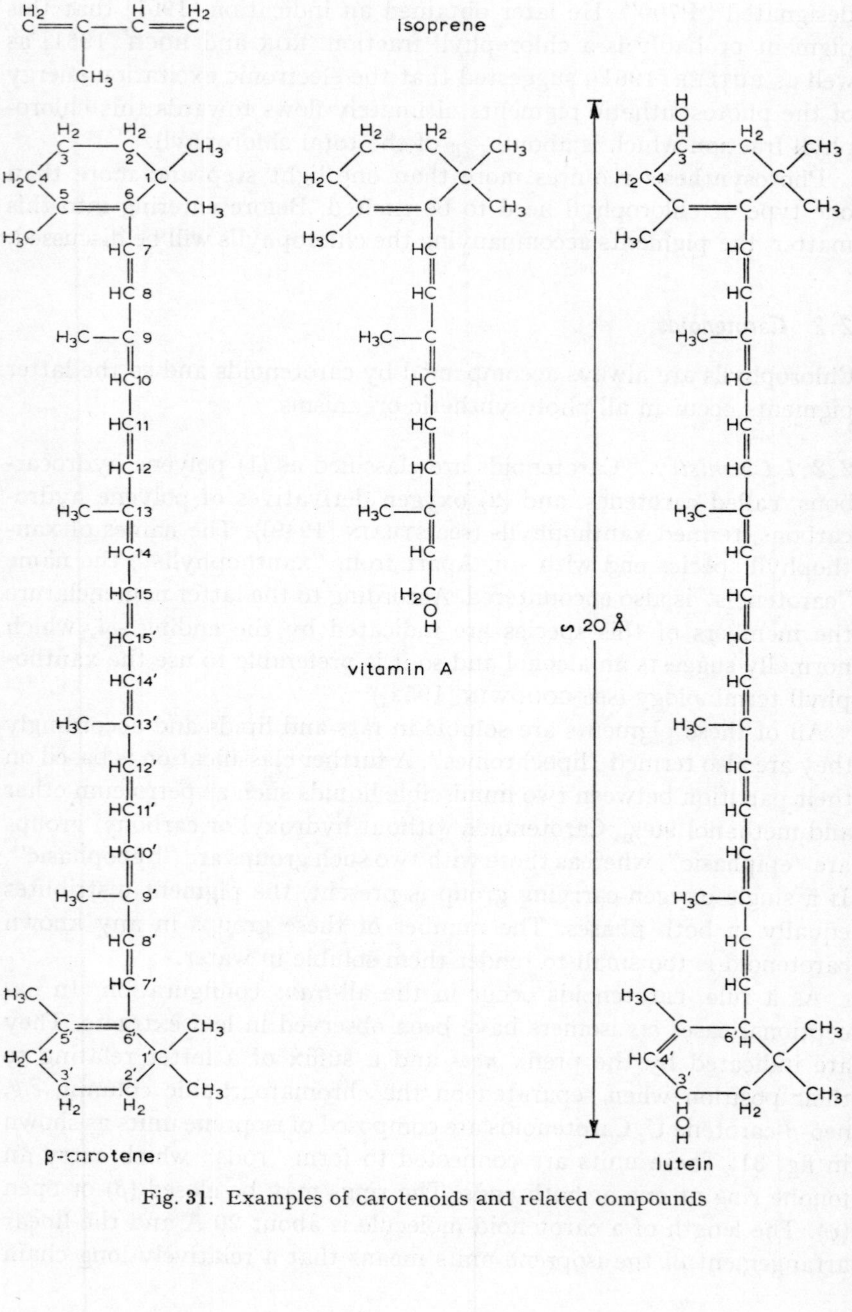

Fig. 31. Examples of carotenoids and related compounds

of conjugated bonds – the polyene chain – is formed. In most cases 11 or more double bonds occur which makes the chain chromophoric and so the carotenoids are coloured.

The carbon skeleton of isoprene is also found in phytol and WILLSTÄTTER and MIEG [1907] suggested a genetic relationship between carotenoids and phytol.

Carotenes occur as isomeric forms of the formula $C_{40}H_{56}$, for example, β-carotene which is depicted in fig. 31. The generally accepted numbering of the C-atoms, suggested by Karrer (see KARRER and JUCKER [1948]), is also indicated. It is worthwhile to note that the carotenes are related to a compound involved in metabolic processes, namely vitamin A. Two vitamin A molecules are formed out of one β-carotene molecule upon hydrolysis as shown in fig. 31.

Xanthophylls are oxygen derivatives of carotenes. Oxygen can be present in the form of hydroxyl-, keto-, epoxy-, carboxy-, or methoxy-groups and consequently there is a much greater variety of xanthophylls than carotenes. As an example of xanthophylls, the structural formula of lutein is shown in fig. 31. According to GOODWIN [1960], the most common xanthophylls are hydroxycarotenes. Ketocarotenes were found in aged conifer needles and in the submersed leaves of *Potamogeton*. Only two epoxycarotenes have been observed in the presence of chlorophylls, whereas methoxycarotenes occur in photosynthetic bacteria. Carboxycarotenes are never observed in photosynthetic cells.

2.2.2 Individual carotenoids accompanying chlorophylls

Carotenes. α-carotene ($C_{40}H_{56}$) differs from β-carotene (fig. 31), in that the bond between C6′ and is single and that between C5′ and C4′ is double, while in α-carotene C6′ is provided with a hydrogen atom, and C4′ carries only a single hydrogen atom. Eleven double bonds, ten of which lie in the conjugated system, are present in the pigment molecule. Only a single asymmetric carbon occurs, and according to STRAIN [1938], α-carotene is dextrorotatory. It is most readily soluble in carbon disulfide and chloroform, readily soluble in benzene and ether, poorly soluble in petroleum ether and nearly insoluble in alcohols. This pigment (see STRAIN [1951]), is found in many leaves and in algae. In some species of the latter, namely some red algae and Siphonales, it is even the principal carotene (STRAIN [1944]).

β-carotene ($C_{40}H_{56}$). The structural formula is given in fig. 31. The pigment contains eleven double bonds in conjugation. As the molecule is symmetric, it is optically inactive. In general its solubility is less than that of α-carotene, though it is readily soluble in carbon disulfide, chloroform and benzene. In ether and petroleum ether it is not so soluble, and it is nearly insoluble in ethanol and methanol. This pigment is the main carotene accompanying chlorophyll-a in all plant species, except for α-carotene in some red algae and Siphonales.

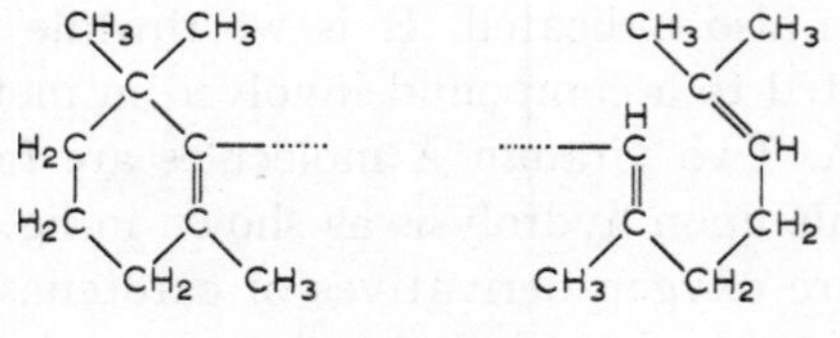

γ-carotene

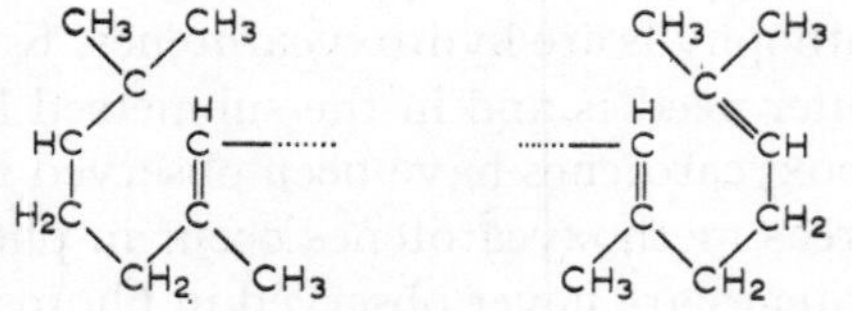

Lycopene

Fig. 32. Terminal moieties of some carotenes

γ-carotene ($C_{40}H_{36}$). In contrast with α- and β-carotene, γ-carotene contains only a single closed β-ionone ring. The ψ-ionone ring is open as illustrated in fig. 32. There are twelve double bonds of which eleven belong to the conjugated system. The pigment is soluble in organic solvents such as carbon disulfide, chloroform, benzene, petrol, petroleum ether and hexanol, though its solubility is less than that of β-carotene. γ-carotene is optically inactive (see KARRER and JUCKER [1948]). This carotene occurs in traces, about 0.1% of the amount of β-carotene, in many higher plants (STRAIN [1949]), and in green algae where it may be present in higher amounts in the gametes or reproductive organs (KARRER *et al.* [1943]). However, according to

GOODWIN and LAND [1956], it is the major carotenoid of green sulfur bacteria.

ε-carotene. Both the chemical and structural formula are unknown. The pigment is soluble in ethanol and has been isolated by STRAIN and MANNING [1943] from a diatom and the green alga *Bryopsis corticulum* (STRAIN [1951]).

Flavacene. Probably a hydrocarbon. According to the absorption spectrum, the conjugated system should contain a smaller number of double bonds than that of β-carotene. The pigment is soluble in carbon disulfide, petrol, and petroleum ether. Traces have been observed by TISCHER [1939] in the blue-green alga *Aphanizomenon flos-aquae.*

Lycopene ($C_{40}H_{56}$). Both ionone residues are open, as shown in fig. 32. Lycopene contains thirteen double bonds of which eleven belong to the conjugated system. It is most readily soluble in carbon disulfide, readily soluble in chloroform, soluble in benzene and nearly insoluble in ethanol and methanol. The pigment is optically inactive (see KARRER and JUCKER [1948]). According to GOODWIN [1959], it occurs in a number of photosynthetic purple bacteria, both Thiorhodacae and Athiorhodacea.

Rhodopurpurene. The chemical constitution is not yet fully elucidated. It is most probably a hydrocarbon of the formula $C_{40}H_{56}$ or $C_{40}H_{58}$. It is soluble in carbon disulfide, chloroform, petroleum ether and benzene. The spectrum resembles that of lycopene. The pigment has been isolated by KARRER and SOLMSSEN [1935a] from the photosynthetic purple bacterium *Rhodovibrio,* where it occurs in very small amounts.

Xanthophylls. Lutein ($C_{40}H_{56}O_2$). This carotenoid is also termed "xanthophyll" (see KARRER and JUCKER [1948]). However, as the designation "xanthopyll" is generally given to the group of oxygen-carrying carotenoids, the name lutein, originally proposed by Kuhn, is the one normally used. The structural formula is depicted in fig. 31. The pigment is readily soluble in carbon disulfide, chloroform, benzene, acetone and ether. Its solubility in ethanol and methanol is poor and it is nearly zero in petroleum ether. As lutein is a derivative of α-carotene, it is optically active and is dextrorotatory. This xanthophyll is the major carotenoid in green leaves, in most of the photosynthetic cells of other green plants and algae, as well as in most of the red algae.

Violaxanthin ($C_{40}H_{56}O_4$). Both ionone rings are closed. Each of them carries an epoxy group at positions 5–6 and 5′–6′ respectively. KARRER and JUCKER [1945] established the formula. All of the ten double bonds belong to the conjugated system. According to STRAIN [1954], violaxanthin from flower petals of *Viola tricolor* is identical with that from leaves. It is a diepoxyzeaxanthin. YAMAMOTO, NAKAYAMA and CHICHESTER [1962] obtained evidence that in spinach and lima bean leaves, violaxanthin is converted to zeaxanthin *via* antheraxanthin in the light and under nitrogen, whereas in the dark and under oxygen this process is reversed. Violaxanthin is readily soluble in ethanol, methanol, carbon disulfide and ether, and is nearly insoluble in petroleum ether. The pigment is dextrorotatory (see KARRER and JUCKER [1948]). It is the second major xanthophyll in leaves.

Neoxanthin ($C_{40}H_{56}O_4$). Its structural formula is unknown (see STRAIN [1938, 1944]) and the carotenoid is soluble in ether and ethanol. It occurs as the third major xanthophyll in leaves and in algae.

Cryptoxanthin ($C_{40}H_{56}O$). Both ionone rings are closed. Their structure, established by KUHN and GRUNDMANN [1933], is depicted in fig. 33.

Eleven double bonds occur all of which belong to the conjugated bond system. This phytoxanthin is readily soluble in chloroform, benzene, and pyridine. Its solubility is somewhat less in ligroin, petroleum ether, methanol and ethanol. Contrary to expectation from the structural formula, cryptoxanthin is not optically active (see KARRER and JUCKER [1948]). The pigment occurs in smaller amounts than the ones mentioned previously in many leaves and green algae.

Zeaxanthin ($C_{40}H_{56}O_2$). The structure has been chiefly established by KARRER *et al.* see [1948]. As shown in fig. 33, both ionone rings are closed. All of the eleven double bonds lie in the conjugated system. Zeaxanthin is soluble in ether, chloroform, carbon disulfide, pyridine and boiling methanol, but is nearly insoluble in petroleum ether and hexane. It is laevorotatory. The pigment occurs in small amounts, comparable with those of cryptoxanthin, in leaves and green algae.

These five xanthophylls are the major ones in green leaves. For example, BICKOFF *et al.* [1954] determined the following amounts of these pigments, expressed as percentages of the total xanthophyll content for alfalfa: lutein 40%, violaxanthin 34%, neoxanthin 19%, cryptoxanthin 4%, and zeaxanthin 2%. Together these pigments amount to 99% of the total xanthophyll content. Though cryptoxanthin and zeaxanthin are absent in a number of species, the cited xanthophyll distribution may be considered quite typical. The remaining

1% consists of traces of other xanthophylls rather than any single one. A large number of such pigments is known (see KARRER and JUCKER [1948]); GOODWIN [1952, 1955, 1959, 1960]; STRAIN [1949]) and with the exception of a few xanthophylls which are characteristic of, or

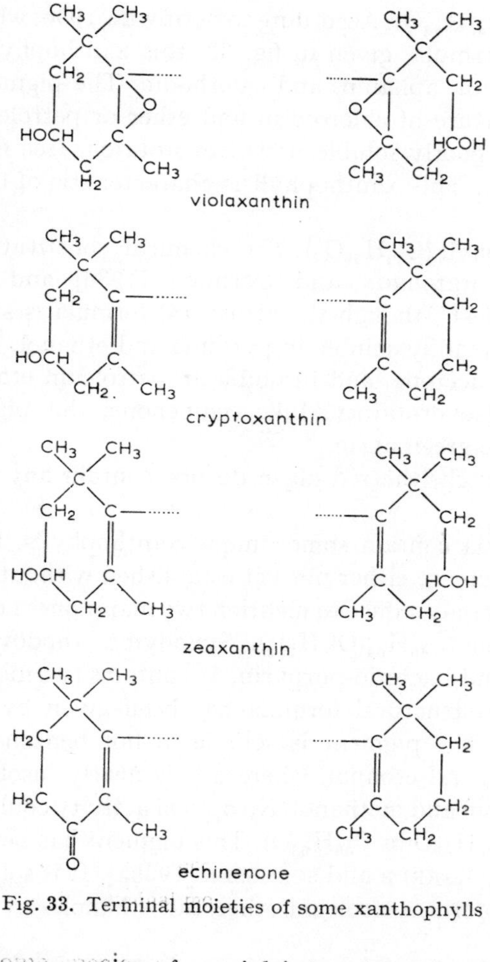

violaxanthin

cryptoxanthin

zeaxanthin

echinenone

Fig. 33. Terminal moieties of some xanthophylls

abundant in, some species of special interest to the study of photosynthesis, they will not be discussed any further here.

Fucoxanthin is the main xanthophyll of diatoms and brown algae. Its chemical structure, however, is not yet well established (see KARRER and JUCKER [1948]). The pigment is readily soluble in ethanol, soluble in carbon disulfide, poorly soluble in ether and insoluble in petroleum ether. The opinions about its optical activity are controversial.

Peridinin ($C_{40}H_{52}O_8$). This xanthophyll occurs in dinoflagellates. It was studied by STRAIN *et al.* [1944]. Peridinin is soluble in ethanol, n-propanol, petroleum ether and ether.

Echinenone ($C_{40}H_{54}O$). According to GOODWIN [1956] who established the structural formula, given in fig. 33, this xanthophyll is identical with myxoxanthin, aphanin, and calorhodin. The pigment is readily soluble in a mixture of chloroform and ether or petroleum ether. In chloroform it is poorly soluble. It is laevorotatory (see HEILBRON and LYTHGOE [1936]). This xanthophyll is characteristic of the blue-green algae.

Myxoxanthophyll ($C_{40}H_{56}O_7$). The chemical constitution has been established by HEILBRON and LYTHGOE [1936] and KARRER and RUTSCHMANN [1944], though the structural formula is still uncertain. The pigment is readily soluble in pyridine and ethanol, less soluble in chloroform and acetone, and insoluble in petroleum ether, ether and benzene. It is laevorotatory. Like echinenone, this pigment is characteristic of blue-green algae.

Curiously enough, the red algae do not contain any unique xantthophylls.

Purple bacteria contain some unique xanthophylls, the structural formulae of which are either not yet established without any doubt or still unknown. It may suffice to mention two major ones here. These are:

Spirilloxanthin ($C_{40}H_{54}(OCH_3)_2$). Synonyms: rhodoviolascin, bacterio-erythrin and bacterio-purpurin. It contains two methoxyl groups and a probable structural formula has been given by KARRER and KOENIG [1940]. The pigment is soluble in hot benzene, chloroform, carbon disulfide and ethanol, whereas it is nearly insoluble in petroleum ether, ligroin and methanol. No optical activity could be observed.

Rhodopin ($C_{40}H_{58}O$ or $C_{40}H_{56}O$). This pigment has been isolated for the first time by KARRER and SOLMSSEN [1935a]. It is soluble in carbon disulfide, chloroform, petroleum ether and ethanol.

2.2.3 Optical properties. Carotenoids owe their colour to the chromophoric properties of the linear conjugated bond system and as a rule, an increase in the number of conjugated double bonds causes the absorption bands to shift to the long-wave side and their intensities to be increased.

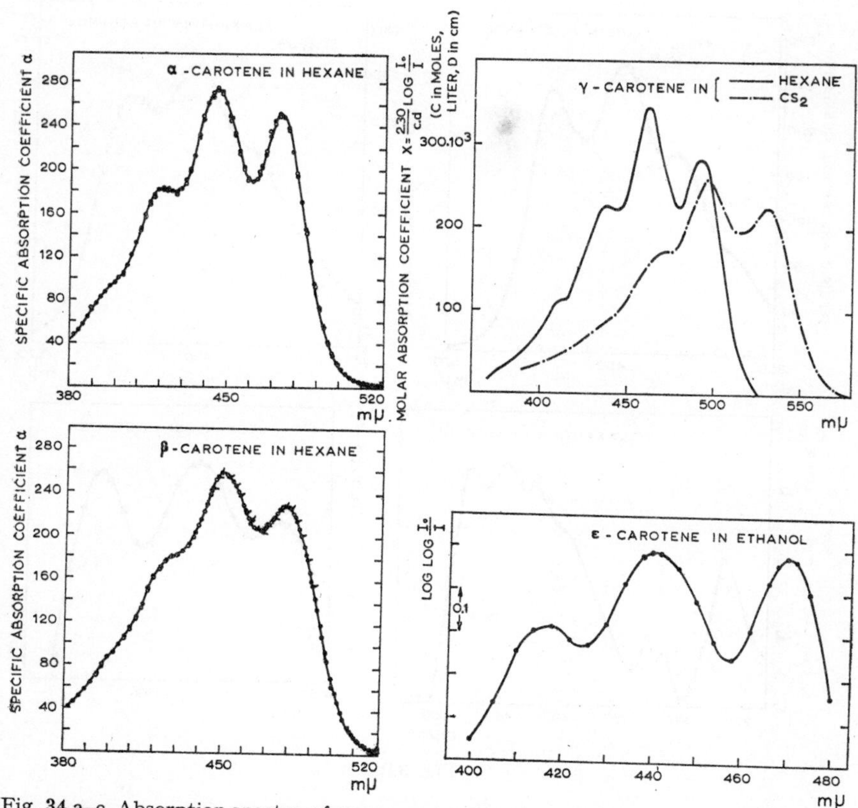

Fig. 34 a–c. Absorption spectra of some carotenes and xanthophylls. α- and β-carotene, cryptoxanthin, lutein and zeaxanthin from ZSCHELLE, WHITE, BEADLE and ROACH [1942]; γ-carotene from KUHN and BROCKMANN [1933]; neoxanthin from STRAIN, MANNING and HARDIN [1944]; spirilloxanthin (rhodoviolascein), rhodopin, violaxanthin and fucoxanthin from KARRER and WÜRGLER [1943]; and, by permission of the American Chemical Society, ε-carotene from STRAIN and MANNING [1943]

Fig. 34a

In the visible region of the spectrum, carotenoids generally show two or three bands located at wave lengths shorter than 550 mμ. The absorption spectra of most of the carotenoids considered are shown in fig. 34. Fluorescence of carotenoids has never been observed under *in vivo* conditions.

2.2.4 Physical state. As we saw in the case of the chlorophylls, the absorption spectrum of a carotenoid in photosynthetic cells or the

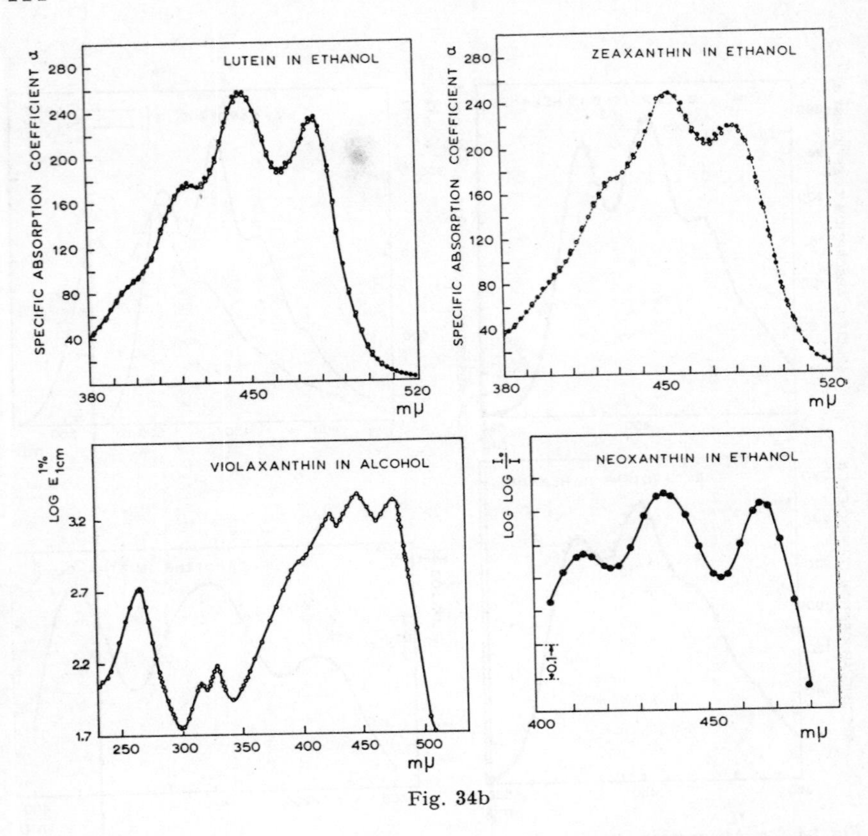

Fig. 34b

aqueous extract of cells is displaced to longer wavelengths compared with its spectrum in organic solvents. For example, fig. 35 demonstrates the difference in the location of the carotenoid maxima between a suspension of live cells of *Rhodospirillum molischianum* and an acetone extract of the same purple bacterium. The shifts are indicated by arrows. For comparison, the Soret band between 350 and 400 mμ as well as the minor absorption maximum between 550 and 600 mμ are shown for bacteriochlorophyll. Such shifts can be explained in the same way as for the chlorophylls.

By analogy with the *in vivo* state of the green pigments, it is considered likely that the carotenoids in the natural state occur in combination with proteins. As chlorophylls and carotenoids are not separated by the aqueous extraction of photosynthetic cells, it seems plausible to suppose that both kinds of pigments occur on one and the same

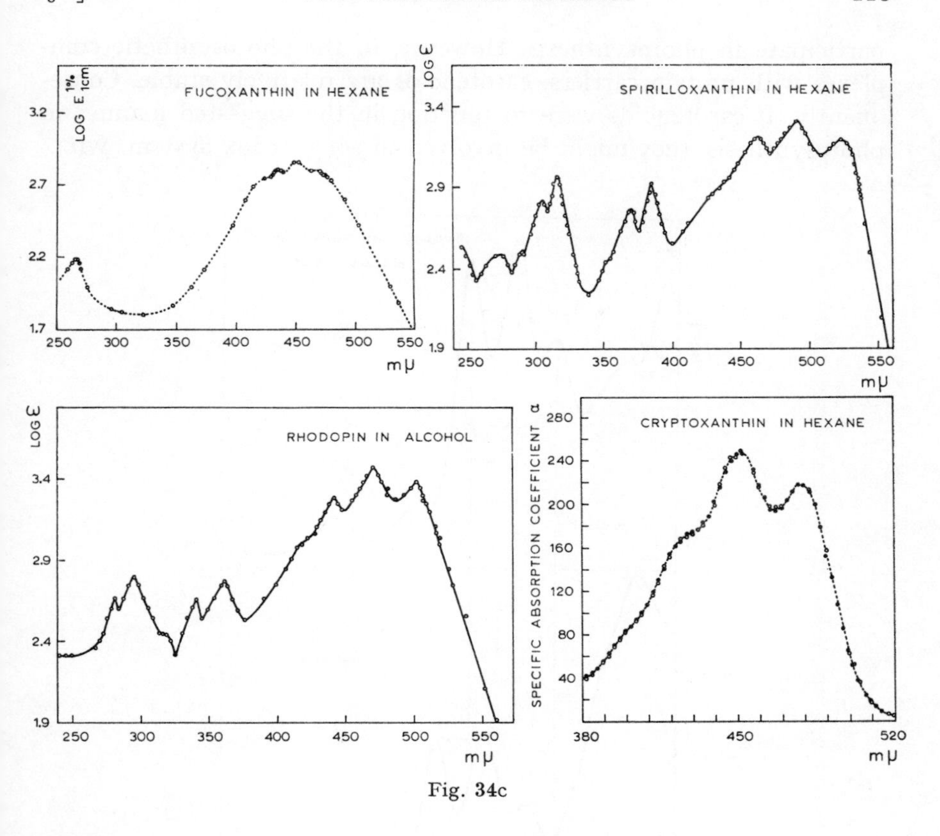

Fig. 34c

protein carrier. NISHIMURA and TAKAMATSU [1957, 1960], however, succeeded in isolating a complex of protein and a carotenoid, namely β-carotene, from green leaf plastids. This result does not necessarily mean that chlorophylls are not attached to the same protein carrier in the living cell. During preparation the green pigments may well have been removed. The authors found for these carotene-protein particles, obtained from spinach chloroplasts, a mean radius of 56 mμ by optical methods and 29 mμ by sedimentation techniques. The particle "molecular" weight was calculated to be of the order of 10^6–10^7.

2.2.5 Photochemistry and photophysics. Much less can be said on these topics for carotenoids than was the case for chlorophylls. *In vitro*, carotenoids are easily autoxidisable which led to the suggestion that carotenoids may function as oxygen transporters and so they might participate in photosynthesis. However, in the photosynthetic complexes with protein carriers, carotenoids are relatively stable. Consequently, if carotenoids were to function in the suggested manner in photosynthesis, they might be involved in some redox system. WILL-

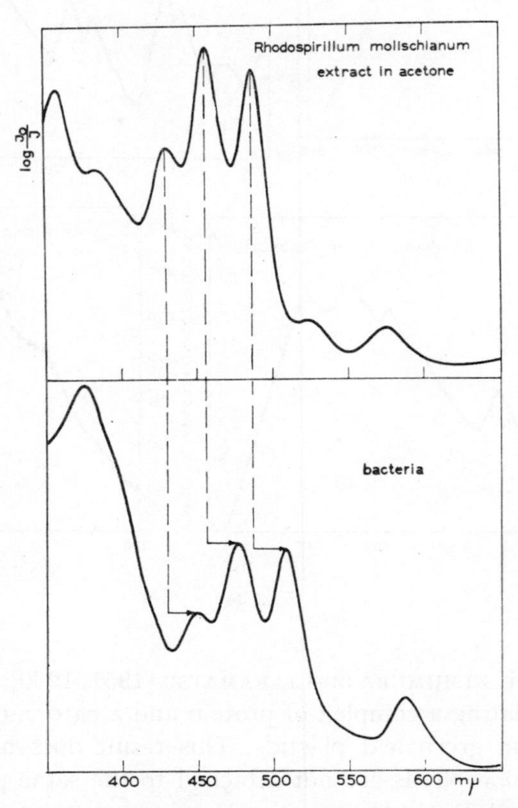

Fig. 35. *In vitro* and *in vivo* spectra of the carotenoids in the purple bacterium *Rhodospirillum molischianum*

STÄTTER and STOLL [1913] were not able to confirm such a hypothesis though SAPOZHNIKOV and LOPATKIN [1950], on the other hand, stated that under adequate photosynthetic conditions, the ratio carotene/lutein increases and on blocking the photosynthetic dark reactions, this ratio declines. The total amount of carotenoid stayed the same in both cases. SAPOZHNIKOV *et al.* [1957, 1958] reported a decrease in the violaxanthin concentration and an increase in that of lutein in the light, and similarly this reaction was reversed in the dark. This result could mean that the oxygen from violaxanthin might become available for oxidation of other compounds in the light. ANDERSON, BLASS and CALVIN [1960] were able to confirm a depression of the violaxanthin concentration in the algae *Chlorella* and *Scenedesmus* in the light but authors did not observe a corresponding lutein increase. Nevertheless, from radioactive labeling experiments they concluded that a light-dark interconversion of violaxanthin and lutein seems very likely. An oxygen transportation system involving the oxygenation of zeaxanthin *via* antheraxanthin has also been suggested by CHOLNOKY *et al.* [1956, 1958]. In the previous paper, Anderson *et al.* proposed a scheme in which both systems are correlated though such proposals are purely hypothetical at the present time. Actually, SHNEOUR and CALVIN [1962] concluded from isotopic oxygen incorporation studies that the xanthophylls of green plants probably do not act as major oxygen transporters in photosynthesis.

COLEMAN and RABINOWITCH [1960] felt tempted to ascribe the shifting of an absorption band from 480 to 520 mμ, deduced from a rather complex light minus dark difference spectrum of *Chlorella*, to a carotenoid change upon illumination. As they remarked, a difficulty of such an interpretation is that carotenoids *in vitro* show two or three maxima. However if one considers the complexity of the difference spectrum in question, it seems quite feasible that the shifts of one or two more carotenoid peaks could be masked by optical changes in other compounds. Such a possibility seems to be even more likely since SMITH and RAMIREZ [1959] observed absorption changes at the three wavelengths corresponding to carotenoids in *Rhodospirillum rubrum* and *Rhodopseudomonas spheroides*. In these, as in other purple bacteria, the carotenoid absorption is better separated from the absorption of bacteriochlorophyll than is the case with the carotenoid and chlorophyll peaks in green algae and higher plants. These authors found that either light or oxygen caused a decrease of the carotenoid absorption bands of these bacteria grown under anaerobic conditions. This suggests that the carotenoids in question are oxidized by light in the living cell. Whether this oxidation plays a role in photosynthesis, and in what way, remains to be investigated.

CLAYTON [1962] also observed a reversible photobleaching of carotenoids in *Rhodopseudomonas spheroides*. This bleaching is effected by light absorbed by bacteriochlorophyll. Deoxycholate inhibits this reaction, probably by a spatial rearrangement of the pigment molecules. Clayton interpreted the carotenoid reaction by assuming a diffusion of electrons or holes from the neighbourhood of a special bacteriochlorophyll component to the carotenoid. At least one function of carotenoids in photosynthesis has been established without doubt. The action spectra given by DUTTON *et al.* [1943], WASSINK and KERSTEN [1946], and THOMAS [1950] show that light absorbed by carotenoids is active in photosynthesis. The absorbed energy, however, is not fed into the chain of chemical processes in a direct way, but *via* the intermediary of chlorophyll-a or bacteriochlorophyll B890. This conclusion is based on the fact that the action spectrum for fluorescence excitation of these chlorophylls shows maxima corresponding with those of carotenoid absorption. The carotenoids thus transport their excitation energy to the chlorophylls. According to DUYSENS [1952], who studied and discussed this matter in a quantitative way, this energy transfer as a rule is either not very efficient (the percentage ranging from 20 to 50%), or only some of the carotenoids pass their excitation energy on with high efficiency, the remainder being inactive in this respect. However in diatoms and brown algae the efficiency of such a transfer is high and TANADA [1951] concluded that in these organisms, fucoxanthin transfers its excitation energy to chlorophyll with an efficiency approaching 100%, while no transfer from the other carotenoids occurs. The conclusion that fucoxanthin is very active in this process was confirmed by Duysens.

A secondary function of the carotenoids, seen from the photosynthetic point of view, has been suggested by STANIER [1959] to be their protective action against photodestruction sensitized by chlorophyll itself. This suggestion is based on experiments with mutant strains of bacteria which are devoid of carotenoids or strains in which carotenoid synthesis was inhibited by poisons or the growing conditions. Though the results are interesting one should keep in mind that beyond changes leading to carotenoid deficiency, others responsible for photodestruction of chlorophyll may occur as well.

Of the surveys of carotenoid studies, the following give readily access to the relevant literature: STRAIN [1938, 1944, 1949], KARRER and JUCKER [1948] and GOODWIN [1952, 1959, 1960].

2.3 Biliproteins

Beyond chlorophyll-a and carotenoids, blue-green and red algae as well as marine microflagellates (the cryptomonads), contain blue and red pigments which are readily extracted by grinding the algae in water. In general, it can be said that the red and blue pigments, termed phycoerythrins and phycocyanins respectively, occur together though the ratio of their concentrations varies greatly as evidenced by the colours of the organisms. In contrast to chlorophylls and carotenoids, these pigments diffuse out of dead cells.

Phycocyanins and phycoerythrins consist of a protein moiety and a chromophoric group. Both parts are linked together much more intimately than in other photosynthetic pigment-carrier complexes. LEMBERG [1928, 1929] was the first to separate the chromophoric group from its carrier. Because of the similarity of these groups with bile pigments, Lemberg termed them "phycobilins". A number of names have been suggested for the chromophore-protein complex. O'HEOCHA [1958] introduced the shortest designation: biliproteins.

The red phycoerythrins and the blue phycocyanins are therefore biliproteins and the corresponding chromophoric groups are termed "phycoerythrobilins" and "phycocyanobilins" respectively.

The phycobilins, like the bile pigments, contain four pyrrole nuclei. These nuclei are written in linear arrangement by convention though since bile pigments are formed from hemoglobin and other hematin compounds by opening the porphyrin ring system, it is likely (LEMBERG and LEGGE [1949]), that the correct structural formula is open-cyclic rather than linear. The four pyrrole nuclei are linked together by three carbon atoms. The skeleton and the numbering of atoms in bile pigments is shown in fig. 36A and a typical one, mesobiliviolin in its bislactam form according to GRAY and NICHOLSON [1958], is shown in fig. 36B.

Much research about these pigments has been carried out, though since the structure of the phycobilins from plants is not yet quite elucidated, it may suffice to quote a few literature sources with regard to their chemistry in general: FISCHER-ORTH [1937], LEMBERG and LEGGE [1949], GRAY [1953], O'HEOCHA [1960], and HAXO and O'HEOCHA [1960].

2.3.1 Individual biliproteins. The light absorption of a particular biliprotein is dependent upon its source and so phycocyanin in blue-green algae shows absorption characteristics different from the phycocyanin in red algae. For this reason the prefixes C (from Cyanophyceae) or R (from Rhodophyceae) are added to the name of the pigment. However there are some exceptions. In certain cases, red algae may contain phycocyanin of the C-type. It may be preferable, therefore, to consider the C and R prefixes as indicators of a certain type of biliprotein rather than an indication of the source of the pigment.

The following forms of the pigments are known:

C-phycocyanin, commonly occurring in blue-green algae. It has also been observed in a few Rhodophyta and Chlorophyta.

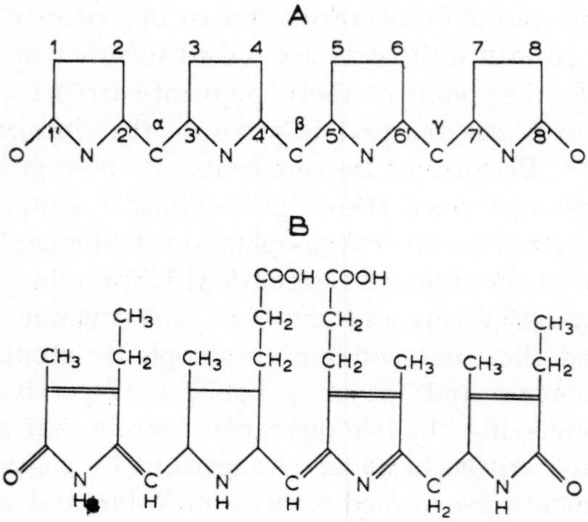

Fig. 36. Skeleton and numbering of atoms in bile pigments (A) and mesobiliviolin (B)

R-phycocyanin, found in a few red algae.

Allophycocyanin occurs in small amounts in many red and blue-green algae.

R-phycoerythrin, the most generally occurring phycoerythrin in red algae.

C-phycoerythrin, present in red-coloured Cyanophyta.

B-phycoerythrin, observed in the red alga *Porphyra naiadum* (BLINKS [1954]).

It should be added that according to HALLDAL [1958], M. BRODY and EMERSON [1959] and FUJITA and HATTORI [1960a, b], the qualitative composition of biliproteins varies with the light conditions during the algal growth.

2.3.2 Optical Properties. The phycocyanins and phycoerythrins can be characterized reliably by their absorption properties though it is the location of the maxima rather than the general shape of the spectra that is more important in this respect. Examples of absorption spectra

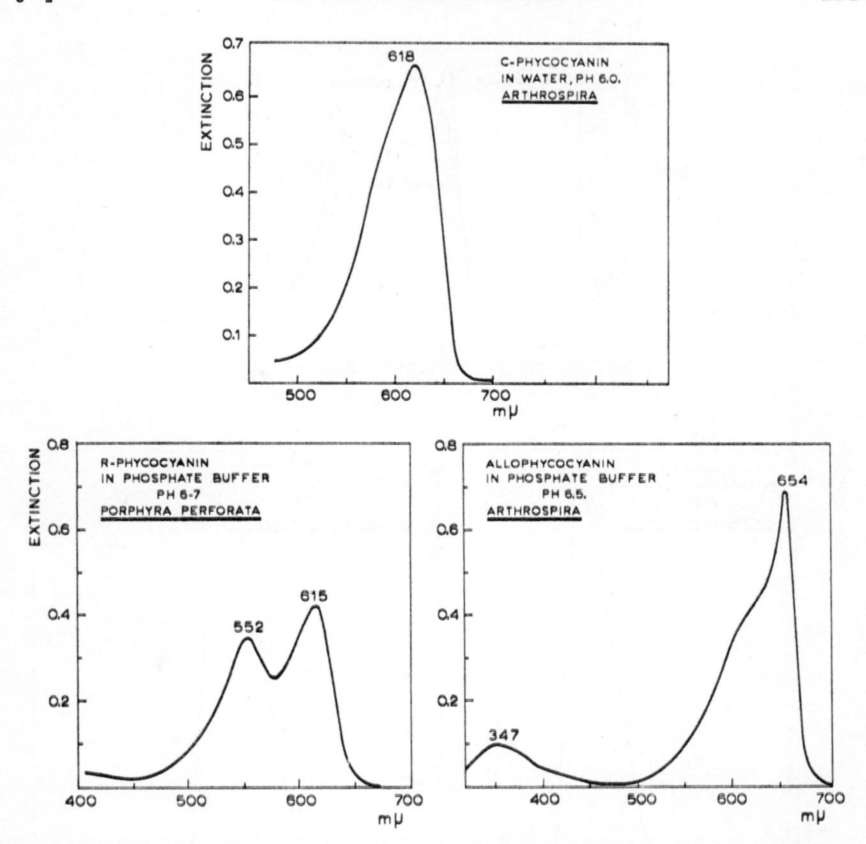

Fig. 37. Absorption spectra of phycocyanins. C-phycocyanin and allophycocyanin from O'HEOCHA [1958]; R-phycocyanin from HAXO, O'HEOCHA and NORRIS [1955]

are shown in fig. 37 for phycocyanins and in fig. 38 for phycoerythrins.

A striking property of the biliproteins is their strong fluorescence. According to BRODY and RABINOWITCH [1957], the fluorescence yields of phycocyanin and phycoerythrin in phosphate buffer, pH 6.0–6.2, amount to 53 and 85% respectively. LEMBERG [1930] observed that fluorescence quenching occurs together with a shift of the absorption spectrum. He suggested that the fluorescence in question depends on the presence of another, more labile bond between the protein and the chromophoric group. This conception is shared by O'HEOCHA [1960].

2.3.3 Physical state. Phycocyanobilin and phycoerythrobilin occur *in vivo* as the chromophoric groups of a protein and are linked rather

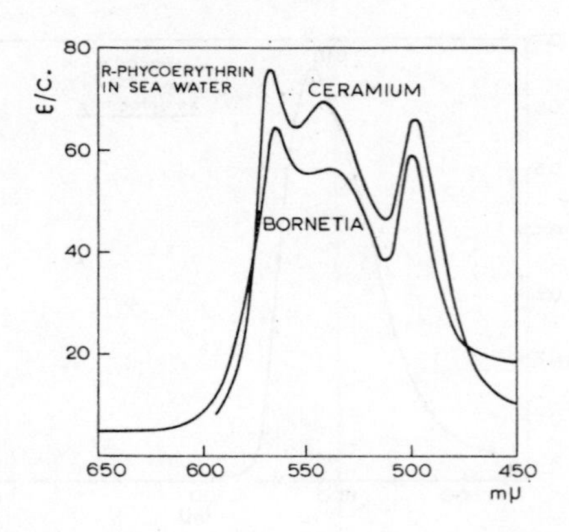

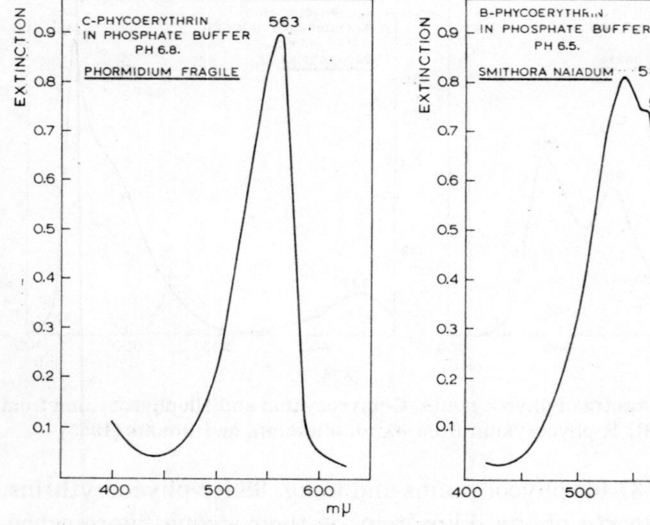

Fig. 38. Absorption spectra of phycoerythrins. R-phycoerythrin from SVEDBERG and ERIKSON [1939] by permission of the American Chemical Society; C- and B-phycoerythrin from O'HEOCHA and HAXO [1960]

strongly to the protein in contrast to the chlorophylls and carotenoids. This phenomenon is expressed in the nomenclature for instead of phycobilin-protein complexes, the pigments are termed biliproteins.

A very efficient energy transfer, approaching 100%, occurs from the biliproteins to chlorophyll-a (see DUYSENS [1952] and FRENCH and YOUNG [1952]). To attain such a high efficiency, the distance between the transferring molecules should not exceed 60–70 Å. TOMITA and RABI-

NOWITCH [1962] found the transfer times in *Porphyridium* from phycoerythrin to phycocyanin and from phycocyanin to chlorophyll-a to be 0.3 and 0.5 nano-sec. respectively. In *Anacystis* the transfer time from phycocyanin to chlorophyll-a was found to be 0.3 nano-sec. As evidenced by the easy selective extraction of the biliproteins by grinding the cells in water, both kinds of pigment do not occur in the same complex. The phycoerythrins and phycocyanins seem to be separated from each other as well. This conclusion is based upon the fact that phycocyanin is leached out of dead *Porphyra perforata* fronds more readily than phycoerythrin (THOMAS and GOVINDJEE [1960]). Nevertheless the highly efficient energy transfer suggests that the pigments should be located in close proximity to each other in the living cell. This means that in the photosynthetic apparatus, they either occur in some very loosely bound configuration or are just located close to each other.

2.3.4 Photochemistry and photophysics. The biliproteins are sensitive to light and oxygen. LEMBERG [1930] stated that this sensitivity is considerably higher for phycobilins, that is, upon removal of the protein moiety. THOMAS and GOVINDJEE [1960] purified phycoerythrin preparations from *Porphyra perforata* as well as phycocyanin extracts from *Anacystis nidulans* by repeated precipitation and washing with ammonium sulfate. Upon final removal of this salt by dialysis, clear, intensely coloured pigment solutions were obtained which showed only a slow aerobic bleaching in the light. KRASNOVSKY, EVSTIGNEEV *et al.* [1952] stated that chromatographically purified phycoerythrin is stable against oxidation by air in the light. The same is true of reduction by ascorbic acid. In conclusion, these results might mean that the more biliprotein preparations are purified, the more photostable they are.

There has been no indication from difference spectra that light-dark changes in biliprotein absorption take place, and fluorescence action spectra clearly demonstrate that energy absorbed by the biliproteins is transferred to chlorophyll-a with an efficiency approaching 100%. Taken together these data suggest that the role of these pigments is to make a larger part of the spectrum available for photosynthetic purposes.

2.4 Phytochrome

There are two reasons for doubting whether it is relevant to introduce the phytochrome system here.

Firstly no definite proof of the participation of phytochrome in photosynthesis has yet been established while secondly, if such a participation might exist, it is a negative one since the pigment might act as an inhibitor. There is only one fact that justifies a brief discussion about phytochrome at this point which is that, provided phytochrome interacts in photosynthesis, this pigment takes part in at least two completely different processes. This is because phytochrome is also a general photomorphogenic agent. It will therefore be discussed in more detail under "photoperiodism".

Phytochrome is the pigment that mediates the effects of red and far-red light on many aspects of plant development. It is a photoreversible compound, occurring in two forms with absorption maximal at either 660 mμ or 730 mμ, (see BUTLER *et al.* [1959], BUTLER and NORRIS [1960], and BUTLER [1961a]). Irradiation with light absorbed by one form makes it change over to the other form. The pigment, or pigment complex, is of a proteinaceous nature.

THOMAS and GOVINDJEE [1960b] obtained results in photosynthetic experiments which seemed to point to the occurrence of a "countereffect" evoked by extreme red light. RABINOWITCH *et al.* [1960] succeeded in showing that in some algae, light of 750 ± 10 mμ indeed reversibly inhibits the photosynthesis produced by light of about 700 mμ. GOVINDJEE *et al.* [1960, 1961] found that the maximum inhibitory effect occurs around 745 mμ. The inhibitory effect can be annihilated by light of shorter wavelengths. Two features of the process, namely its reversibility and the fact that the approximate wavelengths for maximum effect are similar, both correspond with those of the processes controlled by phytochrome in photomorphogenesis. The maximum activity, it is true, occurs in the latter around 730–735 mμ while photosynthesis inhibition is strongest around 740–745 mμ. However in both cases the bands are rather broad and overlap each other to such an extent that the possibility of the same pigment acting in both kinds of phenomena should certainly be considered seriously. On the other hand, it should be emphatically stated that there is no definite proof of the identity of these two pigments.

2.5 Hematin compounds

Apart from the above photoreceptive species, another type of pigment is active in photosynthesis – the hematin compounds. These are proteins with prosthetic groups consisting of tetrapyrrolic iron chelates. As an example, cytochrome-c is depicted in fig. 39. The porphyrin moiety of cytochrome-c is linked to the protein by two thioether bonds (see PAUL [1951]), while the iron is probably linked to two imidazolyl groups of histidine residues to form a hemochromogen (see MARGOLIASH [1955]).

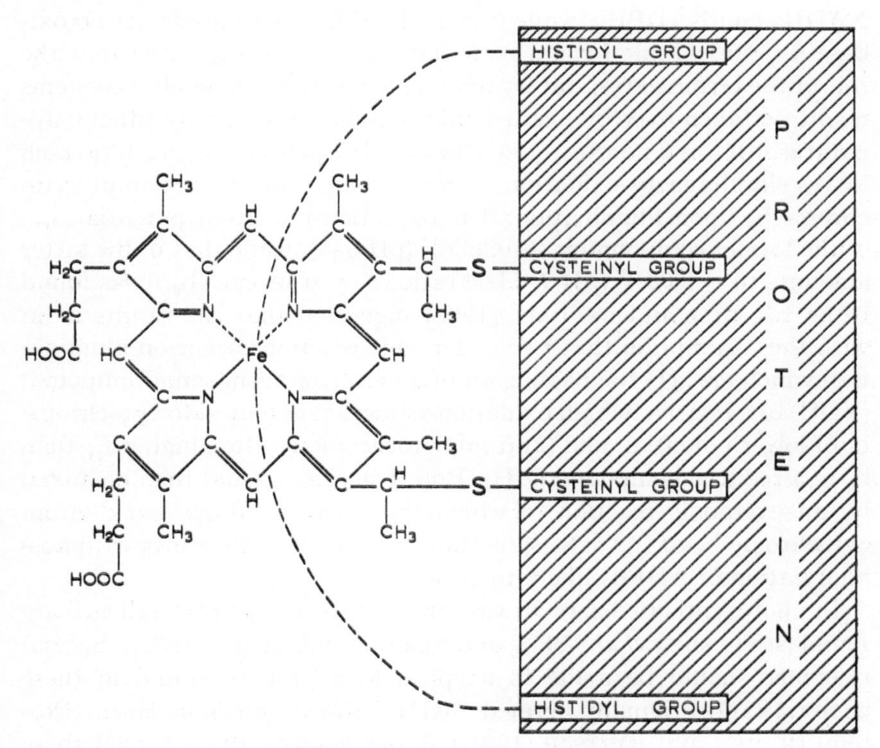

Fig. 39. The structure of cytochrome-c

Though the hematin compounds are pigments, their photosynthetic function does not consist of light absorption but of enzyme activity. Their role most probably consists of linking the light capture phenomenon and the chain of "dark-chemical" synthesis processes.

HILL and SCARISBRICK [1951] succeeded in extracting three cytochromes from green leaves, namely cytochromes c, b_3, and f. DAVENPORT and HILL [1952] purified cytochrome-f and stated that this compound is found only in "green" leaves. Cytochrome-f was localized within the chloroplasts by DAVENPORT [1952] and is a c-type cytochrome. In the same paper, this author reported the occurrence of a second cytochrome which is typical of chloroplasts and this is a b-type one. HILL [1954] studied this cytochrome spectroscopically and termed it cytochrome-b_6. It is highly autoxidizable.

Cytochrome-f is non-autoxidizable. It is reduced by ascorbate, $NADH_2$ and $NADPH_2$, while it is oxidized by ferricyanide. As no oxidase for cytochrome-f could be found, HILL [1956] suggested that the role of the terminal respiratory oxidase found in mitochondrial systems might be taken over by excited chlorophyll in the photosynthetic apparatus. HILL and BONNER [1961] observed in pale yellow-green spinach leaves simultaneous oxidation of cytochrome-f and reduction of cytochrome-b_6 upon illumination. The oxidation-reduction potential, E_O, of the former compound is $+ 0.365$ V (pH 5–8), while that of the latter amounts to -0.06 V (pH 7). The ratio of cytochromes b_6/f was found to be 1.3. HILL and BENDALL [1960] suggested that the results fit in with the assumption that two endergonic reactions occur on illumination which are: (1) the passing on of an electron from some compound (YOH) of a relatively high oxidation-reduction potential to cytochrome b_6 of lower potential, and (2) from cytochrome-f with a higher E_O than b_6 to a reduced compound (XH). Both reactions should then be linked by an exergonic reaction in which the electron "drops back" from cytochrome-b_6 to f. At the same time as this electron transport, phosphorylation of ADP is likely to occur.

In photosynthetic bacteria, varieties of cytochrome-c as well as b are found (see ELSDEN *et al.* [1953] and VERNON and KAMEN [1954]). Special reference should be made to atypical hemoproteins found in these bacteria, and originally termed "RHP" (*Rhodospirillum* Haem Protein) (KAMEN and BARTSCH [1961]). Later KAMEN [1963] named these compounds "cytochromoids". The E_O value (pH 7.0) is -0.008 and -0.005 V for *Rhodospirillum rubrum* and *Chromatium* cytochromoids respectively. In contrast with cytochrome-c, they are readily autoxidizable though the chemistry of RHP indicates that it is a cytochrome-c variant. It might function as a "terminal oxidase".

In their experiments on the occurrence of cytochromes in photosynthetic organelles, Hill and coworkers, *loc. cit.*, only observed them in pale-green tissues. These authors therefore concluded that the cytochrome function in photosynthesis can only be assessed properly after the establishment of their light-induced absorption changes in fully green cells or photosynthetic structures. SMITH and CHANCE [1958] remarked that in fully green leaves and algae there are so many differences between "aerobic" and "anaerobic" spectra due to other pigments that the difference spectra of cytochromes may be impossible to distinguish. These authors also point to a number of methodical uncertainties in assigning the right function in photosynthesis to the cytochromes in question. Without entering into details, it may be stated in conclusion that the data obtained with pale-green chloroplasts as well as the results with purple bacteria (DUYSENS [1954b]) strongly suggest that one or more cytochromes do participate in photosynthesis.

According to KAMEN [1961a], one cytochrome molecule occurs per 100–500 chlorophyll molecules.

Since the function of cytochromes in photosynthesis probably consists of transporting free electrons rather than producing them as a result of light absorption, their function does not strictly belong to the photo-driven processes and a more detailed discussion of the literature concerning these compounds will not be undertaken. It may suffice to quote a few reviews: KAMEN [1956, 1961b], SMITH and CHANCE [1958], and GEST and KAMEN [1961].

Pigment-enzymes other than cytochromes also play a role in the dark processes of photosynthesis but will not be discussed here for the same reason.

3 The photoreceptive structures

The photosynthetic pigments are not homogeneously distributed throughout the cell, but are concentrated in well-organized structures So far, there seems to be one single exception: FULLER *et al.* [1963] stated that in green sulfur bacteria the photosynthetic pigments occur on particles which are randomly distributed throughout the cell. These particles may well represent subunits such as are observed in the organized structures. Four types of such photoreceptive structures are known:

3.1 Grana-containing chloroplasts

These chloroplasts, also termed "granular" or "granulated" chloroplasts, are the most commonly occuring type in "higher" plants. Usu-

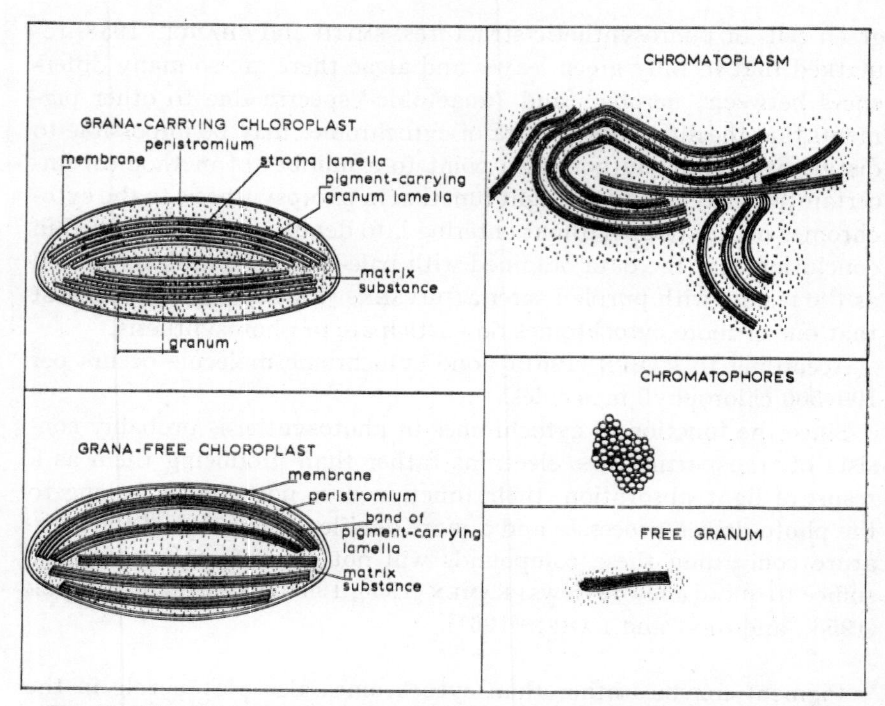

Fig. 40. Schematic representation of the five types of photosynthetic structures

ally they show up as lens-shaped bodies under the electron microscope. The largest dimension may vary from a few μ to more than 10 μ. These chloroplasts consist of both a non-coloured and a coloured part. The former consists of an outer membrane and a proteinaceous substance, termed "stroma".

The membrane shows up as two layers, each of them with a thickness of 50–80 Å, and located at a distance of about 100 Å apart. MCLEAN [1956] however, suggested that by analogy with the proposed structure of the mitochondrial envelope, the surrounding membrane of the chloroplast might consist of three layers, namely two protein layers separated by a bimolecular lipid film. The total thickness of the membrane is found to be about 200 Å in most cases. However values ranging from 100 to 300 Å have also been reported.

The membrane governs the swelling and permeability properties of the chloroplasts, (MERCER *et al.* [1955]) and as the chloroplasts are capable of expanding and shrinking, the area of the envelope is of a variable size. Surprisingly however, the deformations of this membrane are considerably larger than those accounted for by the volume changes of the chloroplasts. Before discussing this phenomenon, the structure of the second non-coloured chloroplast constituent, the stroma, should be considered.

The stroma is defined as the colourless proteinaceous substance in which the pigment-carrying structures are embedded. Electron micrographs show that the stroma consists of a granular-looking matrix material as well as lamellae which connect the coloured bodies. In chloroplasts, particularly in young ones, the lamellae are located somewhat removed from the outer membrane and thus are very clearly surrounded by a "granular" outer stroma layer. This outer layer for which SENN [1908] proposed the name "peristromium", is capable of carrying out amoeboid movements. STRUGGER [1956] suggested that the peristromium is of a sol character, whereas the more centrally located stroma exhibits a gel nature. WILDMAN *et al.* [1962] made a cinematographic study on movements of spinach chloroplasts. They made the astonishing observation that the amoeboid movements of the outer jacket often result in ejaculating stroma matter which means that the surrounding membrane should be capable of undergoing sufficient deformation to prevent damage of the chloroplast structure by leakage of material in either direction.

The membrane can thus undergo three types of deformation, (1) osmotically-controlled volume changes of the chloroplast, (2) amoeboid movements, and (3) ejaculation of stroma substance. The ejaculates do not disintegrate. Just as if they were mitochondria, they carry on for some time by themselves as units, and one should conclude that these mitochondria-like bodies are surrounded by a membrane. This membrane possibly formed part of the original chloroplast envelope. Sooner or later the ejaculates may recombine with the chloroplasts. The authors state that mitochondria are also seen to unite with the chloroplast jacket and so lose their identity. It is tempting to speculate that the formation of such stroma particles might serve as a distribution mechanism for the photosynthetic products. However as yet there is not the slightest evidence to support this. On the other hand, although the ejaculates are able to recombine, not all of them necessarily do so. In this case the stroma content of the plastids should decrease with time. In fact the peristromium is less pronounced in aged chloroplasts. Might this phenomenon be due to loss of stroma in the young ones?

There are other problems. Does the ejaculated stroma contain certain enzymes or cofactors active in photosynthesis? Does their amount therefore decrease during aging in the chloroplasts? Or is the occurrence of these compounds restricted to the "gel" phase of the stroma? Future research may answer these questions, though for the moment we can only say that the function of the stroma is far from understood.

The second component of the stroma, the lamellae, connect the pigment-carrying units with each other. LEYON [1956] suggested that these "stroma-lamellae" or "intergrana-lamellae" may function as flattened channels enabling the transport of photosynthesis products to the outer layer of the chloroplast. In certain cases the stroma lamellae occur in bundles of 4 to 6 and according to VON WETTSTEIN [1957], the interspaces in the bundles may function as temporary storage and transportation facilities for the products. The lamellae are paired to form closed double lamellae which GIBBS [1960] named "discs", MÜHLETHALER [1960] "flattened vescicles", and MENKE [1962] "thylakoids". The lamellae are assumed to consist of proteins and lipids, or lipoproteins. It has been suggested that the lipids are oriented. According to MÜHLETHALER [1960], the lamellae consist of a central sheet of a thickness of 35 Å, bounded by osmiophylic layers of 20 Å thickness. The central layer may consist of protein while the adjoining layers may be composed of lipids.

The occurrence of two apparent components of stroma raises the question whether it is desirable to change the terminology. SAGER and PALADE [1957] proposed that the term stroma be replaced by "matrix" with regard to the non-lamellar material. MERCER [1960] suggested that the denomination "stroma" may be used for indicating this particular material, whereas the lamellae embedded in this stroma may be called "stroma-lamellae". Indeed, this seems preferable to "intergrana-lamellae". The matrix may contain starch vacuoles and spherical bodies probably of a lipoic nature.

The grana are carriers of the photosynthetic pigments. Though some authors, for example MERCER *et al.* [1955] considered the possibility that chlorophyll also occurs at stroma-lamellae, it is assumed by the majority of the investigators that this pigment is concentrated in the grana exclusively. The fact that light- and fluorescence-microscopy reveals the presence of chlorophyll only in the grana in those chloroplasts with sufficiently large grana for these techniques to be of use, strongly supports this view.

The grana consist of stacks of round, closed, double lamellae. These stacks are interconnected by the mentioned stroma-lamellae. In some cases, the number of grana-lamellae equals the number of stroma-lamellae per unit area of cross-section. In other cases, the former number is twice the latter one. For a more detailed review on this matter see THOMAS [1960]. PACKER [1962] observed changes in light scattering by spinach chloroplasts and fragments thereof which are correlated with photosynthetic phosphorylation. He ascribed them to variations in the "membranes" though the nature of the changes is still obscure. According to the author, variations in the structural arrangement of the "membranes" are involved. As to the arrangement of photosynthetic pigments, it will be recalled that GOEDHEER [1957] concluded that chlorophyll occurs at the lamellae in layers of a thickness of the order of that of the pigment porphyrin plate. He observed a relatively poor orientation of these plates in the plane of the lamellae, and no indication of carotenoid orientation could be measured. On a purely hypothetical basis, HUBERT [1935] suggested a carotenoid orientation perpendicular to the lamellar plane.

The lamellae are probably built up of lipoprotein macromolecules which show up as spherical bodies under the electron microscope. By disintegrating spinach grana ultrasonically and measuring the photochemical oxygen liberation by the resulting fragments in the Hill reaction, THOMAS, BLAAUW and DUYSENS [1953] concluded that the size of the smallest fragments capable of performing this reaction is of the order of 10^6 Å^3. This volume corresponds with that of the "globular" particles forming the lamellae (THOMAS [1958]). PARK and PON [1961] suggested that these particles are oblately spherical and estimated the dimensions to be somewhat larger than the earlier authors. Calvin and coworkers (see CALVIN [1962]) termed the chlorophyll-carrying macromolecular constituents of the lamellae "quantasomes", a pretty name, though not quite correct for σωμα means "body" whereas the "quantasome" is a fragment of a body. It will also be recalled that SAUER and CALVIN [1962] suggested from electric dichroïsm experiments that some of the chlorophyll molecules occur highly oriented at one particular site in the "quantasome", while the remainder of the chlorophyll in this structure is randomly arranged.

As the grana-lamellae are closed double lamellae, the question arises whether the chlorophyll occurs at the outer or inner surface, or at both of them. From Hill reaction experiments with grana which were slightly torn up by mild supersonic treatment, and from considerations on energy transfer, THOMAS *et al.* [1958] obtained indication that the chlorophyll is likely to occur at the outer surface of the grana lamellae.

Estimates by various authors agree to the extent that the mean lamellar area available per chlorophyll molecule is of the same order as the area of the porphyrin moiety of this pigment.

The Hill reaction referred to previously consists of oxygen evolution from water in the presence of a suitable hydrogen acceptor and excited chlorophyll. This process is assumed to represent part of the photosynthetic reaction chain. It is enzymic and so at least part of the enzymes responsible for the photosynthetic oxygen liberation are likely to occur together with chlorophyll at the proteinaceous constituents of the lamellae. This conclusion is supported by the fact that repeated washings of chloroplasts do not destroy their capability of performing the Hill reaction. Other enzymes or cofactors, active in photosynthesis, for example those involved in the carbon dioxide reduction, are readily leached out of isolated chloroplasts. These enzymes should either be bound quite weakly to the mentioned macromolecular carriers or occur in the matrix substance. There are some indications, (THOMAS and NUBOER [1959]) that the compounds in question are located in this stroma substance.

3.2 Grana-free chloroplasts

These are also termed "lamellate chloroplasts". The latter designation however dates from the earlier investigations which had not then revealed the stroma lamellae and it therefore seems preferable to discard this name. Grana-free chloroplasts are observed in many algae and less frequently, in higher plants. Like those of the former type, these plastids are surrounded by an envelope. Chlorophyll-carrying double lamellae extend throughout the chloroplast, in most cases in strands of 2 to 6. According to GIBBS [1960], in *Euglena* chloroplasts 10 to 45 of these strands occur. The double lamellae are located quite closely to each other in the bands and so the thickness of the outermost lamellae, which is of the order of 50 Å, seems to be half that of the inner lamellae. In between the lamellar bundles a granulated stroma or matrix substance is found. In certain regions the interlamellar material may be modified so as to form a pyrenoid.

One may formulate the difference between these chloroplasts and the grana-carrying ones as follows: (1) in grana-free plastids the stroma consists of a single granulated component, the matrix substance, whereas in the other type of chloroplast the stroma is made up of two components: (a) the matrix substance and (b) the stroma lamellae. (2) In grana-free chloroplasts, the photosynthetic pigments are most probably distributed evenly along the lamellar surface, while in grana-carrying ones the occurrence of these pigments is restricted to the grana lamellae. Apart from these differences, both types of chloroplasts are very much alike. This also holds for their content of pyrenoids, starch vacuoles, and the globules of high electron-scattering power.

3.3 *Chromatoplasm*

In some algae and green flagellates the photosynthetic structures, instead of being located within a special organelle, are found in the cytoplasm and are spread throughout the cell. These structures consist of winding strands of about 4 lamellae. This system of lamellar bands embedded in the cytoplasm of the cell is termed "chromatoplasm". NIKLOWITZ and DREWS [1956] observed this type of structure in blue-green algae and estimated the lamellar thickness to vary from 120 to 210 Å. This thickness, however, seems to refer to a strand of lamellae rather than to an individual one. Probably the photosynthetic pigments are evenly distributed along the lamellar surface. Earlier studies (THOMAS [1960]), suggested that grana-like bodies occur in the blue-green algae and such structures have been observed in aqueous extracts of these algae under the electron microscope. Obviously, these "grana" are artifacts.

3.4 *Chromatophores*

This name has been assigned by SCHACHMAN *et al.* [1952] to pigment-carrying structures extracted from photosynthetic bacteria. VATTER and WOLFE [1958] prepared ultra-thin sections of photosynthetically active purple and green bacteria. When studied under the electron microscope, the chromatophores were found to be spherical bodies. BERGERON [1959], working with the purple sulfur bacterium *Chromatium,* studied the chromatophores both morphologically and chemically. He assumed the chromatophore is a macromolecule and found the "molecular" weight to be 1.3×10^7. Measurements as well as calculation showed that the average particle diameter is of the order of 300 Å. In each chromatophore the following numbers of molecules occur: chlorophyll–600; carotenoid–300; phospholipids–3000; amino-acids constituting the protein–67000.

3.5 Free grana

In aged cultures of photosynthetic bacteria lamellar systems together with chromatophores occur. Such a lamellar structure consists of a stack of double lamellae. It resembles a granum from chloroplasts of higher plants and is therefore termed a "free granum" (see THOMAS [1960]). NIKLOWITZ and DREWS [1955] were the first to prepare ultra-thin sections of these bacterial organelles and study them under the electron microscope. One gets the impression that with age of the bacteria, the number of free grana increases at the expense of the number of chromatophores. Therefore it may be that chromatophores combine to form lamellae though this is not the only way in which lamellae originate in bacteria. GIESBRECHT and DREWS [1962] observed that bacterial lamellae developed from invaginations of the cell envelope.

The consequences of the presence of free grana to the photosynthetic activity of the bacteria are still obscure. Bacteria containing only chromatophores and bacteria also containing free grana in addition are both capable of photosynthesis. It would be interesting to study the light-intensity dependency of photosynthesis as well as its maximum rate in relation to the formation of free grana.

It has been mentioned before that lamellae have been seen in all the full-grown photosynthetic organisms studied so far. This statement does not hold in the case of young purple bacteria as well as green sulfur bacteria although these are photosynthetically active. Consequently the presence of relatively large flat double lamellae is no prerequisite of the photosynthesis function in these organisms. Such a conclusion need not be contradictory to the suggestion of Leyon mentioned earlier that the flattened channels formed by the lamellae act as transportation routes for the photosynthesis products. It might be that in the tiny bacterial cell no such provisions are required as the transportation area is sufficiently restricted. On the other hand, it should be emphasized once more that the "channel hypothesis" is not supported by any experimental evidence whatsoever.

At present it is hard to say what kind of a structure the bacterial chromatophore actually is in a morphological sense. Should they be considered as short double lamellae? If the area of a double lamella is gradually decreased, a sphere will result when its three dimensions are equal. Alternatively, considering the fact that free grana are absent in young bacteria, are the chromatophores to be considered structures like those in the "crystalline core" from which lamellae may originate in young chloroplasts (see STRUGGER and LOSADA-VILLASANTE [1955/56]) ? However in this case there is a notable difference between the two kinds of structure. Chloroplasts containing the "crystalline core" but still lacking lamellae are photosynthetically inactive, whereas bacteria with chromatophores but without free grana are capable of photosynthesis. Moreover, "crystalline cores" are only observed in chloroplasts which were either developed in the dark or showed "disintegration" of the lamellar system after keeping them in the dark for a prolonged time.

Whichever the case may be, lamellae and chromatophores have certain features in common. Both of them are carriers of pigments, both contain proteins or lipoproteins, and lipids, and last but not least, both exhibit a surface area sufficient to allow spacing and orientation of the pigments relative to each other and to the enzymic centres.

A number of suggestions have been presented in the literature on the most interesting problem of structure on the molecular scale, for example HUBERT [1935], FREY-WYSSLING [1957], BERGERON [1959], CALVIN [1961a], and WOLKEN [1962]. These proposals, interesting as they are, lack experimental support, most of them do not pay any credit to the fact that overall orientation of the pigments is only poor and none of them accounts for the conclusion of SAUER and CALVIN [1962] that the major part of the chlorophyll in the plastid shows random orientation, while only a minor fraction is strongly oriented. For this reason, no discussion on this problem will be presented here. In conclusion it can be said that elucidation of the molecular structure of the photosynthetic apparatus is still far from being achieved.

4 *The nature of the process*

The primary photoprocess of photosynthesis may be regarded as the capturing of light energy and the transformation of it into a type of energy, "chemical energy", needed (a) to provide activation energy for the dark chemical reactions, and (b) to produce a gain of free energy. The fundamentals of these processes rather than their detailed features, will be briefly discussed here.

According to a suggestion of LEVITT [1953], the light energy is converted into chemical energy in photosynthesis by means of the expulsion of an electron from a chlorophyll molecule which has been raised to an excited state by the absorption of a photon. Furthermore he suggested that this electron originated from the magnesium atom. This idea of electrons expelled by excited chlorophyll molecules also underlies a theory proposed by ARNON, see [1961], known as the "electron flow mechanism". Before any further consideration of this theory, one consequence of the removal of an electron from a molecule should be discussed.

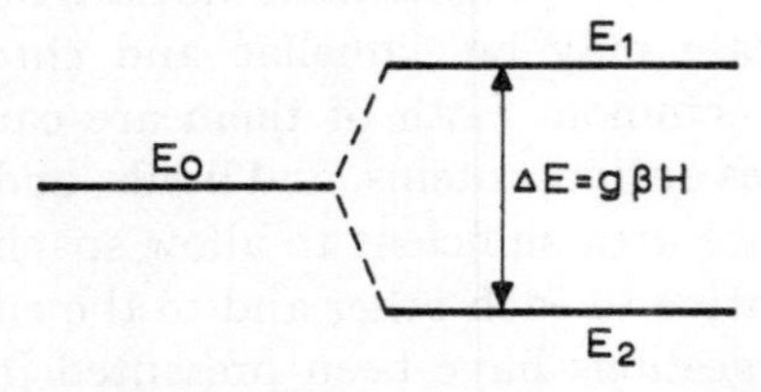

Fig. 41. Splitting of electronic energy levels in an applied magnetic field

In molecules, electrons lie in discrete energy states each of which can be occupied by one or two electrons and in general, electrons occur in pairs. Since an electron spins around its own axis and is a carrier of electric charge, a magnetic momentum results. Usually no such momentum can be detected, since the partners in an electron pair are spinning in such directions that the magnetic momenta are antiparallel and so compensate each other.

If an electron is expelled from its pair, the magnetic momenta of the two electrons are compensated no longer and the molecule as a whole displays a detectable magnetic momentum. The molecule has thus become paramagnetic and is termed a "free radical". A free radical may carry an electric charge and is then called an "ion radical". Paramagnetic substances can be detected by the electron spin resonance (ESR) technique. The ESR phenomenon is based upon the fact that unpaired electrons can take only two orientations in an applied external magnetic field. Under such conditions they arrange their magnetic momenta both parallel and antiparallel to the applied field. The energies related to these two states are slightly different and the magnitude of this difference will be proportional to the applied magnetic field.

In fig. 41, the level E_0 indicates the energy state of a certain electron. On the application of an external magnetic field, orientation of the magnetic moments of the unpaired electrons occurs, resulting in a splitting of the single energy state E_0 into two states E_1 and E_2. The energy difference depends on three parameters as follows:

$$\Delta E = g\beta H$$

in which β stands for the magnetic momentum of the electron, H for the strength of the applied magnetic field, and g is a constant. This constant is called the spectroscopic splitting factor or Landé factor. It amounts to 2.0023 for a free electron. However, because of interactions of the magnetic momentum of the electron spin with the angular momentum of the electron and the magnetic momentum of neighbouring spinning nuclei, the g-value for an unpaired electron in a free radical is different from that of a free electron. This means that the g-value may be an important source of information with regard to the magnetic environment of an unpaired electron.

If a paramagnetic particle in an applied magnetic field is irradiated with microwave energy, electron spin resonance may result.

This resonance actually takes place upon introduction of an alternating electromagnetic field of such a frequency that the quantum energy, $h\nu$, of this radiation equals the gap between the two possible electron spin energy levels, $g\beta H$. For practical reasons, the resonance condition, $h\nu = g\beta H$, is produced by varying the magnetic field strength instead of changing the microwave frequency and results in the energy uptake by the radical from the incident electromagnetic field. This absorption is then detected, amplified and recorded as a function of the strength of the applied magnetic field. The first derivative of the absorption curve is generally recorded as the ESR signal.

As an example, fig. 42 shows such a signal from a layer of a dried chlorophyll preparation excited by illumination with white light.

ESR signals provide three kinds of information: (1) the signal intensity, usually measured from maximum to minimum, is related to the number of unpaired electrons present in the sample, (2) the location of the signal along the abscissa, representing the magnetic field strength reveals the nature of the free radical, and (3) both the width and the "hyperfine" structure of the signal yield evidence of the environment of the unpaired electrons.

A complication arises when two unpaired electrons occur in one and the same molecule, which then is termed a biradical. There is more than one type of biradical. One is a molecule in its triplet state. It will be recalled that two unpaired electrons result upon a singlet-triplet transition, since the spin of an electron raised to an excited singlet state is reversed upon the transition to the triplet state.

The complication in measuring ESR signals of biradicals is based on an interaction of both unpaired electrons. If the distance between these electrons does not exceed 4 Å, and the biradicals do not occur under

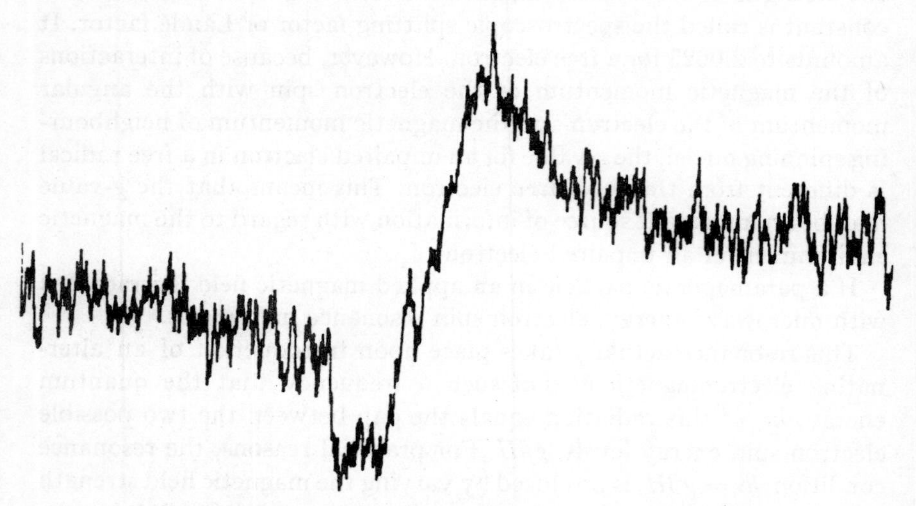

Fig. 42. ESR signal of chlorophyll-a excited by white light

special conditions, such as prevail in crystals, this interaction causes such a broadening of the ESR signal that the latter becomes an approximately straight line. Without entering into details, it can be stated that detection of ESR signals originating from triplet states in biological compounds is very difficult, if not impossible. If, on the other hand, the distance between the two unpaired electrons exceeds 4 Å, the interaction of such electrons is negligible and each unpaired electron is capable of producing its own ESR signal. Then two possibilities exist: (1) Both electrons occur in similar paramagnetic environments. In this case, both ESR signals are identical. They add to one another, and give rise to a signal which, except for its intensity, cannot be distinguished from that of a single unpaired electron. (2) Both electrons occur in different paramagnetic environments. The ESR signals show up separated from each other, that is at different strengths of the magnetic field. They may differ in hyperfine structure.

Details about ESR phenomena and techniques are available in many papers and books, *e.g.* WERTZ [1955], SOGO and TOLBERT [1957], INGRAM [1958], SANDS [1960] and COMMONER [1961].

COMMONER *et al.* [1956] observed ESR signals in suspensions of tobacco chloroplasts upon illumination, while in the dark, only weak signals were detected. Their intensity proved to depend on age and preparation techniques. In the light, the signal grew maximum in about 12 seconds and decayed in about 45 sec. upon cutting off the light. After attaining its maximum value, the signal stayed constant on prolonged illumination. According to the authors, the ESR signals showed saturation at light intensities at which photosynthesis is also saturated. However according to their fig. 6 no true saturation of the paramagnetic resonance occurred but at their "saturation" intensity the rate of further increase of the ESR signal was only reduced. It was concluded that the paramagnetic resonance absorption is caused by either or both excited chlorophyll and redox intermediates.

In a later paper, COMMONER *et al.* [1957] described the occurrence of two ESR responses, a "slow" and a "fast" one, upon illumination of spinach chloroplasts. Separation of the components giving rise to the two signals was brought about by extensive washing and dialization of chloroplast suspensions. The slow signal is present in unwashed suspensions even in the dark but it increases upon illumination. The g-value was found to be 2.005 and again the resonance absorptions showed five hyperfine lines of unequal amplitude and arranged in a group extending over about 25 gauss both in the light and in the dark. The results indicate that this slow ESR signal is due to the presence of organic free radicals in which two chemically equivalent nitrogen atoms are located near to the unpaired electron.

Upon progressive washing and dialization of the suspended chloroplasts the dark ESR signals decreased, whereas the fast-developing absorption in the light persisted. This absorption was maximum at $g = 2.002$, showed no hyperfine structure and extended over only 8–10 gauss. These characteristics are to be expected when no interaction of the electron with neighbouring nuclei occurs and so they may indicate the presence of free electrons. An identical ESR signal was obtained from illuminated preparations of purified chlorophyll-protein complexes. The authors therefore concluded that the second kind of signal is associated with the chlorophyll-(lipo)-protein complex.

In spinach chloroplast preparations which have been washed but not dialyzed, the half-time for establishing the maximum signal is about 15 sec. after turning on the light. The half-life of the decay of this signal in the dark is about the same. Upon dialization however, these half-times are 2.2 and 25.5 sec. respectively.

The above data fit into the hypothesis, suggested by Commoner *et al.*, that illumination of the chlorophyll complex produces unpaired electrons which are transferred by a diffusible compound. Upon removal of this compound by dialysis, draining of the electrons from the excited chlorophyll complex is prevented, or at least diminished. In this way the building-up of an equilibrium-state concentration of unpaired electrons sufficiently high to enable detection by the ESR technique, is possible. The diffusible compound is the free radical which gives rise to the ESR dark signal in unwashed chloroplast preparations. As this ESR signal is enhanced in the light without change of its characteristics, the paramagnetic compound produced upon illumination must be identical with the free radical responsible for the ESR dark signal.

In conclusion, the authors suggested that the excited chlorophyll-protein complex responsible for the fast ESR signal is to be considered the primary product in photosynthesis. The electrons are transferred from this product to the intermediates in the dark chemical processes *via* an electron-transport system. The free radical responsible for the slow ESR signal is a component of this system.

However BRODY *et al.* [1960] when studying light-induced ESR signals in chlorophyll crystals and solutions, pointed to the fact that the observed number of unpaired electrons corresponds with an exitation of less than 0.1% of the number of chlorophyll molecules present. Therefore, the ESR signal at $g = 2.002$ may well be due to the presence of "impurities". They also observed that clear ESR signals only occurred in solutions at concentrations exceeding 10^{-3} M, which corresponds to the concentrations for the quenching of fluorescence. The authors suggested that this quenching is due to the formation of non-fluorescent chlorophyll dimers and so concluded that the ESR phenomenon may be associated with dimers rather than chlorophyll monomers.

COMMONER [1961] confirmed the low yield of unpaired electrons and also considered therefore the possibility of impurities being responsible for the "low-*g*" signal. Moreover he compared light-induced ESR signals in *Chlorella* cells grown in media containing H_2O with those containing D_2O. With heavy water both types of signal appeared to be markedly narrowed. This most probably means that both the slow and the fast ESR components are associated with protons. Consequently none of the signals is likely to be due to conduction electrons. In addition, the results from the D_2O experiments made Commoner conclude that, in contrast with the earlier suggestion, the slow signal originates from an organic free radical containing an unpaired electron associated with four chemically equivalent carbon atoms, each carrying a proton.

Suspensions of chromatophores and "quantasomes" in both H_2O and D_2O media were prepared by ANDROES *et al.* [1962]. No difference between the light-induced resonance signals was observed in the two kinds of media. This means that the protons in the environment of the unpaired electrons which determine the width of the ESR line, cannot be exchanged for deuterons by merely suspending the photosynthetic structures in D_2O-media. In other words, the protons in question are not "labile". The same authors also studied a number of aspects of the light-dependent ESR phenomenon. According to them, the fast signal is probably associated with the oxygen-evolving system in photosynthesis. The ESR signal in bacterial chromatophores is only a single one and corresponds with the fast one in chloroplasts. The action spectrum for producing the fast signal in "quantasomes" shows a maximum at about 675 mμ and probably a shoulder around 730 mμ. The ESR responses to temperature in both chromatophores and "quantasomes" roughly parallel the light-induced optical absorption changes which have been previously mentioned as being assigned to a cytochrome, and so the authors suggested that the fast signal may be associated with photooxidation of a cytochrome. They remarked that because of the small *g*-value of the signal, the unpaired electrons are not likely to reside on the cytochrome iron. Therefore it was deemed more probable that the unpaired electrons are located in molecules associated with the cytochrome in such a way that they are able to receive electrons from the cytochrome upon excitation of the chlorophyll. It was hypothesized that these electrons, either in the chlorophyll molecules themselves or in adjacent acceptor molecules, are responsible for the fast ESR signal. In addition, STOREY *et al.* [1962]

observed that with unwashed spinach chloroplasts, oxygen is required for the establishment of the fast ESR signal. No decision was reached on whether oxygen is directly related to the ESR phenomenon or not. The action spectrum for the production of this ESR signal was found to show a single maximum at 715 mμ.

SOGO *et al.* [1957] measured light-induced ESR signals in spinach chloroplast suspensions at 25° and −140 °C. They found that the signal growth time at these two temperatures is not markedly different, and concluded that no enzymic reactions are involved in the production of these ESR signals.

TREHARNE *et al.* [1960] working with *Chlorella* cells, stated that the light-induced (slow) ESR signal depends on the presence of manganous ions.

The effect of the presence of chlorophyll-b in addition to a was studied by ALLEN *et al.* [1962]. They compared the production of light-dependent ESR signals in both a wild and a mutant strain of *Chlorella pyrenoidosa*, the latter strain being devoid of chlorophyll-b. In the wild variety both types of signal were observed while only a single response – the fast one – was noticed with the mutant strain. This phenomenon made the authors suggest that the fast signal is associated with excited chlorophyll-a whereas the slow one is a response to light absorbed by chlorophyll-b or by the accessory pigments in general. The light-induced ESR of the mutant lacking chlorophyll-b thus resembled that of washed chloroplasts or water-treated *Chlorella* cells. The action spectra for the production of ESR signals in these three cases show maxima of the same intensity at about 625 and 695 mμ. However in "normal" *Chlorella* cells the 695 mμ maximum is predominant by far. Moreover, in the latter case there seems to be an indication of a weak shoulder around 730 mμ. It should be noted that in studies of mutants, one never is sure whether only a single factor is changed. It may well be that there has also been a loss of one or more other compounds, one of which is responsible for the ESR signal. Conversely this compound might now be consumed at such a rate that its equilibrium concentration becomes too low for detection.

The fast ESR signal was assigned to the photooxidized form of a long-wave chlorophyll-a type by BEINERT *et al.* [1962]. These authors assumed that this type, termed P_{700}, acts as the ultimate photoconverter in photosynthesis.

These studies indicate the limited extent of the interpretation of the

ESR phenomenon. At least it is clear that two kinds of light-induced ESR signals appear which correspond to the formation of two free radicals. Their nature is still a matter of speculation, but it seems right to conclude that the one responsible for the slow signal is formed at the expense of the other. The formation of free radicals, in any case, demonstrates that the partners of an electron pair become separated. In other words, an electron is transferred upon excitation of chlorophyll by light.

The step from this conclusion to solid-state physics has been accomplished by ARNOLD and SHERWOOD [1957] and CALVIN [1961b]. The former authors observed thermoluminescence of pre-illuminated layers of dried chloroplasts as well as a decrease in electrical resistance of these chloroplast layers upon heating. The similarity between these effects and those in crystals suggested, but did not prove, that chloroplasts or grana may act as semiconductors. Photoconductivity of such chloroplast layers was indeed observed a few years later by ARNOLD and MACLAY [1959]. Calvin made a number of model experiments with dry preparations of both the chlorophyll-like compound phthalocyanin and of chlorophyll. He observed the phenomenon of photoconductivity in these which shows that light is also able to effect electron migration in such preparations. Calvin suggested that the layered structures of the chloroplasts are essential in photosynthesis since they enable the electrons and holes to become separated from each other by electron transfer rather than by the atomic displacements found in solutions. In this way, recombination of charges is considerably retarded and hence they are able to put into action the dark chemical mechanism with a high efficiency.

Energy absorbed by a chlorophyll molecule is thus assumed to travel by the mechanism of inductive resonance towards an organized array of such pigment molecules located in the environment of a suitable electron acceptor. This acceptor acts like a trap for the conduction electron, just as an "impurity" in a crystal may do in the solid-state picture. The chlorophyll molecule adjacent to such an electron acceptor yields an electron, raised by excitation from the valence band to a conduction band, to this acceptor and the chlorophyll molecule fills the "hole" by transfer of an electron from a suitable donor. This very brief consideration of Calvin's suggestion may suffice here. For a more detailed review, reference should be made to a paper of BASSHAM [1963]. It should be emphasized that the above conception is still purely hypothetical and that KRASNOVSKY [1960] remarked that the semiconductor picture does not account for the biochemical specificity of the photosynthetic processes. According to him, some of the results also can be interpreted as back reactions of intermediate radicals, which are produced by photochemical electron transfer. Whether the fast ESR signal which also occurs in purified chlorophyll preparations can be explained in this way seems questionable. GOEDHEER [1963a] remarked that the solid state picture need not be the only one able to explain the separation of oxidation and reduction reactions upon excitation of chlorophyll *in vivo*. As an alternative, he suggested that the expelled electron leaves the pigment molecule *via* the magnesium atom, whereas the oxidized chlorophyll recaptures an electron *via* the porphyrin ring or its additives. However such an hypothesis implies that the photoconductivity phenomena observed in dried chloroplast layers, need not play a role in wet photosynthesizing chloroplasts. Whatever the mechanism may be, it can be concluded that the above experimental evidence is in accord with the concept of the expulsion of an electron by an excited chlorophyll molecule.

What then, happens to the expelled electron ? This question concerns the essentials of the photosynthetic process. Photosynthesis results in the reduction of carbon dioxide to carbohydrates. Calvin and coworkers (for a review see CALVIN [1962]) established the chemical pathway of the reduction of carbon dioxide in this process. The carbon-cycle proper does not require light energy and therefore, as pointed out by BENSON and CALVIN [1950], need not be typical of photosynthesis. Actually, in the non-photosynthetic sulfur bacterium *Thiobacillus denitrificans* the carbon dioxide assimilation was found to proceed according to the "Calvin cycle" by TRUDINGER [1956] and AUBERT *et al.* [1957]. The brilliant work of Calvin *et al.* on the pathway of carbon in photosynthesis, for which a Nobel prize was awarded to him, does not consider photoreactions *sensu stricto*. As it is beyond the comparative considerations concerning biological photophenomena, the reductive carbon cycle as such will not be discussed here. Instead of this, the way in which energy is fed into this carbon cycle in order to set it in action will be considered. For general reviews see ARNON [1960], [1961] and JAGENDORF [1962].

In non-photosynthetic carbon assimilation, two compounds are essential, namely a reduced phosphopyridine nucleotide, $NADH_2$ or $NADPH_2$ and ATP. The former compound acts as a hydrogen donor while the latter functions as a source of energy stored in its high-energy phosphate bonds (VISHNIAC *et al.* [1957]).

RUBEN [1943] made the suggestion that ATP and $NAD(P)H_2$ may be involved in the production of carbohydrates in the dark-chemical reactions of photosynthesis as well. If so, the difference between the carbon dioxide assimilation in photosynthetic and non-photosynthetic organisms is brought back to the way in which ATP and $NAD(P)H_2$ are formed. In non-photosynthetic cells these compounds are formed with the aid of energy generated by metabolic processes. Carbohydrate synthesis depends on the absorption of light energy in photosynthesis, and it may be that light takes over the role of the metabolic processes to produce ATP and $NAD(P)H_2$.

The formation of ATP, the "energy coin" of metabolism, in photosynthetic organisms upon illumination was observed first by GEST and KAMEN [1948] with *Chlorella* and the Athiorhodacea *Rhodospirillum rubrum*, and by WASSINK *et al.* [1949] with the Thiorhodacea *Chromatium*. ARNON *et al.* [1954] demonstrated that light-induced ATP formation, or photophosphorylation, can occur in isolated chloroplasts, and FRENKEL [1954] observed the occurrence of the same phenomenon in cell-free extracts from photosynthetic bacteria.

The photophosphorylation taking place in illuminated photosynthetic systems differs from phosphorylation in mitochondria. The latter process occurs at the expense of energy produced by the oxidation of substrates in the respiratory chain by oxygen. It is therefore termed "oxidative phosphorylation".

It should be remembered that phosphorylation consists of the synthesis of ATP out of ADP and inorganic phosphate. Therefore the overall reaction of photophosphorylation can be written:

$$\text{ADP} + \text{P} \xrightarrow{h\nu \textit{ via } \text{photosynthetic apparatus}} \text{ATP}.$$

The other compound required for the reduction of carbon dioxide, a reduced NAD(P), is also formed by chloroplasts in the light. TOLMACH [1951], VISHNIAC and OCHOA [1951] and ARNON [1951] observed such a light-induced NAD(P) reduction in the presence of isolated chloroplasts. JAGENDORF [1956] noticed that irradiated chloroplasts are capable of reducing NADP but not NAD. It was also found by LOSADA *et al.* [1960] that NADP, instead of NAD, was needed for reconstituting carbon dioxide assimilation by isolated chloroplast systems in the light. Photoreduction of NAD(P) in photosynthetic cells was recognized by fluorescence measurements as well (*e.g.* DUYSENS and SWEEP [1957]). ARNON, WHATLEY and ALLEN [1957, 1958] obtained simultaneous NADP reduction and oxygen evolution in the light by chloroplast preparations under appropriate conditions, according to:

$$2NADP + 4H_2O \xrightarrow{h\nu \text{ via photosynthetic apparatus}} 2NADPH_2 + O_2 + 2H_2O.$$

Moreover, they noticed that NADP acts as a "catalyst" for photophosphorylation. This means that in illuminated chloroplast systems there is the simultaneous reduction of two moles of NADP, the formation of two moles of ATP and the evolution of one mole of oxygen.

Two processes in photophosphorylation were distinguished by Arnon and coworkers (see ARNON [1961]), namely a "cyclic" and a "non-cyclic" reaction. In cyclic photophosphorylation, the electron expelled from the excited chlorophyll molecule returns to this molecule *via* a series of steps essential to the proceeding of photosynthesis. Without these steps, the expelled electron would return directly to the chlorophyll molecule to which it originally belonged and the excitation energy re-emitted instead of doing any "work". If, on the other hand, the electron "climbs down an electron ladder" before re-entering the chlorophyll molecule, the energy is set free stepwise in a series of reduction-oxidation reactions. A typical step in this descent takes place through a cofactor such as flavin mononucleotide capturing the electron. Each "step" of the "ladder" will be a compound of higher redox potential then the preceding one. Cytochromes are assumed to figure amongst these compounds. In this way, the excitation energy carried by the "descending" electron is distributed over a number of redox reactions leading to phosphorylation. The expelled electron after descending its "ladder" finds its way back to the chlorophyll molecule eager to capture an electron in order to reform its ground state. As the chlorophyll molecule is both donor and acceptor of "one and the same" electron, this type of photophosphorylation is termed "cyclic" by Arnon. In chemical terms one may say that the excited chlorophyll acts as a reducing agent by expelling an electron, but as soon as this happens, the chlorophyll becomes an oxidant.

This photoproduction of ATP does not require nor produce oxygen. TSUJIMOTO *et al.* in ARNON [1961], obtained evidence of a second type of cyclic photophosphorylation in which oxygen acts as a catalyst. In this process the ejected electron returns to the chlorophyll molecule as well.

In non-cyclic photophosphorylation, it is not the same electron that returns to the chlorophyll molecule. The electron freed from the excited pigment molecule is used in the production of $NAD(P)H_2$ by reduction of NAD(P) with the aid of a hydrogen ion derived from water and so remains incorporated with it. The resulting oxidised chlorophyll molecule then accepts a different electron from the cytochromes. Arnon suggests that the latter electron originates from water in green plants and from other sources such as thiosulphate, malic acid or even molecular hydrogen in photosynthetic bacteria. This electron transfer from cytochromes to chlorophyll is coupled with ATP production.

In non-cyclic photophosphorylation ATP production is less than in the cyclic process. ATP is supposed to be formed in the cyclic process by both an electron transfer between a cofactor and cytochromes, and between cytochromes and chlorophyll. In non-cyclic phosphorylation, ATP is only formed during the latter transfer.

A prerequisite for the electron transfer from water to cytochromes in the non-cyclic photophosphorylation of green plants should be that the oxidized cytochromes are capable of attracting electrons, or rather, hydroxyl ions from water. However, a difficulty is encountered here. The E_0 for the reaction: $2H_2O \rightarrow O_2 + 4H^+ + 4\,e$ is $+\,0.815$ V at pH 7. The most oxidizing cytochrome known up to now, cytochrome-f, exhibits an E_0 of only $+\,0.365$ V. ARNON [1961] argued that redox potentials of chlorophyll-cytochrome complexes within chloroplasts might turn out to be lower than the presently measured values. On the other hand, according to this author, one cannot exclude the possibility that additional energy input is required to force electrons from hydroxyl ions to cytochromes. The latter possibility turned out to be the most likely (see LOSADA *et al.* [1961]) and implies that, instead of just one, two photoacts occur, one of which drives NADP reduction, and the other lifts an electron from a hydroxyl ion to a level at which it is able to reduce one or more cytochromes. The wavelength of maximum efficiency for both processes was found to be different. In other words, excitation of more than one pigment is required for non-cyclic photophosphorylation in green plants.

Cooperation of two pigment systems in photosynthesis was discovered by EMERSON *et al.* [1957]. Before this, however, EMERSON and LEWIS [1943] had observed that the quantum yield of photosynthesis drops with increasing wavelength at the long-wave side of the red absorption band of chlorophyll. This result is not obvious for whether a chlorophyll molecule is or is not excited is dependent on the energy of the incident quantum. If it is excited by the absorption of a quantum, an electron is raised to one of the singlet excitation states. It will be recalled that if this level is higher than the first excited state, the electron "tumbles down" to it. In this process part of the energy is released as heat by internal conversion. Once the electron reaches the first excited singlet state, it stays there for a period about a thousand times longer than for the higher states. Chemical energy and fluorescence are released only at the transition of an electron from this first excitation level to the ground state. In other words, in photosynthesis it is only the number and not the energy content of the absorbed quanta that counts. Therefore it would be expected that the quantum of longest wavelength and hence of lowest energy which can be absorbed should be as effective as those of shorter wavelengths. Consequently the so-called "red drop" of the photosynthetic quantum yield, observed by Emerson and Lewis, needs further consideration.

EMERSON *et al.* [1957] argued that the red drop possibly might be due to an interplay with the vibrational energy of the chlorophyll molecules. If a quantum is of just-insufficient energy to be absorbed, additional vibrational energy might be able to assist the quantum in raising an electron into the first excited state. If so, one might expect that raising the temperature would result in shifting the red drop to the long-wave side. The authors made such experiments and found that the result was completely opposite – the red drop shifted to the short-wave side with raising temperature. What then, could be the nature of the red drop?

This question was answered by EMERSON *et al.* [1957] in the following way. *Chlorella pyrenoidosa* cells were irradiated with light of wavelengths at which the red drop occurs, namely from 675 to 720 mμ, and quantum yields for oxygen evolution were determined. Next supplementary light of shorter wavelengths, that is, below 670 mμ was added. The quantum yields in the mixed-light condition were found to be considerably increased. Under favourable conditions the low quantum yields found with the "long-wave" light were enhanced to the "normal" value. This means that long-wave quanta of low efficiency in photosynthesis become fully effective when quanta of shorter wavelengths are added. Furthermore it shows that light which is only absorbed by chlorophyll-a is photosynthetically less effective than light absorbed simultaneously by at least one more pigment. Comparison of these effects in a green alga, *Chlorella*, and a red one, *Porphyridium*, made the authors suggest that in green algae, chlorophyll-b acts as the auxiliary pigment whereas in the red algae which do not contain chlorophyll-b this role is taken over by one of the phycobilins.

This effect of supplementary "short-wave" light has become known as the "Emerson effect" and means, briefly, that the excitation of at least two photosynthetic pigments, chlorophyll-a plus an auxiliary pigment, is needed to establish full photosynthesis. Emerson continued working on this problem up to his death. Rabinowitch, in EMERSON and RABINOWITCH [1960], published his later results which include the determination of action spectra with auxiliary short wavelength light in the enhancement of the quantum yield for algae already receiving light in the red-drop region of wavelengths larger than 680 mμ. To this end, the yield of auxiliary light alone was substracted from that of combined auxiliary and far-red light, and these differences were plotted *versus* wavelength. Such action spectra were determined for a green, a brown, a red, and a blue-green alga, namely *Chlorella, Navicula, Porphyridium*, and *Anacystis* respectively. Distinct maxima occur in these action spectra at wavelengths corresponding to maximum absorption of the auxiliary pigments. These auxiliary pigments proved to be for the green alga: chlorophyll-b, for the brown one: chlorophyll-c and fucoxanthin, for the red one: phycoerythrin, and for the blue-green one: phycocyanin.

As Rabinowitch remarked in this paper, it seems unlikely that the requirement of the excitation by light of two wavelengths for full photosynthesis means that each of the light reactions is initiated by the excitation of a different kind of pigment. This is improbable because light energy absorbed by the auxiliary pigments is almost entirely transferred by inductive resonance to chlorophyll-a. Evidence for this phenomenon is the fact that the fluorescence of chlorophyll-a *in vivo* is enhanced by irradiation with light which is mainly absorbed by auxiliary pigments to such a degree that nearly all of the excitation energy should be transferred to the main photosynthetic pigment. It thus seems most probable that the photosynthetic reaction chain is initiated by a single excited pigment. The existence of the Emerson effect suggests that there are two systems present which contain different types of one and the same "initiating" pigment, chlorophyll-a. One of these is connected with an auxiliary pigment in some way.

The Emerson effect is not confined to photosynthetic oxygen liberation and non-cyclic photophosphorylation in green plants. It has also been observed in the photoreduction of NADP by GOVINDJEE and GOVINDJEE [1962]. R. GOVINDJEE *et al.* [1960] demonstrated its appearance in the Hill reaction. A "two-light" effect is also found on the production of ESR signals (see KOK and BEINERT [1962]) and on the emission of chlorophyll luminescence (GOEDHEER [1962] and BERTSCH [1962]). BLINKS [1960] studied the "chromatic transients" or changes in the photosynthetic rate upon switching from one wavelength to another. This phenomenon will not be discussed any further here, though chromatic transients and Emerson effect are related to each other (MYERS and FRENCH [1960]).

The types of chlorophyll-a *in vivo* have been mentioned in the chapter on photosynthetic pigments and it may be recalled that FRANCK [1958] suggested that chlorophyll-a in the photosynthetic apparatus occurs in two states. Part of this chlorophyll may be exposed to water and dissolved ions, while part of it may be built into a lipoprotein carrier and "protected" from water. The state of the exposed and the protected chlorophyll may differ with respect to the location of the n,π^* level relative to the first excited π,π^* one. If the former level occurs above the latter mainly excited singlet states will result upon irradiation. On the other hand it was suggested that the opposite arrangement occurs in the protected chlorophyll and so triplet states will be preferentially formed. Energy from excited pigment molecules in the singlet state may then be transferred to a molecule already in the triplet state and so raise it into an excited triplet state. The energy of such a doubly excited molecule would be sufficient for direct activation of a reaction such as the electron transfer from water to carbon dioxide bound to some acceptor. Rabinowitch, in EMERSON and RABINOWITCH [1960], remarked that the absorption band of the chlorophyll-a type C_a695, observed by FRENCH [1959] most clearly in aged *Euglena* cells, might be the n-π band of Franck's protected chlorophyll. Chlorophyll in this state is assumed to be non-fluorescent, the singlet excited state being converted into the non-fluorescing triplet state.

It should be noted that if this hypothesis is correct, it is in contradiction with the interpretation of French who assigned a clear additional fluorescence maximum at 705–710 mμ to C_a695 in aged *Euglena* cells. This might be comparable with a long-wave fluorescence at about 720 mμ observed in irradiated *Chlorella* cells at liquid-air temperature by BRODY [1958] which was shown to be also emitted by chlorophyll-a. Brody moreover noticed a similar additional emission in illuminated concentrated chlorophyll solutions at low temperature, though not with dilute solutions, and so he suggested that the additional fluorescence is emitted by a polymer, probabiy a dimer, of chlorophyll-a. By analogy he suggested that chlorophyll-a occurs in both monomeric and dimeric forms *in vivo*.

Whatever the nature of the different chlorophyll types, if the conclusion that the Emerson effect is due to the excitation of two forms of chlorophyll-a is correct, it should be possible to observe the enhancement of the quantum yield by irradiation at the two characteristic wavelengths. GOVINDJEE and RABINOWITCH [1960] working with monochromatic bands far narrower than those used by Emerson, succeeded in verifying this prediction. They also re-established the action spectrum for the Emerson effect in *Chlorella* and *Navicula*, and observed a distinct band at 670 mμ apart from the maximum due to the absorption of the auxiliary pigment. This wavelength coincided with that of maximum absorption of one of the known chlorophyll-a types, namely C_a670. This is direct evidence that excitation of at least two chlorophyll a types, namely a "long-wave" type and C_a 670, is required for fully efficient photosynthesis. The identity of the long-wave type is not yet certain though the following have been suggested by different authors: C_a680, C_a695, or C_a700 (P700).

Elucidation of the function of the two chlorophyll-a systems is mainly based on studies of difference spectra. DUYSENS *et al.* [1961] concluded from such experiments with the red alga *Porphyridium cruentum* that two pigment systems, termed 1 and 2, co-operate in photosynthesis. System 1 includes a non- (or weakly) fluorescent type of chlorophyll-a and system 2 contains a fluorescent type. The phycobilins which can act as auxiliary pigments are unevenly distributed over both systems, but will be left out of consideration here. Upon excitation, system 1 promotes cytochrome oxidation whereas system 2 effects cytochrome reduction. The maximum activity of system 1 occurs at 680 mμ and that of system 2 at 560 mμ, which is in the region of phycoerythrin absorption. In the latter case, the electronic excitation energy is transferred to the fluorescent type of chlorophyll-a. A two-light system functioning *via* reduction and oxidation of cytochrome f was proposed earlier by HILL and BENDALL [1960] as a working hypothesis. DUYSENS and AMESZ [1962] and AMESZ and DUYSENS [1962] further concluded from experimental results that the excited cytochrome-oxidizing system 1 reduces carbon dioxide *via* NAD(P), whereas excitation of the cytochrome-reducing system 2 causes dehydrogenation of water resulting in oxygen liberation. The cytochrome in question is of an f- or c-like type. The authors suggested that such systems also operate in other algae and higher plants. Probably photosynthetic purple bacteria, which do not evolve oxygen in the light, have only a single system comparable with system 1.

According to Duysens and his associates, systems 1 and 2 contain a mixture of phycoerythrin and C_a680 in *Porphyridium*, and in *Chlorella* a mixture of C_a680 and C_a670. However, the ratio of the amounts of both components is different for the two systems. BISHOP and WHITTINGHAM [1963] concluded from experiments with isolated spinach chloroplasts that one of the systems contains chlorophyll-b and C_a670, while the other one includes C_a670 and a long-wave type of chlorophyll-a.

A slightly different idea about the two-light effect was suggested by WITT *et al.* [1961a], see also RUMBERG *et al.* [1962]. These authors also concluded that a C_a680 system oxidizes cytochrome, but they proposed that a C_a670 system reduces cytochrome only indirectly. A detailed discussion of their work is outside the scope of this book and it is only noted that they suggest that the oxidation and reduction of cytochromes occupies a key position in the early photochemical events of photosynthesis.

French and his associates (see FRENCH [1962]) suggested a different explanation of the Emerson enchancement effect based on the interaction of two photoproducts or two basically different processes rather than on redox reactions of cytochromes. A more detailed discussion of this matter would also be out of the present scope.

According to GOEDHEER [1962] two chlorophyll systems govern the luminescence intensity. One of them acts as a luminescence-promoting ("p") system, while the other one, the "q" system, quenches the luminescence evoked by the excited "p" system. The "p" system is excited by light of wavelengths mainly absorbed by auxiliary pigments and may be identical with system 2 of DUYSENS *et al.* [1961], while system "q" is excited by far-red light around 700 mμ. The latter may be identical with Duysens' system 1. The luminescence effects are tentatively explained by Goedheer in a hypothetical photosynthesis scheme in which cytochrome oxidation and reduction are again the central reactions. The "p" system is suggested to bring about cytochrome reduction and the "q" system is correlated with cytochrome oxidation.

When studying the kinetics of chromatic transients, and induction and other effects in luminescence, GOEDHEER [1963b] concluded that a third system is involved in photosynthesis. The character of this system is that of a "feed-back" mechanism of products formed by the excited "p" and "q" systems into a dark chloroplast respiratory system, termed the "r" system. Evidence of the occurrence of a light-sensitive respiration has been obtained by a number of authors. Although this "photorespiration" is closely associated with photosynthesis, it does not seem to be a photoprocess in a direct sense and, for this reason, will not be discussed here.

Summarizing, it can be stated that the nature of photosynthesis consists of converting light energy into chemical energy by way of the expulsion of one electron per chlorophyll molecule excited either directly by light or indirectly *via* inductive resonance. Cooperation of at least two chlorophyll-a types in separate systems is required for the establishment of fully effective photosynthesis. One system promotes cytochrome oxidation and the other one, cytochrome reduction. The subsequent reactions, viewed as an electron flow, lead to the formation of ATP as a carrier of energy and to the production of $NADPH_2$ as a reducing agent. The subsequent steps in the reduction chain in which carbon dioxide is ultimately reduced to carbohydrates are the same as those occurring in carbon dioxide assimilation in non-photosynthetic systems. The specific role of light in photosynthesis thus consists of the formation of both adenosine triphosphate and reduced nicotinamide adenine dinucleotide phosphate.

5

Vision

1 *Introduction*

Vision is one of the senses. In general, senses serve to receive information about the physical conditions of the environment of an organism. They transform data from outside into a form which can be fed into the central nervous system. As a consequence there need not be any quantitative relation between the ultimate reaction and the energy taken up by the receptor.

This statement is certainly an oversimplification. In some cases, for example in the pigmented muscle fibres of the eel iris sphincter upon which SELIGER [1962] states the action of light is a direct one. In vision however, the processes are much more complicated because the way in which the information which is dealt with is so complex. On the other hand, the energetic properties of vision, at least for the overall visual process, are not important. This is the basic difference with photosynthesis. Both phenomena are photoprocesses but photosynthesis is a typical energetic process, whereas vision is a cybernetic one.

In vision, the contact between the organism and its surroundings occurs in the visual sensory cells, and it is here that the energy conversion and the primary photoprocesses occur. Consequently only this part of the intricate visual chain of events will be considered.

The history of this aspect of vision is relatively short. It is true that the anatomy of the eye was explored many centuries ago, and the study of the morphology of the light-sensitive part of the eye dates from 1674 when Anthony van Leeuwenhoek observed the retinal cells with his microscope. Curiously enough, two centuries passed after this investigation before the general morphology of the rods and cones was described by SCHULTZE [1866]. Ten years later the foundation of the study of the visual processes was laid by BOLL [1876] who observed the fading of the rose colour of the frog's retina in bright light. He thus discovered a direct photoreaction in vision. Kühne and co-workers, (see KÜHNE [1879]) started a most extensive study following their first report of 1877. They noticed that the rose pigment "visual purple" is found exclusively in the retinal cells and that it bleaches in the light. In the dark, this bleaching is reversed provided the retina is kept *in situ*, that is, in contact with the pigment epithelium. Kühne also succeeded in preparing a clear solution of visual purple by solubilization with bile. The light-induced bleaching of the dissolved pigment took place in the same way as in the *in situ* retina, though the reversibility of the bleaching reaction was lost.

The study of the visual processes developed from these investigations and a large amount of data has accumulated since then, although most of the research has been done since 1920. General information about this subject can be found in a number of excellent reviews and handbooks, in particular: HECHT [1942], RUSHTON [1959], WALD [1953a, 1959, 1961a], DAVSON [1962], WALD *et al.* [1963], and DARTNALL and TANSLEY [1963].

2 The visual pigments

2.1 Chemistry

The pigments of the vision apparatus are of a carotenoid nature though not all of them are involved in the visual chemical process proper. For example, WALD and ZUSSMAN [1937] isolated three carotenoids, a red, a golden and a yellow-green one from the chicken eye. These carotenoids are light-stable and seem to function as light-screens for the light-sensitive pigments. In this section only the latter – the true visual pigments – will be dealt with.

All known visual pigments are aldehydes of vitamin A. There are two vitamin A compounds: A_1, $C_{19}H_{27}CH_2OH$, and A_2, $C_{19}H_{25}CH_2OH$. They differ in that vitamin A_2 contains a second double bond in the β-ionone ring as shown in fig. 43.

Both vitamins are depicted in the all-*trans* configuration. However other isomers are also found. Two of them, namely the 11-*cis* or *neo*-b and the 9-*cis* or *iso*-a configuration are given in fig. 44. The photosensitive pigments are formed in particular from the 11-*cis* isomers by three processes: dehydrogenation, isomerization and complexing with special proteins, the opsins. Light enters into part of these processes and the

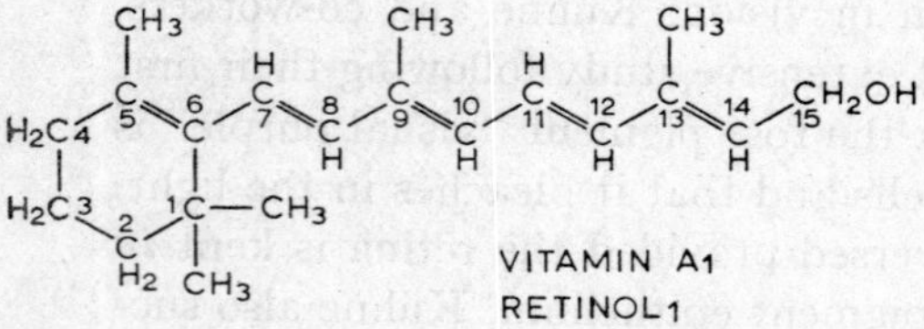

VITAMIN A_1
RETINOL$_1$

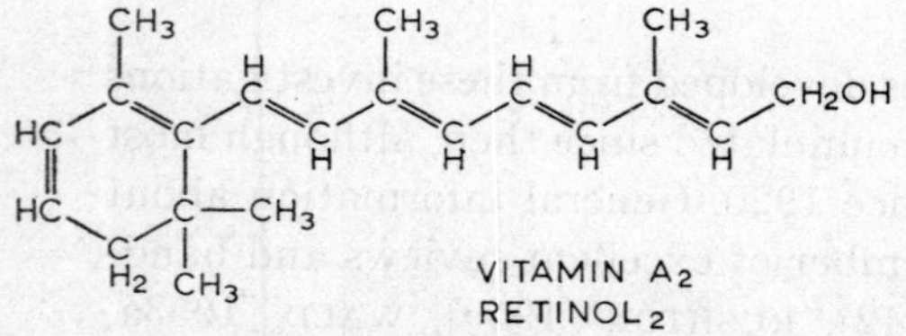

VITAMIN A_2
RETINOL$_2$

Fig. 43. All-*trans* retinol$_1$ and retinol$_2$ (vitamins A_1 and A_2)

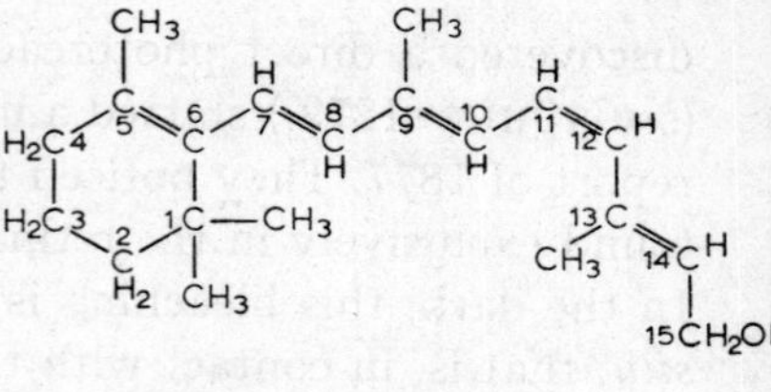

11-cis (neo-b) VITAMIN A_1
11-cis (neo-b) RETINOL$_1$

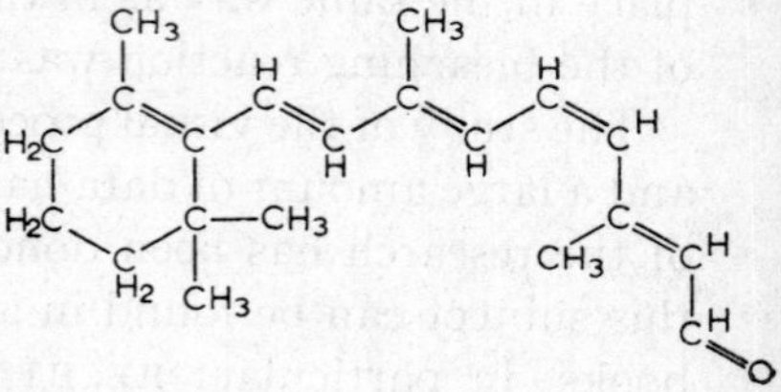

11-cis (neo-b) RETINAL$_1$

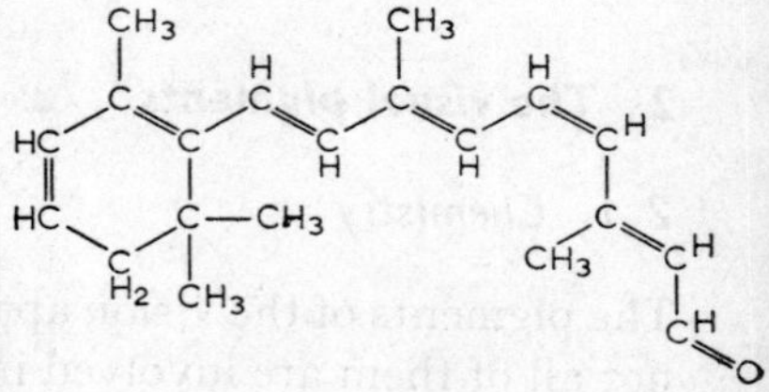

11-cis (neo-b) RETINAL$_2$

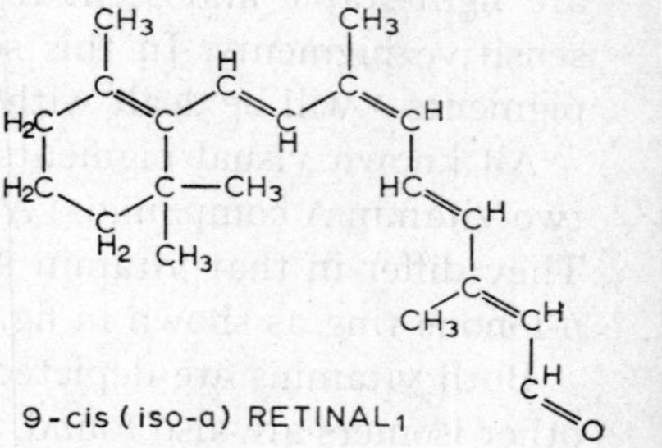

9-cis (iso-a) RETINAL$_1$

Fig. 44. 11-*cis* retinol$_1$, retinal$_1$ and retinal$_2$

pigment is left changed after receiving light. The situation is much more intricate than with photosynthetic pigments which occur *in vivo* as stable complexes with lipoproteins. In vision the chromophore groups can be reversibly detached from their carriers. Consequently one should distinguish between the prosthetic chromophore groups and the opsins. The state in which these compounds occur determines their colour. It can be easily understood why terms such as: visual red, visual purple, visual violet, visual blue, visual yellow, transient orange, indicator yellow, and visual white have been given for these states. However, as WALD [1953a] remarked, these names may be applicable to various states of the retina or extracts from it, but they are no longer adequate in a biochemical sense. Moreover, he pointed to the fact that a number of the designations do not agree with the actual colour of the compound. For instance, visual purple looks red, while visual violet looks purple. Furthermore the same term has been used for different pigments. In order to avoid these difficulties, the nomenclature of Wald will be used below. This has limitations as DARTNALL [1962a] remarked, for the absorption spectra of visual pigments from different sources may overlap to such a degree that Wald's terminology does not apply. Dartnall therefore named each pigment by adding the wavelength value of maximum absorption, for example "pigment 467".

One more general remark remains to be made. The Committee on Nomenclature of the International Union of Pure and Applied Chemistry, taking into account the relationship between vitamin A and the visual pigments, recommended the following nomenclature: for vitamin A: retinol; for vitamin A aldehyde, formerly retinene: retinal; and for vitamin A acid: retinoic acid, (see YOSHIZAWA and WALD [1963]). Accordingly, these terms will be used here.

2.2 *Prosthetic groups of visual pigments*

2.2.1 Retinal$_1$. Its formula is $C_{19}H_{27}CHO$. This compound is formed by oxidation of retinol$_1$ to its aldehyde (see BALL *et al.* [1948]). WALD [1935, 1938] established the carotenoid nature of this pigment. He succeeded in isolating the retinal by extracting dark-adapted retinas with petroleum ether and then with chloroform. Retinol was eluted in very small amounts by the first extraction and the retina retained its colour. The second extraction removed the rose colour from the retina and the chloroform became greenish-yellow. The pigment responsible for this colour showed carotenoid properties. Once extracted, it is readily soluble in petroleum ether and carbon disulfide.

A second way of isolating this pigment is based on the action of light. Wald observed that photobleaching of dark-adapted retinas to an orange-yellow colour renders the retinal directly extractable from the retina by petroleum ether and carbon disulfide. Apparently the visual pigment should be bleached, either by chloroform or by light, before it can be removed from the retina. If bleached retinas are stored at room temperature in the light, they fade still further until retinal is no longer present. The retina contains retinol in relatively large amounts instead. Wald established that the thermal conversion of retinal to retinol is stoichiometric and concluded that retinol is the precursor of retinal as well as its decomposition product. Consequently the visual processes apparently form a cyclic system.

2.2.2 Retinal$_2$. Its formula is $C_{19}H_{25}CHO$. Except for the fact that retinal$_2$ is the aldehyde of retinol$_2$, all that has been said of retinal$_1$ is applicable to retinal$_2$. CAMA *et al.* [1952a] succeeded in preparing it by the oxidation of retinol$_2$. The occurrence of this retinal was believed originally to be restricted to freshwater fishes but WALD [1942] found that it is present in certain saltwater species, for example the sea lamprey which is considered a primitive vertebrate form.

2.2.3 Compounds from the pigment layer. Kühne observed that the reversibility of the photobleaching of the retina only occurs provided its contact with the adjoining pigment layer is undisturbed. WALD [1935, 1936, 1937] stated that this layer contains lutein, $C_{40}H_{54}(OH)_2$, a flavin, presumably riboflavin, and relatively large amounts of retinol.

2.3 Opsins

Very little is known of the carrier compounds for the prosthetic groups. Only the fact that these carriers are proteins has been established without doubt (see WALD [1953a] and DARTNALL [1962b]). A protein band in the UV absorption spectrum of the visual pigment rhodopsin occurs at 280 mμ and this can be simulated by mixtures of two parts tyrosine and one part tryptophane. COLLINS *et al.* [1952] when performing these experiments, stated that the nearest mixture contained 6% tyrosine and 3% tryptophane expressed in percentage dry-weight of rhodopsin. These percentages are typical of animal proteins.

A serious drawback to the study of the chemical constitution of these proteins is the fact that the amounts available for analysis are only very small. On the basis of the spectral properties of the protein-prosthetic group complexes, WALD [1953b] proposed that two classes of the opsins should be recognised. These are: *scotopsins*, which are the carrier proteins occurring in the rods exclusively, and *photopsins*, which are typical of the visual pigment complexes in the cones.

Attempts to determine the molecular weight of the visual pigments are made difficult by the fact that digitonin or other solubilizers have to be used in order to prepare clear pigment extracts. The presence of micelles of the solubilizer seriously interfere with the determinations of the particle weights. Making allowance for these difficulties as far as possible, HUBBARD [1954] gave a preliminary molecular weight of about 40000 for the cattle visual pigment. The molecular weight of the chromophore group, retinal$_1$, is only 284 and so it can be concluded that the molecular weight of the scotopsin is also of the order of 40000.

The quantitative relationship between cattle scotopsin and retinal$_1$ has been studied by the same author who concluded that an opsin molecule will only combine with one retinal molecule.

The thermal stability was studied by HUBBARD [1959] who demonstrated that both scotopsin and its complex with retinal$_1$ are more thermostable when in the rods than after extraction. In both cases, however, the stability of the scotopsin is far less than that of the pigmented complex. Consequently the chromophore group, retinal$_1$, must protect the protein from denaturation. This holds for the 11-*cis* isomer in particular, though the 9-*cis* (*iso*-a)isomer also stabilizes the scotopsin to a lesser degree.

2.4 *The retinal-opsin bond*

Retinal, as an aldehyde, readily condenses with amino groups to yield Schiff bases according to:

$$\underset{\text{retinal}_1}{C_{19}H_{27}HC{=}O} + \underset{\text{amine of amino-acid protein}}{RNH_2} \rightarrow \underset{\text{Schiff base}}{C_{19}H_{27}HC{=}NR} + H_2O.$$

This reaction was recognized by BALL *et al.* [1949] who studied the condensations of $retinal_1$ with a variety of amino compounds. These authors found that the colour of the resulting products depends on the pH of the solution. In alkaline, neutral or weakly acidic, and more strongly acidic media the complexes show up nearly colourless, yellow, and bright orange respectively. CAMA *et al.* [1952b] observed similar effects with $retinal_2$. These phenomena are not characteristic of retinal.

According to BALL *et al.* [1948] the colour of free synthetic $retinal_1$, which displays properties identical with the natural $retinal_1$, is insensitive towards pH. Nor is the pH-dependent colour change typical of the free carrier compounds. Therefore the experiments suggest that the colour reaction is due to the way in which the artificial chromophore-carrier complex is constituted.

Other reactions of aldehydes also have to be considered as possible means of forming a retinal-opsin bond. One of particular interest is the reaction of aldehydes with SH-groups. As proteins contain such groups, it is quite possible that sulphur bridges account partially, or perhaps completely, for the complexing of retinal and opsin. Since the formation of nitrogen bonds as well as sulphur linkages is accompanied by hydrolysis, both types of bonds are sensitive towards pH.

In turning to the natural visual pigments, LYTHGOE [1937] observed a pH dependency of the colour of bleached solutions of the visual pigment rhodopsin. Such solutions show up pale yellow in alkaline and bright orange in acid media. This pH sensitivity makes the pigment resemble a pH indicator and so Lythgoe termed it "indicator yellow". DARTNALL [1948] suggested that in indicator yellow the bleached chromophore group is still in contact with its opsin. COLLINS and MORTON [1950a] observed that immediately upon bleaching of extracted rhodopsin, free retinal cannot be detected. This result, in combination with those of bleaching experiments at different pH, make it seem very probably that the chromophore-protein link of rhodopsin is still present in indicator yellow. The analogy between the pH dependency of both the artificial and natural chromophore-carrier complexes strongly suggests that in rhodopsin, retinal is linked to opsin by a Schiff base ($-CH{=}N-$) bond.

The possibility of sulfhydryl groups being responsible for the formation of linkages between chromophore and opsin was studied by WALD and BROWN [1952]. Amino- and SH-groups ionize in different pH ranges. Amino groups form $-NH_3^+$ ions below pH 6–7. On the other hand, no marked ionization of SH-groups occurs below pH 8–9. Since molecules, not ions, react readily with aldehydes, Wald and Brown argued that the pH sensitivity of the retinal-opsin condensation may provide information about the type of bond. A concentrated retinal$_1$ solution and buffers of various acidity were added to rhodopsin extracts in the dark. Next the various aliquots were completely photobleached in order to obtain free opsin. The bleached solutions were allowed to regenerate the chromophore-opsin complex in the dark at room temperature for about two hours. After this period, the percentage regeneration of rhodopsin was determined. It was found that about 45% regeneration occurred at pH 6.0, at both pH 4.8 and 6.8 about 40% rhodopsin was recovered, whereas above pH 7.9 and below pH 4.5 rhodopsin was formed only slightly or not at all. This result suggests that sulfhydryl groups rather than amino groups are active in taking part in the retinal-opsin condensation. Additional arguments in favour of such a suggestion were provided by the fact that compounds reacting with SH-groups, for example p-chloromercuribenzoate, inhibited rhodopsin regeneration by way of competing with the chromophore for the SH-sites at the opsin.

The same authors also observed that bleaching of rhodopsin results in the liberation of SH-groups at the carrier surface. Removal of the chromophore, either wholly or partly, from the opsin apparently effects the exposure of previously occupied SH-sites. Two sulfhydryl groups became exposed for every retinal molecule removed. In conclusion, Wald and Brown suggested that SH-groups are engaged in binding retinal to opsin and that the linking reaction may proceed in two ways: (1) by establishing a direct bond, or (2) by yielding hydrogen atoms for a reduction of the retinal into the prosthetic group, and simultaneously forming a disulfide bond.

Some difficulties still remain for if the SH-groups were to react with the carbonyl moiety of retinal, the conjugated character of the latter group would be lost. This would mean a shortening of the conjugated bond system of retinal, which would probably result in a shift of the absorption spectrum to the short-wave region. On the contrary, in practice this spectrum shifts to the long-wave side upon condensation of retinal and opsin to the visual pigment.

Another problem is raised by the results of a further estimation of the number of liberated SH-groups at bleached rhodopsin by WALD and BROWN [1954]. These estimations yielded values between 2 and 3 for the number of sulfhydryl groups per photobleached rhodopsin molecule. The authors inferred that, as a consequence of a denaturation of the visual pigments, the bleaching of rhodopsin might result in the exposure of additional sulfhydryl and other groups on the protein which were previously inaccessible to reagents.

The conclusions of the two groups of investigators on the chromophore-protein link seem to be in conflict with each other although they are all based on sound experimental evidence. Therefore an explanation of the discrepancy, or a reconcilation of both points of view was needed. This has been attempted in two ways.

First, COLLINS *et al.* [1954] suggested that the condensation product initially formed is "retinene-S-opsin". Immediately this complex is transformed into "retinene-N-opsin" by intramolecular rearrangement. The latter compound is assumed to be identical with the visual pigment rhodopsin.

Second, DARTNALL [1957] put forward another hypothesis. He emphasized that the experiments of WALD and BROWN [1952] on rhodopsin synthesis were performed with extracts of retinas. The fact that rhodopsin was found to be optimally regenerated around pH 6 seems to be in contradiction with the conception of condensation of retinal with amino groups. The pH ranges for condensation of aldehydes with SH- or amino-groups refer to spontaneous reactions in prepared mixtures of both reactants. However, other compounds from the retina may be present in the rhodopsin extracts. If an enzyme catalyzing aldehyde-amino condensation were present, such a process may take place in a pH range unfavourable for a spontaneous reaction. The pH dependency of the rhodopsin regeneration, as observed by WALD and BROWN [1952], would then be the pH sensitivity of the condensation enzyme.

The undeniable participation of sulfhydryl groups in rhodopsin formation is suggested to consist of providing linkages between the chromophore and the opsin at sites in the retinal moiety other than the aldehyde group. As a consequence of his hypothesis, DARTNALL [1957] proposed that in rhodopsin the chromophore is linked to its carrier by both amino and SH-groups, whereas in "indicator yellow" the sulfhydryl bonds are opened, but the retinal remains attached to the protein by the Schiff-base bond.

2.5 The individual visual pigments

2.5.1 Rhodopsin. This pigment, originally known as "visual purple" is the condensation product of scotopsin and 11-*cis* retinal$_1$, (see WALD [1953b]). In general, it is found in the visual rods of land animals and salt water fishes.

The molecular weight was tentatively estimated to be 40000, (see HUBBARD [1954]. A solubilizer has to be employed in order to extract rhodopsin from the visual rod outer segments, for example sodium cholate, sodium deoxycholate, digitonin, pure-white saponin or cetyltrimethylammonium chloride. The rhodopsin "solutions" thus obtained are clear and quite stable when stored in the dark at low temperature and the solutions can be kept in the refrigerator for more than a year without any appreciable loss of the pigment.

According to MCCONNELL and SCARPELLI [1963], rhodopsin displays enzymic activity in being able to catalyze phosphorylation. The authors worked with digitonin extracts of frog rhodopsin. In the light, the ATP-ase activity of the pigment may be twice that in the dark. The wavelength for maximum ATP production was found to coincide with that of maximum light absorption of rhodopsin. Opsin extracts were incubated with all-*trans* retinal, and illuminated. In the light, the retinal is partly transformed to its 11-*cis* isomer and so combines with the opsin to produce rhodopsin. The enzymic activity of the mixture increased proportionally to the development of the rhodopsin absorption band. The authors therefore suggested that rhodopsin is an ATP-ase requiring the attachment of retinal as a prosthetic group to the opsin. According to them, the retinal may have two functions: as a light absorber and as a cofactor for the enzyme. One may wonder whether the cofactor function is also inherent in one or more of the photoproducts.

According to HUBBARD and WALD [1951], the mechanism of rhodopsin synthesis works as follows. Retinol$_1$ is oxidized by retinal reductase (alcohol dehydrogenase) and NAD to retinal$_1$. The latter compound combines with scotopsin to form rhodopsin. The rhodopsin synthesis can thus be written as two steps:

$$\text{retinol}_1 \underset{\text{NADH}_2}{\overset{\text{NAD}}{\underset{\text{alcohol dehydrogenase}}{\rightleftharpoons}}} \text{retinal}_1 \tag{1}$$

$$\text{retinal}_1 + \text{scotopsin} \overset{\text{Light}}{\rightleftharpoons} \text{rhodopsin}. \tag{2}$$

The colour of rhodopsin is red. Upon illumination, a series of rhodopsin derivatives are produced which may vary in colour and stability. Five of these compounds are recognised at the present time:

Pre-lumirhodopsin. This is at present taken to be the primary compound formed upon irradiation of rhodopsin. It decomposes rather fast at room temperature, but is stable at temperatures lower than −140 °C (YOSHIZAWA *et al.* [1961], KITO *et al.* [1960] and YOSHIZAWA and WALD [1963]). If rhodopsin in a glycerol-water glass at liquid nitrogen temperature is irradiated with 440 mμ light, about 57% of the rhodopsin chromophore is isomerized to all-*trans* pre-lumirhodopsin. This isomerization can be reversed by 600 mμ light. The chromophore stays attached to its carrier. The pigment shows a red colour.

Lumirhodopsin. At temperatures between −140 and −20 °C pre-lumirhodopsin is transformed in the dark to lumirhodopsin, a compound with an orange-red colour (see HUBBARD *et al.* [1959]). The chromophore remains attached to the carrier.

Metarhodopsin. When lumirhodopsin is warmed to about − 15 °C in the dark an orange pigment, metarhodopsin, is formed (see HUBBARD *et al.* [1959]). Metarhodopsin is stable at room temperature if it is in a dry state. The chromophore is attached to the protein. It is evident from the exposure of two new SH-groups as well as one proton binding group with a pK of about 6.6, that the structure of the scotopsin moiety of the pigment is changed from that of the preceeding compounds. Metarhodopsin might be identical with "transient orange" first observed by LYTHGOE and QUILLIAM [1938]. Metarhodopsin was found to have two tautomeric forms, called metarhodopsins I and II (YOSHIZAWA and WALD [1963] and MATTHEWS, HUBBARD, BROWN and WALD [1963]). Metarhodopsin I is formed first and then goes over to configuration II until an equilibrium between the two forms is reached. This equilibrium is shifted in favour of metarhodopsin II on increasing the temperature, the acidity and the glycerol content of the medium. Unless it is stated to the contrary references to "metarhodopsin" mean configuration I. In this form just the two new SH-groups are exposed, and the proton-binding group is probably only exposed in addition in metarhodopsin II.

Isorhodopsin. Irradiation of a rhodopsin solution frozen to −70 °C produces metarhodopsin which when stored at room temperature in the dark for about 1 hour regenerates "rhodopsin". However, the absorption spectrum of this regenerated pigment is slightly shifted to the short-wave side. COLLINS and MORTON [1950b] therefore termed this compound "isorhodopsin". WALD [1951] found that regeneration in fact, gives rise to a mixture of natural rhodopsin and isorhodopsin. The chromophore moiety of the latter compound is the 9-*cis* (*iso*-a) isomer of retinal which according to Wald, should be considered an artifact.

N-retinylidene-opsin. It was mentioned earlier that LYTHGOE [1937] observed the pH sensitivity of a bleached product of rhodopsin which he termed "indicator yellow". MORTON and PITT [1955] studied this product in alkaline as well as in acid media. They concluded that only in acid media is "indicator yellow" a true derivative of rhodopsin. They termed it N-retinylidine-opsin. As "indicator yellow" is formed in the dark from" transient orange", N-retinylidene-opsin is to be considered a dark-conversion product from metarhodopsin.

In alkaline media, on the other hand, hydrolysis of the chromophore-opsin complex occurs. As a consequence, migration of retinal to free amino groups of rhodopsin may occur. Morton and Pitt suggested that the designation "indicator yellow" be retained for the Schiff bases formed upon alkaline treatment.

2.5.2 Porphyropsin. Otherwise visual violet. This pigment has a purple colour and was studied by WALD (see [1953b]). He concluded that the protein carrier is so closely related to that of rhodopsin that both of them can be considered to belong to the family of the scotopsins. The pigments differ only in the structure of the chromophore which is $retinal_2$ in the case of porphyropsin. In most respects these visual pigments resemble each other very closely. It has been proved possible to make $retinal_2$ combine with the opsin moiety of cattle rhodopsin.

Porphyropsin has been found in the rods of freshwater fishes, lampreys, and some larval and adult amphibia.

Wald and his coworkers, see WALD [1953b], prepared a mixture of $retinal_2$ isomers. Two of them proved to be active in combining with opsin from a freshwater fish. One of these, the "cis_1 fraction" yielded porphyropsin when incubated with the opsin in question in the dark, while the "cis_2 fraction" formed iso-porphyropsin.

2.5.3 Iodopsin. In the chicken retina a relatively large number of cones occur. Upon extraction in the dark, a mixture of two visual pigments is obtained, see WALD *et al.* [1952]. One of them is readily bleached by "deep red" light, whereas the other needs the shorter wavelengths of white light for bleaching. The latter pigment is the rod pigment rhodopsin. The red-sensitive component is the cone pigment, termed "iodopsin" by Wald. Its colour is violet and the chromophore is identical with that of rhodopsin, namely 11-*cis*-retinal$_1$. On the other hand, the protein moiety of iodopsin differs from that of rhodopsin in being a photopsin.

According to WALD [1953b], *iso*-retinal$_1$-a combines with photopsin upon incubation to yield *iso*-iodopsin in a similar way to rhodopsin. HUBBARD *et al.* [1959], (see also HUBBARD and KROPF [1959]), studied the products formed upon illumination of iodopsin. These are, by analogy with those of rhodopsin, lumi-iodopsin and meta-iodopsin.

2.5.4 Cyanopsin. This pigment has never been observed *in vivo*. It was synthesized by WALD *et al.* [1953]. These authors irradiated digitonin extracts of chicken retinas with "deep red" light which does not appreciably affect the rhodopsin, but bleaches iodopsin to photopsin and all-*trans* retinal$_1$. 11-*cis* retinal$_2$ was added to this mixture in the dark. After a short incubation period, a new blue "visual" pigment was formed and was termed "cyanopsin". According to WALD *et al.* [1953], the failure of several workers to extract this light-sensitive product may be due to the fact that extracts of retinas are generally prepared under red light and so the cyanopsin would be bleached and decomposed into a mixture of all-*trans* retinal$_2$ and photopsin. The authors therefore suggested that cyanopsin is present in any retina containing retinal$_2$ and photopsin.

In the same way, but using the adequate *iso*-retinal isomer, isocyanopsin was prepared by WALD *et al.* [1953].

Summarizing, Wald and his associates claim that there are four visual pigments, namely the rod pigments rhodopsin and porphyropsin and the cone pigments iodopsin and cyanopsin. As either a direct or an indirect consequence of light absorption, these compounds pass through a number of states which, for rhodopsin at least, are termed the pre-lumi-, lumi- and meta-pigments in the order of their appearance. According to DARTNALL [1962], N-retinylidene-opsin might be identical with metarhodopsin.

Quite a number of retinae from various sources have been studied. The colour of the extracted visual pigments differs somewhat from one source to another which has given rise to a variety of terminology based on the colours of the pigments. However, the various pigments seem to fit into the general scheme of Wald. Moreover, the use of denominations after the colour of the compound interferes with the simplicity of the picture suggested by experimental evidence up to now and so such terms will not be used here.

The differences between the visual pigments must be due either to the nature of the prosthetic group or to the properties of the opsin. At the present time it seems that only one or two isomers of the two retinals participate in the formation of the visual pigments while the variety of the opsins is considerably greater. The existence of a large number of opsins is demonstrated by the fact that the locations of the absorption maxima of rhodopsins, porphyropsins, and iodopsins from different sources may coincide with each other. For this reason, DARTNALL [1952] proposed to name the pigments purely by their wavelength of maximum absorption, though MUNZ [1958] wanted to improve this terminology by indicating the type of chromophore by a subscript, for example, "visual pigment 500_1". This still gives no information about the type of opsin present. DARTNALL [1962] argued that this omission need not be disadvantageous. As an example he pointed to the fact that the absorption maxima of the rhodopsin from hamsters and the iodopsin of grey squirrels coincide. He concluded that the opsins from both sources are identical, and thus a distinction between rod opsins and cone opsins may not be meaningful. Though this suggestion may turn out to be right, the conclusion is still premature. The nature of a carrier protein is not solely defined by the character of a bond with a prosthetic group which is the only property determined by the absorption spectrum of the complex. The similarity of the spectra of two complexes only indicates that the structural type and the immediate surroundings of the binding site are identical, but does not provide any further information about the structure of the protein. The present author prefers to retain a nomenclature which includes the opsin moiety. Moreover, although Dartnall's terminology is certainly more exact than that of Wald, the latter has the advantage of surveyability and for these reasons will be used here. It should be emphasized that in each class of pigments variations occur and so to indicate a special pigment, the wavelength of maximum absorbtion is often added to the name, for example rhodopsin 502.

2.5.5 Optical properties. The chromophores are characterized by two absorption bands: (1) a major maximum in the visible region, around

380 mμ, and (2) a minor one in the ultraviolet, around 260 mμ. In the *cis*-isomers the major bands lie to the short-wave side of those of the all-*trans* configuration, while the shifts of the minor bands are in the opposite direction. Fig. 45 shows the absorption spectra of all-*trans* and 11-*cis* retinal$_1$ in ethanol. The 255 mμ peak of the latter chromophore is the highest *cis* maximum observed in the stereoisomers of retinal.

The opsin shows no appreciable absorption in the visible region, a maximum being located around 280 mμ. In fig. 46 the absorption spectrum of cattle opsin is given.

Rhodopsin shows three absorption bands: a "main" (α) band in the visible region, a minor (β) one which represents the *cis* peak in the near UV, and a maximum (γ) around 280 mμ due to the absorption of the protein moiety. As shown in fig. 47, these bands occur at 498, 340, and 278 mμ respectively for cattle rhodopsin. Upon photobleaching, in this case at pH 9.2, the short-wave protein band remained unchanged. Comparison with the absorption of tyrosine and tryptophane suggests that the opsin band is principally composed of absorption due to these amino-acids. The photoproduct displays a new single absorption maximum at 370 mμ. This product is the "alkaline indicator yellow" for which MORTON and PITT [1955] proposed retaining the term "indicator yellow".

The absorption spectra of the various products formed upon illumination are shown in figs. 48 and 49. Figure 48 is the spectrum of pre-lumirhodopsin, established by YOSHIZAWA and WALD [1963]. The authors obtained the spectrum of the early photoproduct, which is only stable at low temperatures, in the following way. Rhodopsin in a glycerol-water mixture was cooled down to liquid-nitrogen temperature. The resulting glass was irradiated with blue light, to give a mixture of rhodopsin and pre-lumirhodopsin. After recording the absorption spectrum, this mixture was warmed to room temperature in the dark. At this temperature, pre-lumirhodopsin disintegrates to retinal and opsin. Added hydroxylamine reacted with the freed retinal to form retinaldehyde oxime which does not combine with opsin. The absorption spectrum of the residual rhodopsin was determined at room temperature as well as after re-cooling to −195 °C. This was because the absorption maximum of rhodopsin shifts from 498 to 505 mμ upon cooling down to liquid-nitrogen temperature while the extinction coefficient rises considerably and so the re-cooling procedure was essential

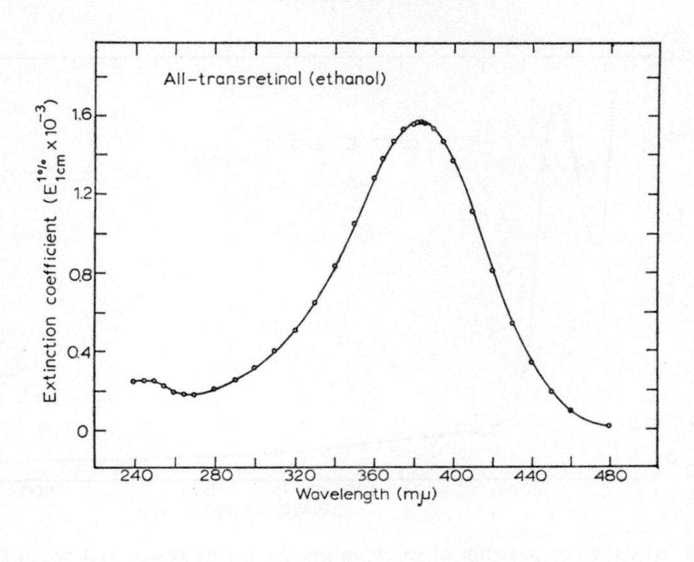

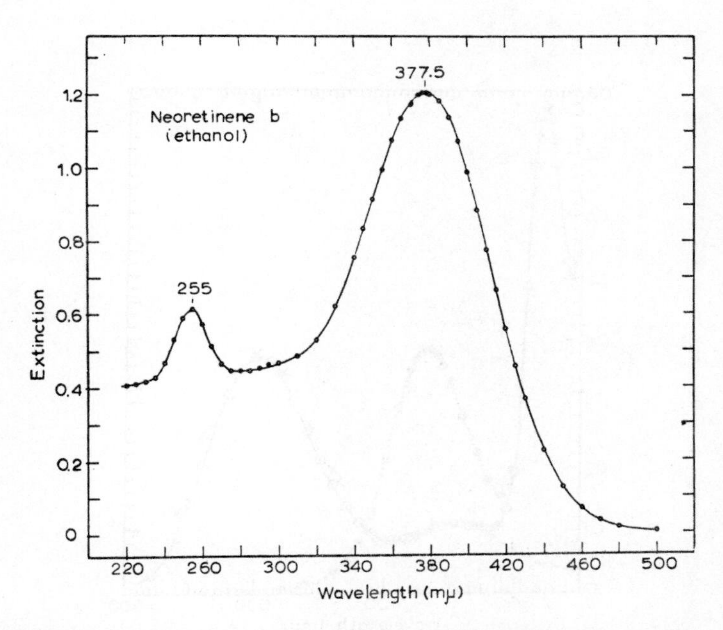

Fig. 45. Absorption spectra of all-*trans* and 11-*cis* retinal$_1$ in ethanol. From: HUBBARD and WALD [1953]

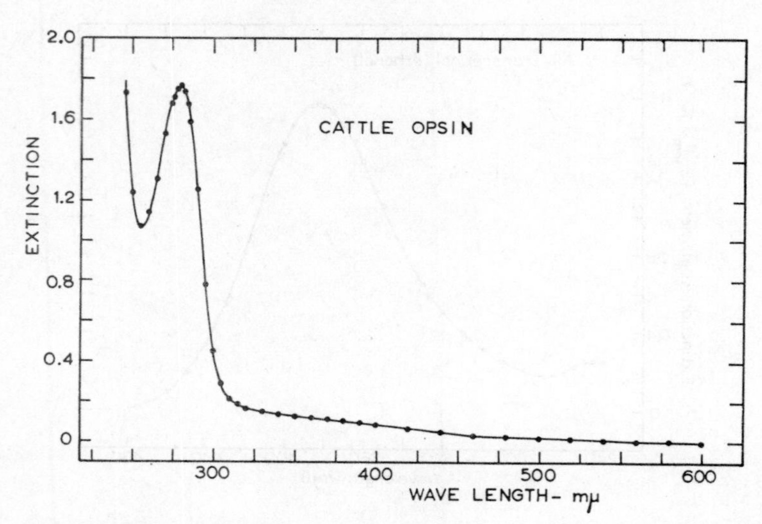

Fig. 46. Absorption spectrum of cattle opsin. From: HUBBARD and WALD [1953]

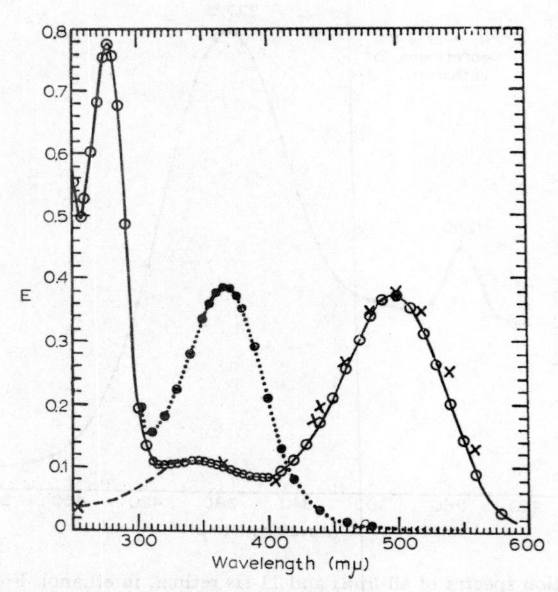

Fig. 47. Absorption spectra of cattle rhodopsin (open circles) and its bleached product "indicator yellow" (black dots) at pH 9.2. Crosses, relative photochemical efficiencies; broken line, probable absorption of the rhodopsin chromophore below 320 mμ. From: COLLINS *et al.* [1952]

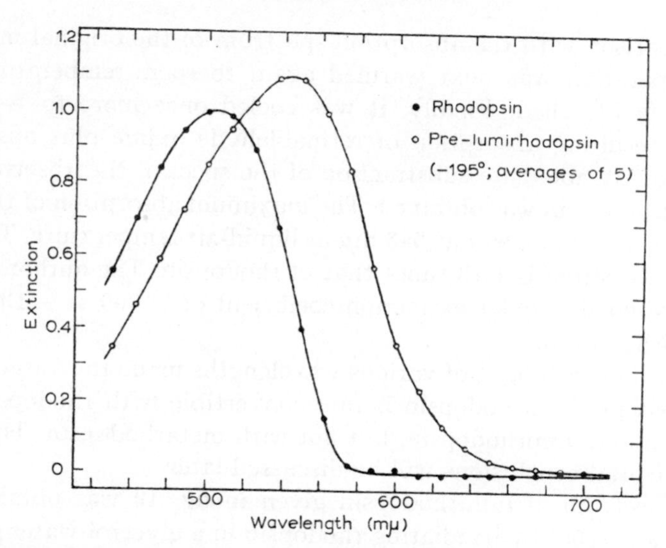

Fig. 48. Absorption spectra of pre-lumirhodopsin and rhodopsin from cattle. From: YOSHIZAWA and WALD [1963]

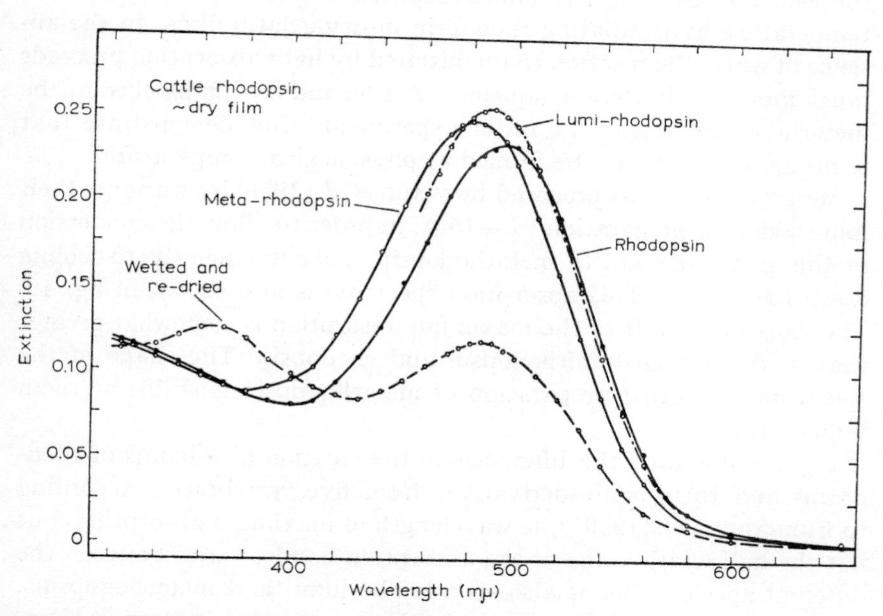

Fig. 49. Absorption spectra of lumirhodopsin, metarhodopsin, rhodopsin, and the final product upon irradiation of cattle rhodopsin. From: WALD *et al.* [1950]

for comparison with the absorption spectrum of the original mixture. The preparation was next warmed again to room temperature and completely bleached. Finally, it was cooled once more to −195 °C and the resulting absorption of retinaldehyde oxime plus opsin was measured. By adequate substraction of the spectra, the absorption of pre-lumirhodopsin was obtained. The maximum absorption of this pigment was found to occur at 543 mμ at liquid-air temperature. The maximum extinction is 1.13 times that of rhodopsin. The authors tentatively assigned a molar extinction coefficient of 72000 at —195 °C to pre-lumirhodopsin.

Irradiation with light of various wavelengths made the authors conclude that pre-lumirhodopsin is interconvertible with rhodopsin, isorhodopsin and lumirhodopsin, but not with metarhodopsin. These experiments and conclusions will be discussed later.

The spectrum of lumirhodopsin given in fig. 49 was obtained by WALD *et al.* [1950] by irradiating rhodopsin in a glycerol-water glass at —40 °C. The α-band of lumirhodopsin occurs at slightly shorter wavelengths than that of rhodopsin at low temperature. The same authors succeeded in observing the lumirhodopsin absorption spectrum at room temperature by irradiating rhodopsin in dry gelatin films. In the absence of water the reaction chain initiated by light absorption proceeds much more slowly than in aqueous solution and is even blocked at the metarhodopsin stage. The latter experiments thus demonstrate that lumirhodopsin can also be formed at physiological temperatures.

Metarhodopsin was prepared by WALD *et al.* [1950] by warming their lumirhodopsin preparation to −15 °C in order to allow the conversion of this pigment state to metarhodopsin, and subsequently re-cooling down to −55 °C. This absorption spectrum is also shown in fig. 49. The short-wave shift of the maximum absorption is somewhat greater than that between lumirhodopsin and rhodopsin. The shape of the spectrum of a dried preparation of metarhodopsin is stable at room temperature.

Fig. 50 illustrates the differences in the location of α-bands of rhodopsins and their photo-derivatives from five vertebrates. According to HUBBARD *et al.* [1959], the wavelength of maximum absorption, but not the half-width value of the absorption bands, varies between the different species. This is also seen in the lumi- and metarhodopsins. The results with cusk pigments may be somewhat exceptional. However, the authors deemed it likely that the spectrum of cusk "metarhodopsin" is in fact that of a mixture of lumi- and metarhodopsin. Such a possibility may well be due to the fact that cusk metarhodopsin hydrolyzes relatively readily and so some may have been hydrolyzed to retinal and opsin before all the lumirhodopsin had been converted. This would explain both the half-width value of the absorption band

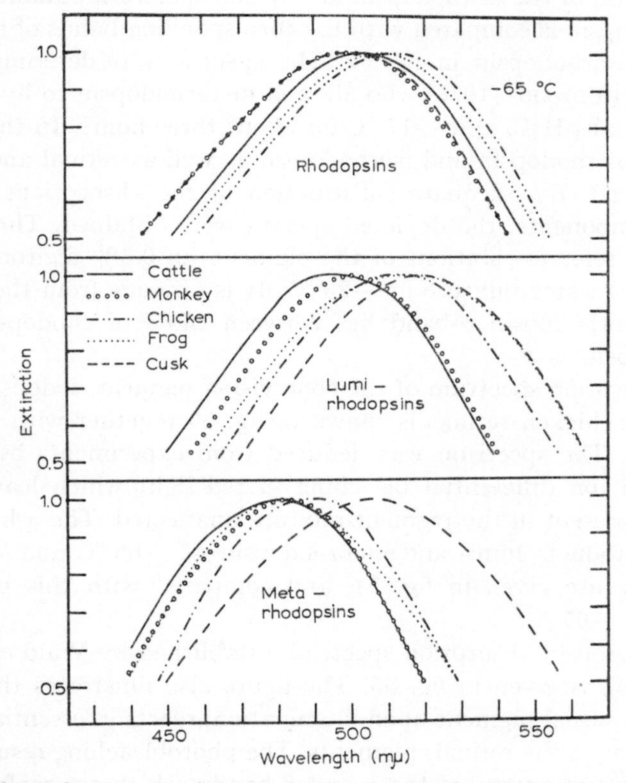

Fig. 50. Absorption spectra of rhodopsins, lumirhodopsins, and metarhodopsins from various vertebrate sources. From: HUBBARD and KROPF [1959]

as well as its location. In any case, the variation of maximum absorption in the different rhodopsins is not due to their having different retinals, and must be due to variation in the opsins.

The absorption spectrum of the bleached products in acid medium, termed N-retinylidene opsin by MORTON and PITT [1951], is shown in fig. 51. This compound is a protonated Schiff base at pH 3.2, and was obtained by BROWN and BROWN [1958] upon acid treatment of the relatively stable *Octopus* metarhodopsin. The "indicator yellow" is a mixture of Schiff bases indiscriminately produced between retinal and opsin moieties at pH 9. It should be emphasized that the vertebrate metarhodopsins are considerably less stable than those of the invertebrates studied so far.

The α-band of the isorhodopsin absorption spectrum obtained from cattle rhodopsin is compared with the corresponding bands of rhodopsin and metarhodopsin in fig. 52. The spectra were determined by KROPF and HUBBARD [1958] who allowed metarhodopsin to hydrolyze in the dark at pH 13 and -17 °C for about three hours. In this way, a mixture of rhodopsin and isorhodopsin as well as retinal and opsin was produced. By adequate substraction of the absorptions of the various components, the depicted spectra were obtained. The molar extinctions refer to solutions of the pigments in 0.3% digitonin in a 2 : 1 glycerol-water mixture at -20 °C. It is obvious from the figure that the isorhodopsin α-band lies between those of rhodopsin and metarhodopsin.

The absorption spectrum of the cone vision pigment, iodopsin, prepared from chicken retinas is shown in fig. 53 together with that of isoiodopsin. The spectrum was deduced from experiments by WALD *et al.* [1955] on differential bleaching in red light which leaves the rhodopsin present in the pigment mixture unaffected. The α-bands of the photoproducts lumi- and meta-iodopsin at -65 °C and -38 °C respectively are given in fig. 54, and compared with this band of iodopsin at -65 °C.

A porphyropsin absorption spectrum established by Wald *et al.*, in WALD [1959], is given in fig. 55. The figure also illustrates that this retinal$_2$ rod visual pigment upon illumination, reacts in essentially the same manner as the retinal$_1$ pigments. The photobleaching results in a complete disappearance of the α and β bands, which are replaced by the absorption band of free retinal$_2$ around 400 mμ. The γ band, due to opsin absorption, is not affected by illumination.

The absorption spectrum of cyanopsin, the "synthetic" cone visual pigment with retinal$_2$ as a chromophore group, established by WALD *et al.* [1953], is shown in fig. 56. The solid portion of the cyanopsin curve represents the accurate spectrum of pure cyanopsin. Due to the fact that other absorptions occur in the region of the dashed part of the curve, there is some doubt about the exact shape of the cyanopsin spectrum in this range. On the left of the figure the absorption spectrum

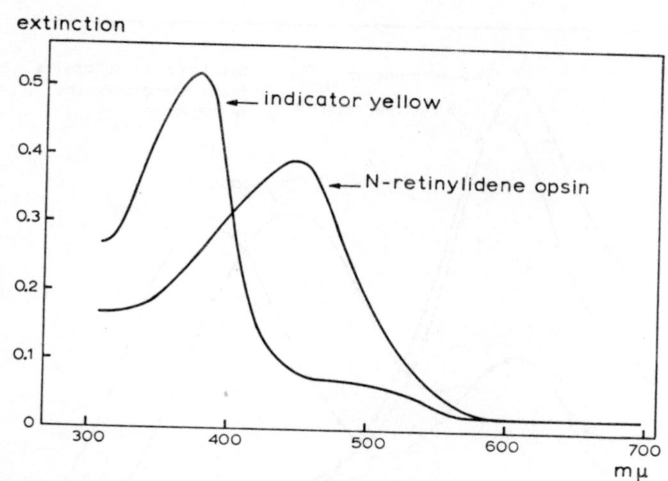

Fig. 51. Absorption spectra of *Octopus* N-retinylidene opsin (pH 3) and "indicator yellow" (pH 9) according to the terminology of MORTON and PITT [1951]. Spectra replotted from data of BROWN and BROWN [1958]

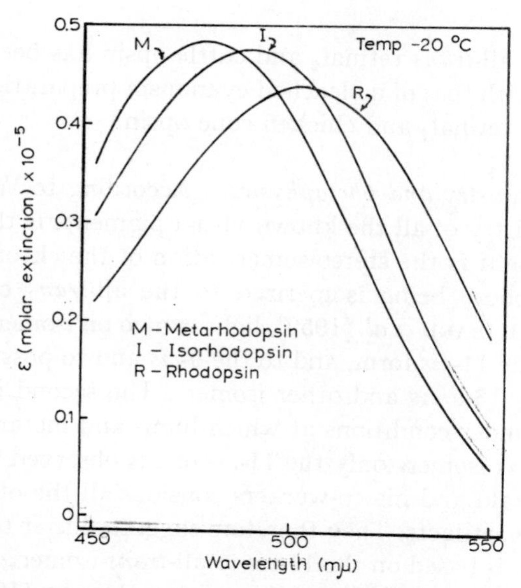

Fig. 52. Absorption spectrum of cattle isorhodopsin compared with the corresponding spectra of rhodopsin and metarhodopsin at −20 °C. From: KROPF and HUBBARD [1958]

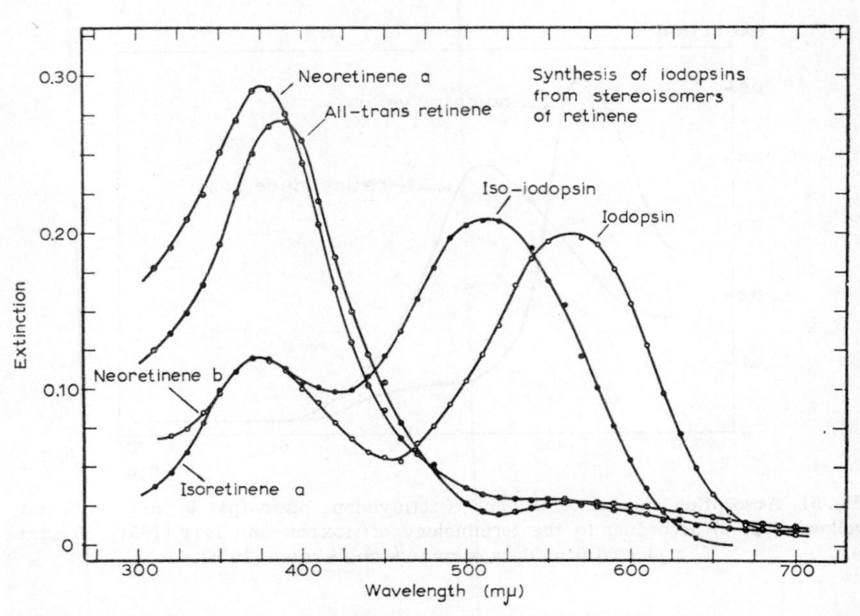

Fig. 53. Absorption spectra of chicken iodopsin and isoiodopsin. From: WALD *et al.* [1955]

of a mixture of all-*trans* retinal$_2$ and cattle opsin has been plotted. It is comparable with that of a bleached cyanopsin preparation consisting of a mixture of retinal$_2$ and chicken cone opsin.

2.5.6 Photochemistry and photophysics. According to Wald's school, the photochemistry of all the known visual pigments is the same. The only effect of light is the stereoisomerization of the chromophore, the 11-*cis* chromophore being isomerized to the all-*trans* configuration. However, see HUBBARD *et al.* [1959], light can go on isomerizing the all-*trans* back to the 11-*cis* form, and to the 9-*cis* and to possibly give traces of 13-*cis*, 9-,13-*dicis* and other isomers. The second isomerization happens only under conditions at which lumi- and metarhodopsin are stable. Of the *cis* isomers only the 11-*cis* one is observed in the *in vivo* state and so Wald and his co-workers consider all the other *cis* configurations to be artifacts. They therefore suggested that the "physiological" photoact is based on the 11-*cis* to all-*trans* isomerization. In this respect, it will be recalled that YOSHIZAWA and WALD [1963] observed an isomerization of the 11-*cis* chromophore of rhodopsin to a steady-

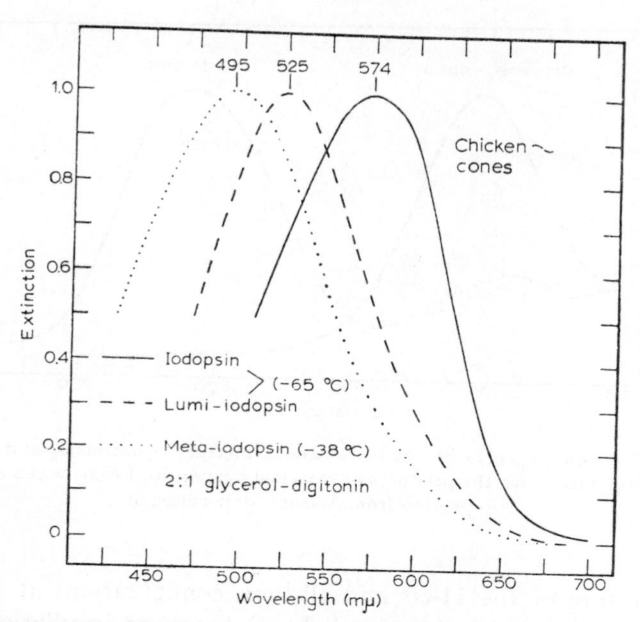

Fig. 54. α bands of the absorption spectra of chicken lumi- (−65 °C) and meta-iodopsin (−38 °C) compared with that of iodopsin at −65 °C. From: HUBBARD and KROPF [1959]

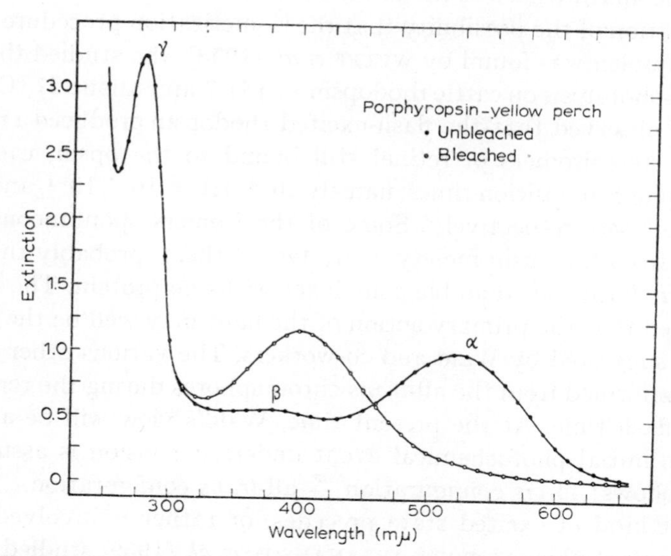

Fig. 55. Absorption spectra of yellow perch porphyropsin and its bleached products. From: WALD *et al.* In: WALD [1959]

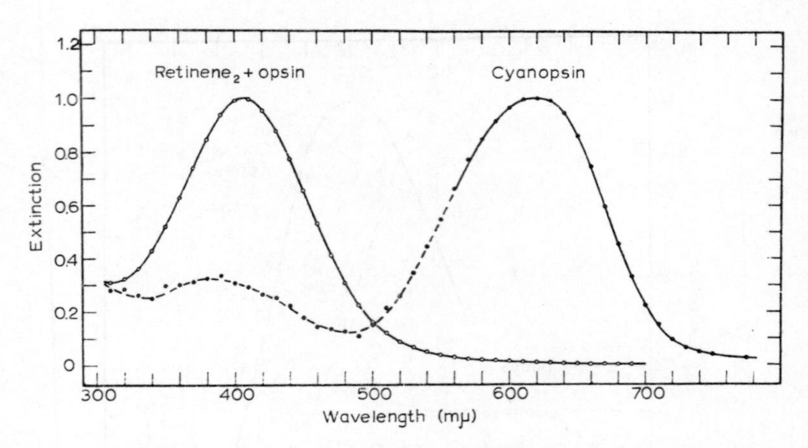

Fig. 56. Absorption spectra of cyanopsin and a mixture of retinene$_2$ and cattle rhodopsin, comparable with the products of bleached cyanopsin. From: WALD *et al.* [1953]. Reprinted from *Science* by permission

state mixture of the 11-*cis* and all-*trans* configurations at —195 °C, when irradiating with 440 mμ light. Subsequent irradiation at this temperature with 600 mμ light isomerized the all-*trans* chromophores in the mixture back to the 11-*cis* form.

Indication of the possibility that the isomerization procedure is even more complex was found by WULFF *et al.* [1958] who studied the effect of flash-photolysis on cattle rhodopsin at pH 7 and about 27 °C. These authors observed that the flash-excited rhodopsin produced a mixture of four stereoisomers of retinal still bound to the opsin, each with different decomposition times, namely 10^{-4}, 1.1×10^{-2}, 10^{-1}, and about 3.5×10^{3} sec. respectively. Some of the isomers spontaneously dissociate from the opsin moiety. Only two of them, probably the 11-*cis* and 9-*cis* forms, yield stable complexes with the protein. The authors remarked that the primary action of the light may well be the isomerization suggested by Wald and co-workers. The various other isomers are then formed from the all-*trans* chromophores during the remainder of the flash time. At the present time, Wald's view will be accepted and the initial photochemical event underlying vision is assumed to be as follows: 11-*cis* configuration $\overset{h\nu}{\rightleftharpoons}$ all-*trans* configuration.

What kind of excited state precedes, or rather is involved in the isomerization phenomenon? ABRAHAMSON *et al.* [1959] studied the optical changes of all-*trans* retinal upon flash illumination. Only in solutions completely free from oxygen was the retinal absorption maximum at 380 mμ reversibly replaced by a band at 440 mμ. The product responsible for the latter absorption band decayed in about 10 μ sec., to give back the original retinal spectrum. The oxygen-sensitivity of the phenomenon, the lifetime and the spectral shift indicate that the intermediate product was a metastable electronic excitation state, probably the triplet state, of retinal. This metastable state could not be detected in either retinol or the protonated Schiff base between retinal and *p*-toluidine. The negative result with the latter compound is of particular interest with regard to rhodopsin. This is because on the basis of the large shift of the absorption maximum upon linking free retinal to opsin to form rhodopsin, PITT *et al.* [1955] made it likely that the chromophore-opsin bond consists of a protonated Schiff base linkage. LINSCHITZ [1960] suggested that the absence of any detectable triplets in protonated retinal Schiff bases and retinol, as well as their occurrence upon flash-illumination of free retinal may be due to the particular location of possible n,π^* levels. With protonated Schiff bases and alcohols, these levels might be situated slightly above the first excited singlet states. If so, they will not favour triplet formation. On the other hand, with the free aldehyde retinal, they might lie below the first π–π^* transition and therefore increase the probability of metastable state production. In any case, it seems very unlikely that triplet states of rhodopsin are involved in the photoisomerization and other visual processes.

Carotenoids, as WALD [1959] remarked, are not likely to be substances capable of initiating nervous stimulatory processes. The spectral changes upon light absorption as well as temperature- and pH-induced variations of the spectrum are found only in chromophore-opsin complexes. Moreover, proteins contain many reactive sites and so attention is focussed on the role of the opsins. Light, as well as heat, affects the configuration of these proteins, see HUBBARD [1959], and also their properties (see RADDING and WALD [1956 a,b]). This phenomenon is not just a result of freeing the opsins from the visual complex for HUBBARD and ST. GEORGE [1958] observed changes in the opsin properties upon conversion of squid rhodopsin into the stable squid metarhodopsin.

More knowledge of the behaviour of opsins upon illumination of the visual pigments was gained by studying the photo-induced optical changes at low temperatures (see HUBBARD and KROPF [1958] and HUB-

BARD *et al.* [1959]). Irradiation of rhodopsin in glycerol-water-digitonin glasses below −45 °C yields stable lumirhodopsin. On illumination at −65 °C this lumirhodopsin is inter-convertible with rhodopsin. If the temperature of the lumirhodopsin preparation is raised to about −20 °C the glass melts and lumirhodopsin changes to metarhodopsin. At the latter temperature and upon illumination, metarhodopsin is interconvertible with rhodopsin. However, at −65 °C such a conversion does not occur. These phenomena were interpreted to mean that, at temperatures at which lumirhodopsin is stable, illumination only causes the isomerization of the chromophore group. This causes the opsin to become labile, but, as a consequence of the low temperature, it is impossible for the opsin to attain a new stable configuration. As soon as the temperature is raised, a thermal rearrangement of the opsin resulting in the formation of metarhodopsin becomes possible. The interconvertibility of metarhodopsin and rhodopsin at these higher temperatures, about −20° C, upon irradiation would mean that both the 11-*cis* configuration of the retinal group and the original opsin structure can be regained. This means that both the temperature-independent photo-isomerization as well as the temperature-dependent rearrangement of the opsin can take place. However, cooling the metarhodopsin preparation to −65 °C would fix the opsin configuration of the meta-pigment and so prevent the back reaction to rhodopsin. Since low temperature irradiation of rhodopsin does not yield metarhodopsin, it was assumed that the rearrangement of opsin is blocked in both directions. In other words, in order to convert the two pigments into each other a thermal "loosening of structure" of the opsin is required.

Lumirhodopsin is thus inter-convertible with rhodopsin. According to YOSHIZAWA and WALD [1963], the same is true of pre-lumirhodopsin with both rhodopsin and lumirhodopsin. It is not inter-convertible with metarhodopsin at low temperatures as would be expected from the preceding discussion. The authors suggested that upon photo-isomerization of rhodopsin at −195 °C, side-chain interactions still hold the all-*trans* chromophore and the opsin together, but that the geometry is rather constrained and distorted. In lumirhodopsin at about −65 °C, these constraints are assumed to be partially relaxed, and the opsin configuration could then have changed slightly towards that of the free protein, while the chromophore may have gained its "usual" all-*trans* geometry to some extent.

What is said of rhodopsin holds for isorhodopsin as well. Upon irradiation of pre-lumirhodopsin, a certain amount of isorhodopsin is formed together with the rhodopsin. The ratio of the amounts of these pigments depends on the wavelength of the actinic light. This equilibrium is governed by two phenomena. First, with light of a given wavelength, the quantum efficiencies of isomerization of pre-lumirhodopsin to rhodopsin or isorhodopsin are different. Second, the pigment mixture tends to absorb as few quanta as possible. For example, neither rhodopsin nor isorhodopsin appreciably absorb 600 mμ light at -195 °C whereas pre-lumirhodopsin does. This means that upon irradiation with light of this wavelength it is converted to rhodopsin and isorhodopsin in the proportion 5 : 1. The isomerization from the 11-*cis* (neo-b) to the 9-*cis* (iso-a) configuration of the chromophore proceeds only *via* the all-*trans* state. Consequently, isorhodopsin is formed from rhodopsin *via* pre-lumirhodopsin.

Both rhodopsin and isorhodopsin are stable at room temperature, whereas all other forms of the visual pigments are labile, except for the metarhodopsin of certain invertebrates. The exceptional behaviour of this metarhodopsin was suggested to be due to an opsin structure slightly different from "normal" opsins by HUBBARD and ST. GEORGE [1958]. Leaving this special case out of consideration, YOSHIZAWA and WALD [1963] concluded that only the 11-*cis* or 9-*cis* configurations of retinal are capable of combining with opsin in such a way that both chromophore and protein assume fitting geometries which are stabilized by mutual interactions. However, the authors remarked that, apart from its isomerizing effect, light might have another function in the interconversion reactions between the various states of the visual pigments. This suggestion is based on the fact that the isomerization reactions are not of a highly endergonic type and a considerable part of the energy of an absorbed quantum is left over after the isomerization of the chromophore. This excess energy might activate rearrangement of the opsin, either by localized protein excitation or on being degraded to heat, thermally loosening the opsin structure near to the binding site of the chromophore.

The electronic ground states of *cis* isomers lie at higher energy levels than that of the all-*trans* configuration of retinal. The *cis* isomers display a "blue shift" relative to the all-*trans* state. As a consequence, the electronic excitation states of the *cis*-forms should be at still higher energies above those of the all-*trans* retinal than their respective ground states. Apart from the blue shift on isomerization, a marked red shift occurs as soon as retinal becomes bound to opsins. KROPF and HUBBARD [1958] tentatively ascribed this phenomenon to a lowering of the energy of the excited state of visual pigments due to interaction between the appropriate *cis* isomers and the protein. As a consequence of this hypothesis, one would expect that the stronger these interactions are, the more the absorption band should shift to the long-wave side. Thus, lumirhodopsin, in which the chromophore apparently fits the opsin better than it is the case with metarhodopsin, should absorb at longer wavelengths. For the same reason, rhodopsin should absorb at longer wavelengths than lumirhodopsin. In fact, this does happen, though for prelumirhodopsin things are different. According to the above reasoning, one might expect that the absorption band of prelumirhodopsin will lie between those of lumirhodopsin and rhodopsin, but on the contrary, pre-lumirhodopsin absorbs at longer wavelengths than rhodopsin. YOSHIZAWA and WALD [1963] explained this by suggesting that the highly constrained geometry of the pigment makes the ground state of prelumirhodopsin occur at a much higher energy level than that of rhodopsin, though no such difference will exist between their first electronic excitation levels. The energy gap between excited and ground levels will thus be smaller with pre-lumirhodopsin than with rhodopsin and a quantum of lower energy, that is, of longer wavelength will be absorbed by the former pigment. However, it should be noted that this reasoning is purely hypothetical.

Fig. 57 summarizes the effect and consequences of light absorption by rhodopsin. The responses of the other visual pigments have not been studied so extensively, but the reaction pattern is apparently the same. In short, it can be stated that the first event in vision consists of photo-isomerization of the chromophore of the visual pigments. This reaction is followed by thermal processes in which the chromophore-protein bonding becomes gradually loosened until, at least with the vertebrate visual pigments, the retinal is freed from the opsin. Two new SH-groups as well as a proton-binding group are ultimately exposed as a consequence of the thermal reactions.

3 The photoreceptive structures

It is not easy in some cases to decide whether or not a particular photoreceptor should be rated as "visual". For example, this difficulty arises in the case of photoreceptor neurons in the abdominal nerve cord of the crayfish (see KENNEDY [1963]). Photostimulation, and thus photoreception in this invertebrate was observed as changes of the impulse activity of the nerve cells. BRUNO and KENNEDY [1962] determined the spectral sensitivity of this phenomenon. The action spectrum exhibited a maximum around 500 mμ and resembled the absorp-

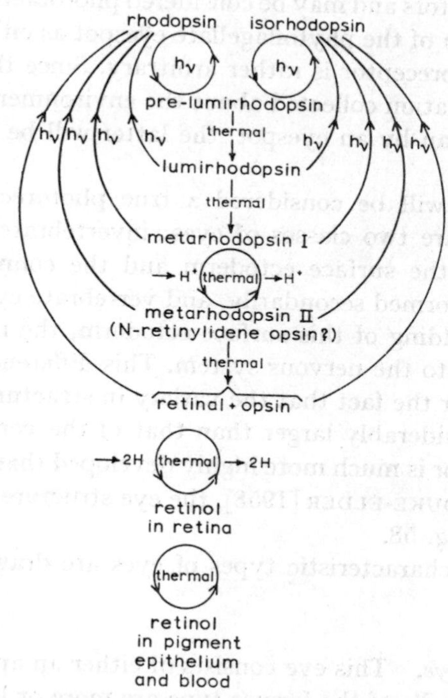

Fig. 57. Summary of the various photo- and thermal reactions found with rhodopsin

tion spectra of rhodopsins occurring in the compound eyes of decapod crustacea. Although a visual pigment seems to be involved, one can hardly consider such a neuron reaction as vision.

The situation becomes more intricate when attempting to classify the eyespot of phytoflagellates. With the aid of such an organnelle, these organisms are capable of directing themselves towards favourable light conditions. WOLKEN [see 1963], carried out spectrophotometry of the receptor and observed a major maximum at 480–490 mμ as well as minor ones around 510 and 530 mμ. The photosensitive pigment, however, was not identified. Because of the directory nature of the photoprocess in question, it seems that one has to deal with phototaxis rather than with vision. However, associated with the eyespot, a flagellum occurs. According to WOLKEN [1963], the combination eyespot-flagellum represents a photoreceptor-effector system which, in both structural and functional respect may be considered analogous to a retinal rod. On the other hand, certain insects are equipped with true visual photoreceptors and may be considered phototactic as well. Therefore, classification of the phytoflagellate eyespot as either a visual or a phototactic photoreceptor is rather arbitrary. Since there is considerably more information collected about the environmental situation by the insect eye than by an eyespot, the latter will be discussed under phototaxis.

Only the eye will be considered a true photoreceptor of vision. Basically there are two classes of eyes: invertebrate eyes which are developed from the surface ectoderm and the connection with the nervous system formed secondarily, and vertebrate eyes which originate from an infolding of this surface ectoderm, the neural ectoderm, and thus belong to the nervous system. This difference in origin may be responsible for the fact that the variety in structure of the invertebrate eye is considerably larger than that of the vertebrate eye, but the latter receptor is much more highly developed than the former one.

According to DUKE-ELDER [1958], the eye structure can be classified as indicated in fig. 58.

A number of characteristic types of eyes are drawn schematically in fig. 59.

The unicellular eye. This eye consists of either an apolar or a bipolar visual cell. The cells of the former type are more or less spherical and are either isolated in the epithelium, for example in *Lumbricus*, or aggregates in close connection with nerve fibres adjacent to the epidermis. Such is the case with *Hirudo*. A dense pigment layer is located under the epithelium. As a rule, the bipolar photosensitive cells are ciliate or brush-shaped at one of the poles and are covered with a pigment cap. Actually it may be somewhat arbitrary to consider these types of eyes as organelles basically different in a functional way from the photoreceptor neurons of the crayfish. The reason for doing so is that in certain respects the unicellular ocelli resemble those of the multicellular "simple" eyes, whereas the latter organelles generally show structures which are undeniably related to true eyes.

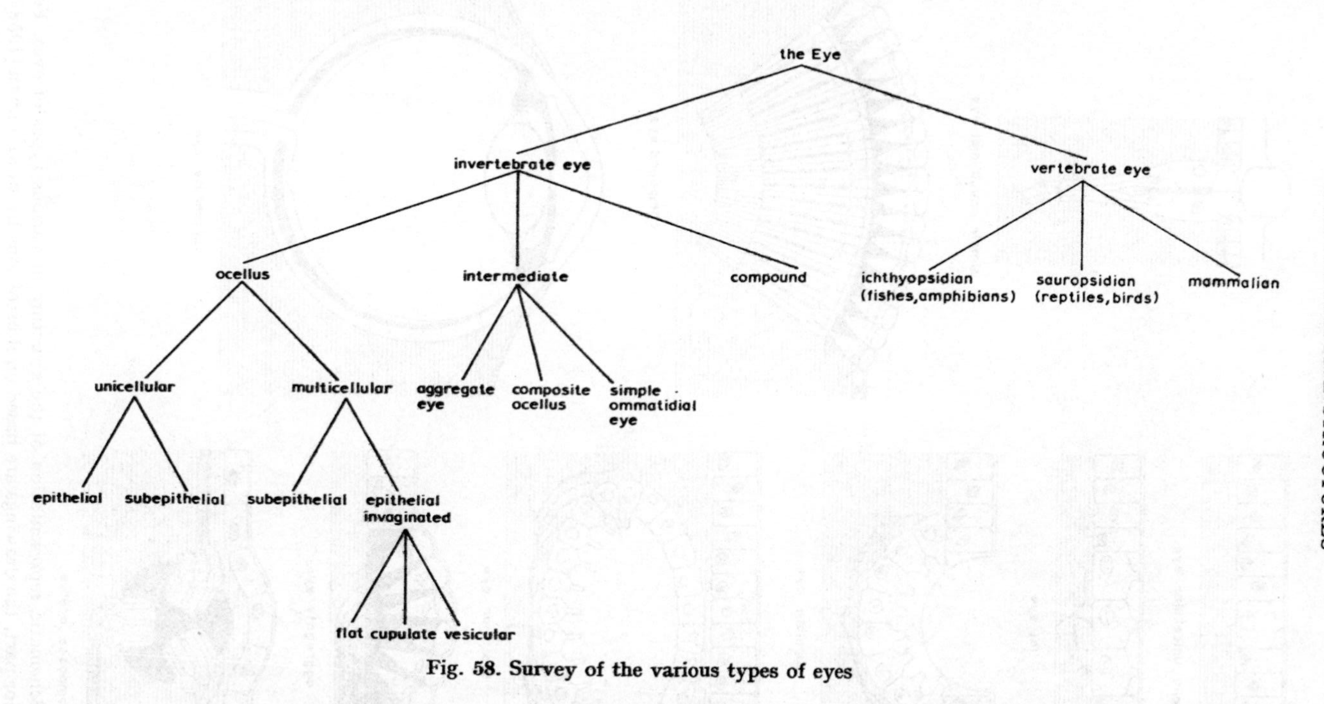

Fig. 58. Survey of the various types of eyes

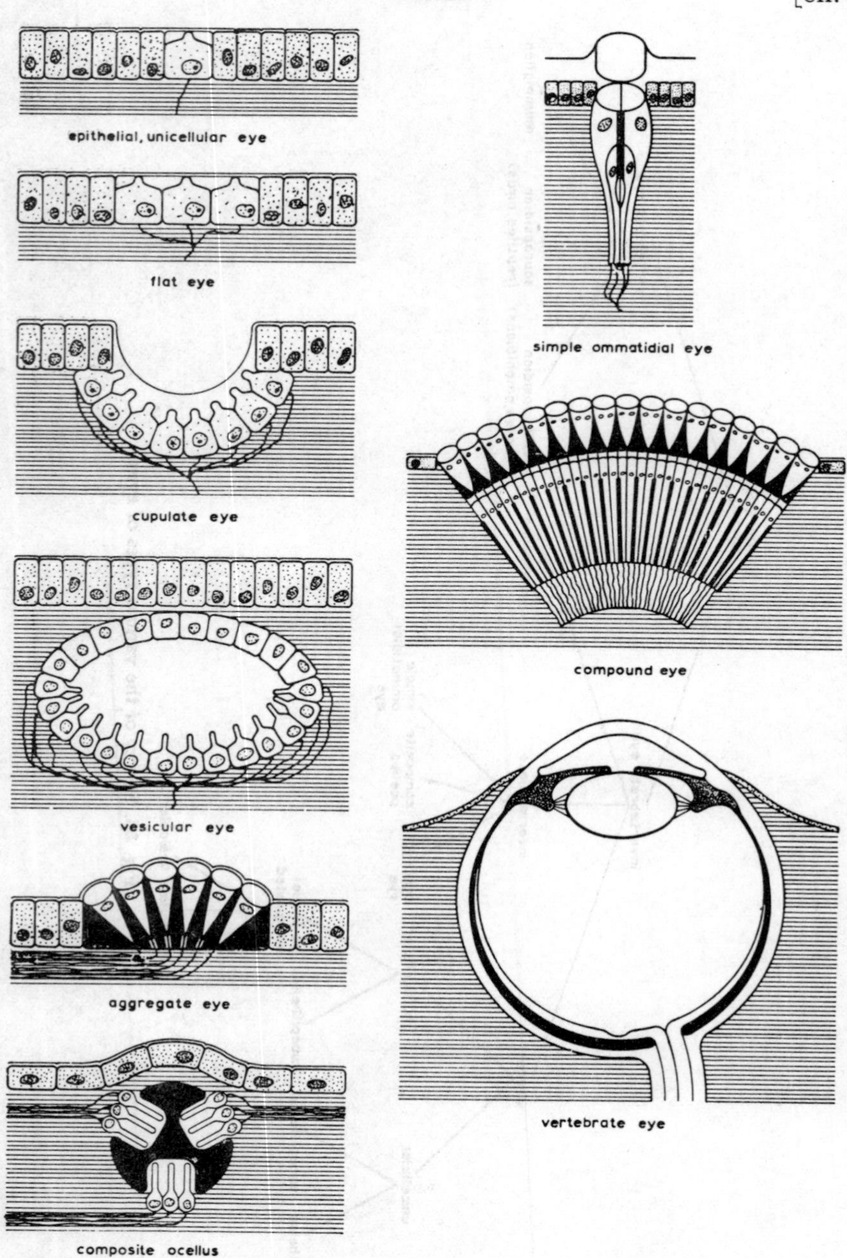

Fig. 59. Schematic representation of the structure of various types of eyes. For the major part, the drawings are based on illustrations by DUKE-ELDER [1958]

In the multicellular "simple" eyes, the individual visual cells co-operate, *via* the nerves, in such a way that a greater number of photoreceptor cells give rise to an improvement of the image of the environment. In order to improve the quality of the image, various optical arrangements, ranging from translucent secretion layers which cover the assembly of visual cells, to pin-hole dark chambers and finally to systems equipped with lenses are found.

The flat eye. This is the simplest assembly type and is found for example in the Annelid *Stylaria*. The covering cuticle may be thickened, for example in the medusan *Lizzia*, to form a kind of lens.

A pin-hole type of eye is encountered in the mollusc *Nautilus*, whereas a vitreous body functioning as an imperfect lens occurs for example in the eye of the polychete worm *Nereis*. In many cases the visual cells are considerably elongated at the pole opposite to the connection with the nervous system in such a way that rods are formed and so a retina may occur. A true lens may be present, instead of the vitreous body, which may be cuticular as with the blow-fly *Calliphora*, or cellular as in the onychophore *Peripatus*. As a rule, pigment layers or pigment-carrying cells surround the eyes or are incorporated in them.

The vesicular eye. Much more complicated and better adapted with regard to image formation are the many varieties of vesicular eyes. The highly adapted ones even show a considerable number of features in common with the vertebrate eye. Such is the case with the eye of the cephalopod *Octopus* which contains a cornea, an iris, a lens, an optical chamber and a retina, although the lens is composed of two halves, one formed from the surface epithelium the other one from the vesicular epithelium.

The aggregate eye. Like that of the asteroid *Asterias*, it is a combination of closely packed ocelli, each provided with a lens. It resembles the compound eye, but differs from it in that the sensory cells are independent of one another.

The composite ocellus. This is seen for example in the ostracod *Cypris*, and consists of a complex of a few groups of ocelli, each of them with a simple retina and separated from each other by a pigment mantle.

The simple ommatidial eye. It occurs for example in many Lepidoptera as a lateral ocellus, is made up of a cuticular thickening, the cornea, a "crystalline" lens and a number of photoreceptor cells surrounding a rhabdome. A rhabdome is a collective secretion product of the visual cells. It has a rod-like structure and functions as a light conductor. Since rhabdomes are characteristic of the compound eye, the simple ommatidial eye should be classified rather close to the compound type.

The compound eye. This is typical of arthropods. It is made up of units which, in their turn, consist of a facet-shaped cornea covering a "crystalline" core under which a group of light-sensitive cells is aligned in such a way that the axis of the central rhabdome coincides with that of the "crystalline" core. The group of photoreceptors is termed the retinule. The entire unit is called "ommatidium". The ommatidia are separated from each other by a pigment sheath and are arranged radially. The corneal facets fit into each other so as to form a mosaic and since in such a "faceted eye" the tube-shaped elements are shielded by pigment layers, the image is also built up to form a mosaic. The retinules together comprise the retina. The inner side of the eye is bordered by the fenestrated basement membrane.

The vertebrate eye. It is the most highly organised and can be divided into three main groups, listed in fig. 58. These groups are basically different only so far as they are adapted to vision in different media: water, air, or both. Essentially, this type of eye contains: cornea, iris, lens, dark chamber, and retina with nerve connections. Nutritive and protective elements are added to the basic structures. The eyeball as a whole can be moved and accomodation facilities often occur. As an example, the human eye is schematically represented in fig. 59.

This very brief review may demonstrate the range of types of visual structures although considerable variety is found within each type. For detailed discussion reference is made to the many elaborate reviews and handbooks, to cite a few: POLYAK [1941], MILNE and MILNE [1956], and DUKE-ELDER [1958].

The organelle of primary interest to this discussion is the photoreceptive cell. By far the most extensively studied of these are the light-sensitive elements from the vertebrate retina, and so only these cells will be discussed.

The primate retina is represented in fig. 60. Ten layers may be distinguished. The inner surface layer consists of pigment epithelium, and covers the photoreceptor cells. Two kinds of such cells are known, namely: rods and cones. Both types need not be present simultaneously. In nocturnal animals such as the bat, a pure-rod retina may occur. In

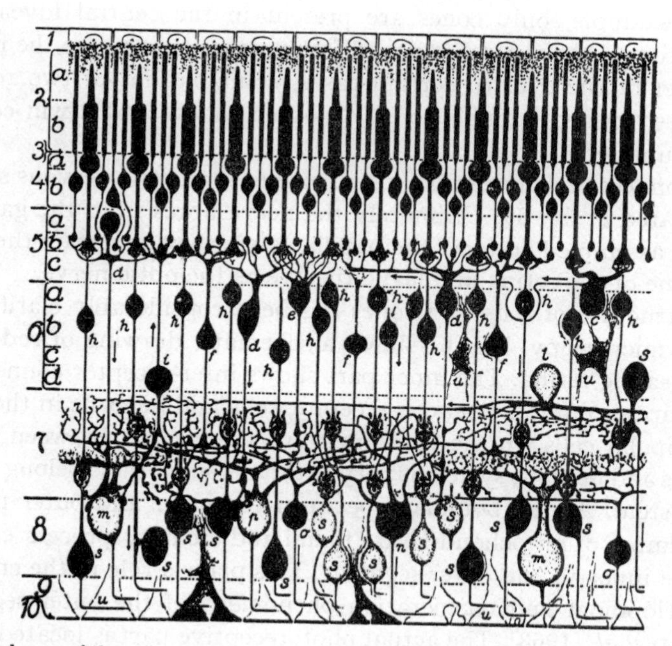

Fig. 60. Scheme of the primate retina. Arrows indicate the probable direction of nervous impulses. 1, pigment layer; 2, rod and cone layer; 2a, outer zone; 2b, inner zone; 3, outer limiting membrane; 4, outer nuclear layer; 4a outer zone; 4b, inner zone; 5, outer plexiform layer; 5a, outer zone; 5b, middle zone; 5c, inner zone; 6, inner nuclear layer, four zones; 7, inner plexiform layer; 8, layer of ganglion cells; 9, layer of optic nerve fibers; 10, inner limiting membrane. a, rods; b, cones; c, horizontal cells; d–h, bipolar cells; i and l, amacrine cells; m–s, ganglion cells; u, radial fibers of Müller. From: POLYAK [1941]

entirely diurnal types a pure-cone retina may be encountered, for example in the marmot eye. However, the retina is normally duplex, the ratio of the number of rods and cones varying between different species. As a rule the retina of species adapted to life at low light intensities contains a predominant number of rods, while cones predominate in that of species living under bright light. In the duplex retina the distribution of rods and cones need not be homogeneous and in many cases, a closer packing of receptor cells is found in an "area centralis" than in other regions of the retina. Within this area a depression, the "fovea centralis", may be formed, as in the human eye. Moreover the ratio of the number of rods and cones in these regions may differ considerably from that elsewhere in the retina. In the human eye for example, only cones are present in the central fovea. The composition of the central area and fovea serves to increase the resolving power of the eye. In certain cases, combinations of two rods or two cones, termed "double rods", "double cones" and "twin cones", are encountered.

The connection between the visual elements and the nervous system is illustrated in fig. 60. Ultimately the nerve fibres from the ganglion cells are assembled to form the papilla where they penetrate the inner membrane of the retina and leave the eye as the optic nerve.

The structure of rods and cones has been considerably clarified by electron microscopy. Fig. 61 shows a schematic drawing of rods from the guinea pig retina. The inner part shows inter-receptor connections and synaptic contacts between receptor cells and neurons in the layer of the bipolar cells. In the vertebrate eye the contact between photoreceptors and nervous system is very intimate since they belong to the same system. At the boundary between the inner and outer parts a large number of mitochondria are found and a ciliary process extends from the inner to the outer segment. This plays a role in the embryonic development and regeneration phenomena of the outer segment, see WALD *et al.* [1963]. The actual photoreceptive part is located in the outer segment which contains a pile of lamellae. These lamellae are the carriers of the visual pigments and are found in the outer segments of cones as well. As an example of the photoreceptive structures in the vertebrate eye, a more detailed schematic drawing of the outer segments, of the receptor cells from the *Necturus* eye is depicted in fig. 62. The lamellae are originally formed by the infolding of the plasma membrane, (see SJÖSTRAND [1961] and FERNÁNDEZ-MORÁN [1961]). The photoreceptive parts of visual cells all have a thickness between 5 and 20 mμ, (see WOLKEN [1962, 1963]) and consist of lamellar plates or discs which form rods and cones in vertebrates, and in invertebrates, tubes or rods. Analysis showed that the retinal rod outer segments are composed of 40 to 50% protein, 20 to 40% lipids – for the major part phospholipids – and 4 to 10% retinal. They also contain nucleic acids.

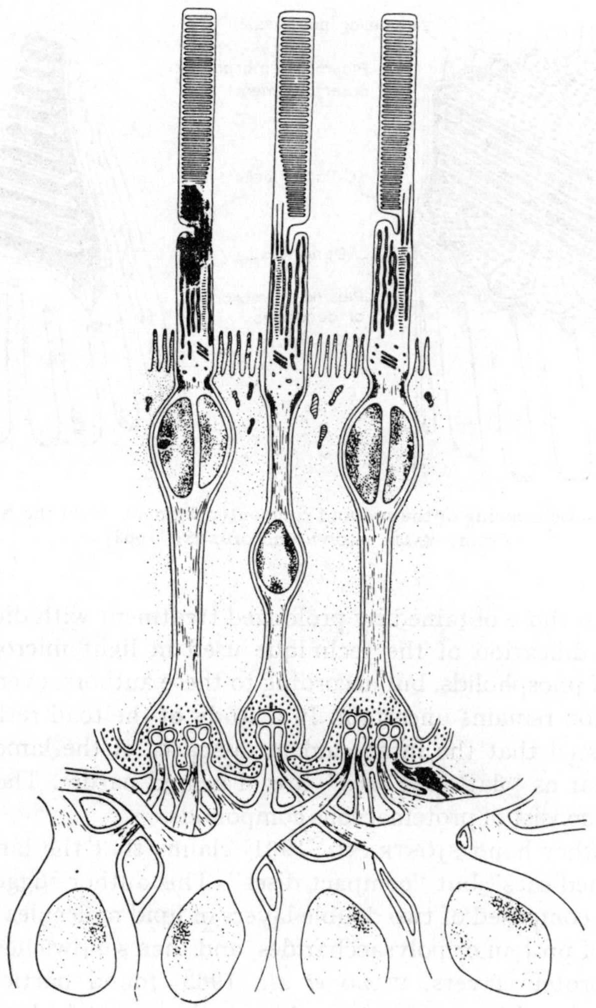

Fig. 61. Schematic picture of rods from the guinea pig retina. From: SJÖSTRAND [1961

The interpretation of the lamellar composition is based on electron microscopial investigations. One particular problem which has not been resolved by this technique is that the dark and light bands in the electron microgram of osmium-fixed outer segments are very hard to interpret in terms of regions consisting of either proteins or lipids. DE ROBERTIS and LASANSKY [1961] compared the results of osmium

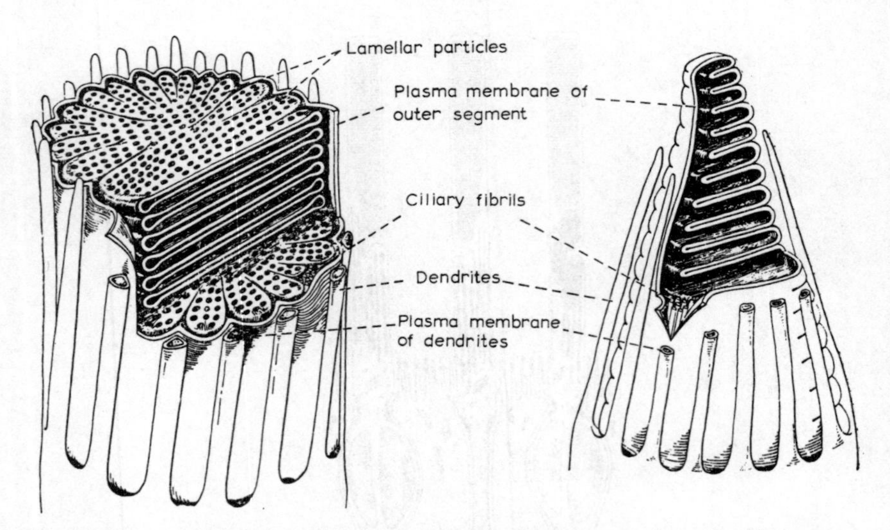

Fig. 62. Schematic drawing of the rod and cone outer segments from the *Necturus* eye. From: WALD, BROWN and GIBBONS [1963]

fixation with those obtained by prolonged treatment with dichromate, a slight modification of the technique used in light microscopy for detection of phospholids, but according to these authors, even then the interpretation remains uncertain. In a study of the toad retina, it has been suggested that the inter- and intra-spaces of the lamellar discs which appear as "flattened sacs", are of a lipid nature. The lamellae themselves consist of proteinaceous compounds.

On the other hand SJÖSTRAND [1961] claims that the lamellae are not "flattened sacs" but "compact discs". This author suggested that each disc is composed of two double layers of lipid molecules separated by a layer of protein or polysaccharides, and then sandwiched between two thin protein layers. WALD *et al.* [1963] found particles which stained deeply with osmium tetroxide on these protein layers in the rod outer segments of the visual cells from the *Necturus* retina. These particles were not observed in cones and were therefore termed "rod-lamellar particles". The particles are circular with a diameter of 30 mμ and a thickness of, presumably, 5 mμ. They are arranged so evenly over the surface of the lamellae that they suggest a crystalline array.

Are the rod-lamellar particles carriers of the visual pigments? There is no direct evidence for such an arrangement though the latter authors pointed out two facts in favour of it. Firstly, with *Necturus*, the only highly organized structures in the rod outer segments seem to be the disc membranes. The interspaces between the discs are very narrow and of varying size. These spaces contain the "ordinary" intracellular ground substance. As the visual pigments, (porphyropsin in the case of *Necturus*) are known to display a high orientation perpendicular to the long axis of the rod (see SCHMIDT [1935] and DENTON [1954]), it is to be expected that they are found in well-organized structures. Secondly, a protein which is a carrier of such highly unsaturated compounds as the visual chromophores, is expected to stain with osmium tetroxide rather intensely. A calculation based on the assumption that the visual pigments are actually located in the rod-lamellar particles, showed that in the *Necturus* rods, these particles would be entirely made up of porphyropsin.

The bases of the outer segments from rods and cones are surrounded by protrusions of the cytoplasm of the inner segments, see CARASSO [1958], COHEN [1961] and WALD *et al.* [1963]. Though they do not imply that these processes are reponsible for the conduction of excitation, the latter authors termed them rod and cone dendrites. With rods, the dendrites occur at the junctions of the outer segment lobes and probably extend from the base of the outer segment to about half of its length. In cones they reach from the base to the tip of this segment. On the average, the numbers of dendrites surrounding the *Necturus* rods and cones were found to be 27 and 30 respectively.

A second system of cytoplasmic protrusions surrounds the visual cells, but these filaments originate from the pigment epithelium, and thus extend "downwards". Their number increases with decreasing distance from the epithelial cells.

Consequently there is a basic difference between the two filamental systems. The dendrites are surrounded by the same membrane which envelops the outer segment of the visual cells, whereas the filaments of the second system are enclosed by the membrane of a neighbouring epithelial cell. On both kinds of structures, small bodies which stain densely with osmium tetroxide were observed by WALD *et al.* [1963]. In dendrites they are button-shaped, while in the epithelial processes they are lens-shaped. Their diameter is of the order of 20 Å. The enveloping filaments are not shown in fig. 61, while in fig. 62 only the dendrites are depicted.

The function of the two filament structures has not yet been elucidated. Tentatively, Wald *et al.* suggested that the major role of the dendrites is to facilitate the exchange of material between outer and inner segments, and the processes of the pigment epithelium enable a similar exchange between this tissue and the outer segment.

Somewhere the absorbed light energy must evoke the stimulus which is to be introduced into the nervous system. There is no argument against the hypothesis that the plasma membrane of the visual cells is responsible for the conduction of this stimulus.

4 *The nature of the process*

Vision is a trigger process for the energy of the ultimate reaction is not proportional to that absorbed by the visual pigments. While only a single molecule may be changed by the light, this change can start a chain reaction. The energy needed for running the latter reaction is supplied by metabolism. There is evidence that a single quantum suffices for stimulating a retinal rod (see HECHT *et al.* [1942] and WALD [1961b]), although stimulation by a single quantum does not result in vision. According to DE VRIES [1943], VAN DER VELDEN [1944, 1946], BOUMAN and VAN DER VELDEN [1947] and BOUMAN [1949] vision is a two-quantum process for rods and cones, the effective absorption of the second quantum being limited in space and time relative to the first absorption act. However, for reasons based mainly on summation variations in different regions of the retina and on quantum fluctuation, other possibilities have been suggested. HECHT *et al.* [1942] and BRINDLEY [1954] arrived at the conclusion that the minimum number of quanta should be about twice that assumed by the previous authors, and BAUMGARDT [1959] suggested that absorption of several pairs of quanta, limited in space and time, is needed for light perception. According to him, the second quantum of a certain pair may function at the same time as the first one of another pair and so the total number of quanta required for vision can be odd or even. For a more detailed review of this matter, reference is made to BOUMAN [1961] and PIRENNE [1962a, b]. Interesting as it is, a further discussion exceeds the scope of this book.

According to EINSTEIN [1905], the activity of each quantum absorbed by the photoreceptor is restricted to changing only the molecule by which it is captured, and so it follows that the stimulation of a rod or cone results from the change of only a single molecule. Considering the fact that the visual pigments are the only receptor constituents known to be changed by light absorption, they must be involved in the primary act of vision.

According to Wald and his associates, light absorption causes stereoisomerization of the chromophore group of the visual pigments. The isomerized product is finally released from its carrier, the opsin. Before this release occurs, two SH-groups and one proton binding group of the opsin moiety become exposed. These phenomena will now be considered from their functional aspect.

The fact that absorption of a quantum under normal conditions results in both the release of the chromophore from the opsin and the exposure of chemically active sites in this protein, shows that some change of the opsin reactivity towards its medium has taken place. It may be expected that such a change is accompanied by alterations of the protein structure. A light microscopical observation by WOLKEN [1961a] showed that illumination transforms the straight cylindrical rod outer-segments of the frog into crumpled structures with many transverse "breaks", as if the lamellar discs have tended to fall apart. The effect is most striking and fits well into the suggestion by HUBBARD and KROPF [1958, 1959] that a light-induced structural change of the opsin has occurred. The combination of such a change and the reaction of the chromophore group upon illumination is schematically illustrated in fig. 63. This picture is based on the ideas of Wald and his school.

In rhodopsin, the retinal is depicted in its 11-*cis* configuration. It fits into a site in the opsin molecule and covers three reactive groups, while its tail is linked to the protein with a Schiff-base bond. Upon absorption of a quantum, stereoisomerization to the all-*trans* form of retinal occurs and the chromophore no longer fits into the protein. This is pre-lumirhodopsin. Next, dark reactions commence in which the protein changes in structure *via* lumirhodopsin to metarhodopsin. These changes result in exposure of the three reactive groups of the protein, manifested by their appearance on the surface of opsin. According to Wald's picture, the exposure of these groups may be responsible for triggering visual excitation. Finally the retinal-opsin link is broken by hydrolysis and the chromophore in its all-*trans* configuration diffuses from the opsin. This release of the pigment is the reason for its bleaching.

According to WALD [1956], visual excitation may result from amplification of the light signal, that is the formation of metarhodopsin, in

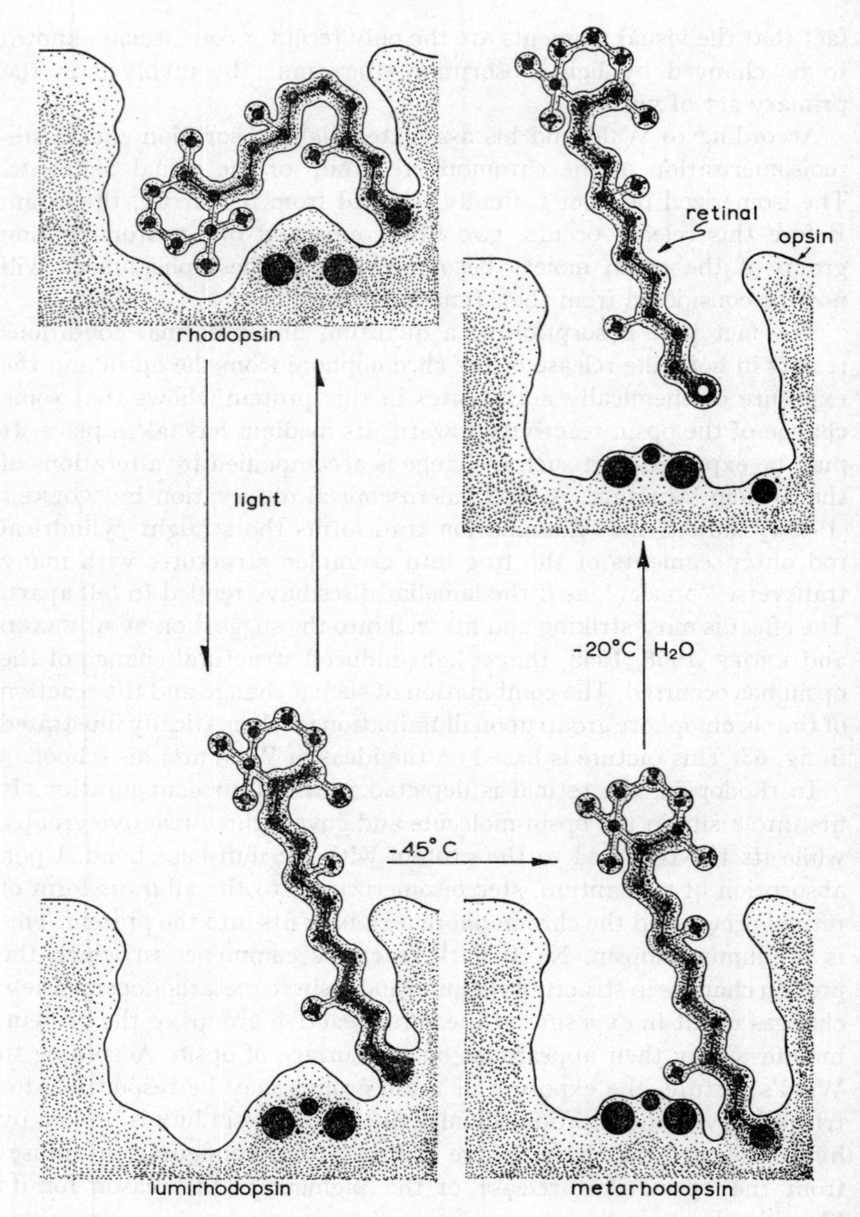

Fig. 63. Schematic representation of the primary photochemical events in vision, based on the concepts of the Harvard School

two ways. The first mechanism may operate biochemically and the visual pigment should be considered a pro-enzyme. By the action of light, the reactive sites are "uncorked" and the opsin becomes an active enzyme. Since an enzyme is capable of effecting the turnover of a large number of substrate molecules, it acts as an amplifier. Such a mechanism is in keeping with the previously mentioned results of MCCONNELL and SCARPELLI [1963], who observed increased ATP-ase activity of rhodopsin upon illumination.

The second possible mechanism is of a more physical type and requires that the outer proteinaceous layers of the lamellar discs, consist mainly of visual pigment molecules. As a result of light action, a unimolecular hole might be punched in such a layer. Through this hole, ions may start to flow in such a number that local depolarization or loss of resistance results. This phenomenon would also mean amplification, and if sufficiently large, might cause excitation. It will be recalled that the layers in question are in rather intimate contact with, or belong to, the photoreceptor membrane. This membrane in its turn is adjacent to that of the nerve cells. Therefore excitation might be transferred to the nervous system *via* the enveloping membrane of the outer segment. In this respect, mention should be made of a suggestion by TAGAKI [1963] that the presence of water is required for the denaturation and bleaching of the chromophore-opsin complex. This phenomenon seems to be related to the hydration and dehydration theory of nerve excitation, postulated by TOBIAS [1951].

In any case, the above discussion illustrates that the nature of the excitation process still lacks a generally accepted explanation.

With respect to a physical concept of the photoreceptor, it has been remarked by a number of authors (see WOLKEN [1962]) that the ordered structure of the photoreceptor lamellae closely resembles crystallinity, and thus a solid state system. If so, solid state phenomena such as photoconductivity and exciton transfer might play a role in vision. However, WALD *et al.* [1963] concluded from experiments with polarized light that the crystallinity is incomplete and they termed the structure in question "quasi-crystalline". The lamellae seem to contain well-ordered "crystalline" regions but these mixed with less orderly ones and the authors hesitated to take solid state phenomena into serious consideration before these are actually demonstrated in visual cells.

Up to now, the visual processes have been considered without discrimination between black-and-white and colour vision. The pattern of the primary processes seems to be the same for both kinds of vision. The problem of colour vision is a very intriguing one, especially since it has not proved possible to extract more than one rod pigment and one cone pigment from the retina. However, thanks to a large number of studies, a general conception of the basic mechanism of colour vision is developing.

According to the "duplicity theory", colour vision is restricted to cones. This theory, originally proposed by SCHULTZE [1866], is based among others on the following facts. Under bright light conditions, the human eye sees colours. When fixating an object, the image is formed on the fovea. Thus, the fovea is capable of colour discrimination. If one fixates a dim star at night, it vanishes which means that the fovea is unable to function under weak light conditions. However, if the image of the star is formed in regions other than the fovea, it can be seen. Anatomy of the human retina shows that the visual cells of the fovea consist only of cones, whereas rods are predominant in other parts of the retina. Schultze thus formulated his duplicity theory that the rods are scotopic receptors giving rise to black-and-white vision and the cones are photopic receptors responsible for colour vision. A strong argument in favour of this concept that visual perception is a dual phenomenon arises from the fact that a shift of spectral sensitivity occurs upon dark adaptation. In honour of its discoverer, this effect has been termed the "Purkinje shift", (see PIRENNE [1962c]).

With progress in the study of vision, some exceptions have become known. For instance, according to ARDEN and TANSLEY [1955a, b], the retinae of the grey squirrel and the souslik actually are pure-cone structures. In eyes of cats and rabbits, DODT and ELENIUS [1960] observed changes of the threshold during dark adaptation and concluded from electroretinograms that either the "cone phase" of such retinograms should be ascribed to a mixture of cones and rods, or that it is the same for both cones and rods. DODT and JESSEN [1961] stated that under bright light conditions the retinogram of the nocturnal gecko changes from the scotopic type to the photopic one. They suggested two possible explanations: (1) upon exposure to bright light a transformation from rod to cone occurs, and (2) there is no change of the visual cells, but only of the bipolars, (see fig. 60).

From the above it seems that either the duplicity theory does not hold for all cases or the duplicity may refer to two systems, the scotopic and the photopic, rather than two structures, the rods and cones.

Moreover, WEALE [1958] concluded that the visual threshold value of a cone equals that of a rod. The difference in sensitivity of the photopic and scotopic systems is probably based on differences in summation of the stimuli rather than properties of the individual rods and cones.

Whatever the case may be, the problem remains to be solved that two visual pigments at the most are responsible for the discrimination of a large number of colours. Only one kind of rod pigment and one kind of cone pigment have ever been isolated. The cone pigment differs from that of the rods only in the properties of the opsins but these do not function as light absorbers, and a quantum once absorbed does no more than effect stereoisomerization of the chromophore regardless of the energy content of the quantum. The colour discrimination therefore cannot be a function of the protein proper. The only possible way in which one and the same pigment is capable of discriminating between colours requires (1) a provision which takes care of the quanta selection, and (2) an arrangement by which visual cells, adapted to a certain wavelength region, are able to feed their stimulus, separate from those of other cells, into the optic centre where colour perception can be effected. The second requirement is a problem of structure and properties of the nervous system and so does not fit into the field under discussion. Therefore only the first possibility will be considered.

There are three ways in which a wavelength region can be selected, namely: (1) by selective absorption of other wavelengths (2) by refraction, and (3) by interference. The first way is analogous to using coloured filters, the second one to using a prism and the third one to employing a diffraction grating.

The selection of spectral regions by using coloured filters does seem to occur in the retinae of chicken, certain other birds and in turtles. In this type of retina WALD [1953b] observed the presence of oil globules which contain carotenoids of different colours, namely light-yellow, orange, and red, and also colourless ones. These droplets, "chromatophanes", were suggested to function as light filters enabling colour vision. The colourless ones were assumed to act as absorbers of UV radiation. However such oil globules are not found in the retinae of other vertebrates.

Reflection, possibly in combination with refraction phenomena, may play a role. The reflection properties of the cat's eye can be clearly observed at night. Still there is no experimental evidence favouring such an hypothesis as yet.

Finally, interference was suggested as the means of colour discrimination in the presence of only a single pigment, (for instance ENOCH [1960] and MYERS [1962]). The diameter of the visual cells is of the order of the wavelength of visible light and so they could act as waveguides. Hence the light which is transmitted by these cells may not be uniformly distributed but forming an interference pattern or "mode transmission". This mode depends upon the form and the dimensions of the photoreceptive cells. If such a mechanism could work, there is no reason to consider the cones as the only receptors affiliated with colour vision for, as WEALE [1958] remarked, the cones of the human fovea are more rod-like than the rods are.

So far, only the colour-vision receptors have been discussed. But the visual process involves much more than the consequences of absorption of different wavelengths. An intricate nervous system operates between light absorption and perception. This is easily demonstrated by applying a pressure to the eyeball in darkness when one sees colours without any light absorption.

There are many theories of colour perception and only a brief survey can be made there. For greater detail, see for example, TEEVAN and BIRNEY [1961] and MARRIOTT [1962]. Theories of colour vision which have been proposed fall into three groups: the trichromatic type, the opponent-process type, and the zone or stage type.

The trichromatic or Young-Helmholtz theory is based on colour matching. It states that any colour achieved by some spectral energy distribution can be matched by a mixture of three "primaries". These primaries must be chosen so that the colour impression due to one of them cannot be obtained by any mixture of the other two primaries. Two different spectral energy distributions that produce the same colour impression are said to constitute a metameric match. In physical terms, colour matching can be understood on the basis of three independent colour receptor systems in the photoreceptor layer. There has been a lot of speculation on how these systems differ from each other. The most obvious hypothesis suggests the presence of three visual pigments.

Evidence for the occurrence of three pigments in the human fovea was obtained by RUSHTON [1961]. By measuring reflectivity in monochromatic light before and after bleaching with a bright beam focussed on the fovea, he concluded to the presence of three photosensitive pigments, termed chlorolabe, erythrolabe and cyanolabe. These results were confirmed by BROWN and WALD [1963] who also studied the monkey retina.

It has already been pointed out that these pigments have never been isolated, although the reason for this failure is not clear. One may wonder whether three kinds of photopsins which are denatured upon extraction might be responsible for the formation of three visual pigments with the same chromophore. The pigments may be distributed one by one over three types of photoreceptor cells originally assumed to be cones, or these types may contain pigment mixtures of different composition. Each type of cone is assumed to be connected with its own nerve fibre, while each of the cone-fibre systems is responsible for the perception of one of the fundamental colours: red, green, and blue. Nearly simultaneously, MARKS *et al.* [1964] and BROWN and WALD [1964] obtained evidence of the occurrence of three types of cones in the parafoveal region of the retinae of primates and man respectively. Each type was found to show maximum sensitivity for one of the mentioned colours.

Without going into details, it is mentioned that a theory was suggested on the basis of tetrachromatic effects in the perifery of the retina due to differences in light adaptation of rods and cones. This theory does not essentially differ from the trichromatic one. A fundamentally different "chromatic" hypothesis is the polychromatic or Hartridge theory, which is based on the existence of seven types of receptors.

The opponent-colour or Hering theory assumes that colour vision is based on three pairs of visual processes, each of them associated with a particular sensory phenomenon. The partners of a pair are antagonistic, both physiologically and sensorily. The three pairs are associated with the following colours: red-green, yellow-blue, and white black. The opposing characters of these pairs was suggested to be based on opposite reactions of the pigments to light, namely by anabolic and catabolic processes. This idea assumes that positive and negative neural responses can occur, and so emphasizes the role of the nervous system to some extent. A modernized version of the Hering theory has been formulated by HURVICH and JAMESON [1961].

The zone or stage theories include elements from both the Young-Helmholtz and Hering conceptions. These theories combine the receptor responses proper with a recording of the stimuli by neural processes. Various investigations suggest that the chromaticity and the luminicity of the image are handled separately in this recording (WALRAVEN [1962]).

In conclusion it can be stated that the basic visual processes are likely to be the same for scotopic and photopic vision and seem to be satisfactorily understood, while colour vision needs much further research.

6

Phototaxis

1 Introduction

Phototaxis is defined as the light-induced motion or change of motion of a free biological object. This body may be either an entire organism or a cellular constituent. Two kinds of phototaxis are distinguished: topophototaxis and phobophototaxis, and each of these may be either positive or negative.

With topophototaxis the direction of motion is determined by the direction of the light beam. If the object moves towards the light source, the taxis is said to be positive. If the object flees from the light source, the motion is considered negative.

KUHN [1929] recognised three kinds of topophototaxis in animals, namely (1) tropophototaxis, (2) telophototaxis, and (3) menophototaxis. In tropophototaxis, a bilaterally symmetrical organism orients itself in a symmetric position relative to the light beam. Such an orientation may be parallel or perpendicular to such a beam. If parallel, the organism may move towards the light source, that is show a positive taxis, or away if negatively phototactic. With telophototaxis, the image of a light spot, or a light field differing in intensity from that of the surroundings, is fixated with the eyes, and the direction of locomotion is corrected in such a way that the image remains focussed on the same fixation spot of the retina. Menophototaxis consists of the maintainance of a certain stimulus pattern on the retina, and so the organism is capable of orienting itself according to the spatial distribution of the light intensity.

In the case of phobophototaxis, the object moves in a direction which is not related to that of the light beam. The direction of motion is determined by the condition and organization of the object. The phenomenon is a "boundary" effect, for the object shows a shock reaction on reaching the boundary between two light fields of different intensity, intensity zero included. The effect is to cause the object to change so that the boundary is not crossed. If the shock reaction occurs on crossing the boundary from a bright to a dim field, the phobophototaxis is called positive. On the contrary, if the direction of motion is changed at leaving a dim region and entering a bright one, the process is termed negative. The locomotion of the object may be entirely at random when in the dark or in the light. In case of positive phobophototaxis, the objects present in the bright field do not enter the dark field. The objects moving around in the latter field may accidentally cross the boundary without being prevented from doing so by a shock reaction. The overall effect therefore consists of accumulation of the objects in the field which is brighter than its surroundings, which thus functions as a light trap or "preferendum". Negative phobophototaxis would result in the emptying of such a field.

In practice, it is sometimes difficult to find out which kind of phototaxis one is dealing with. The phenomenon of photokinesis, that is the effect of light intensity on the rate of motion may seriously interfere with phototaxis. Photokinesis will not be considered any further in this section.

Phototaxis of one and the same object may change from positive to negative and *vice versa* under certain conditions. One of these conditions depends on the light intensity itself. In dim light as a rule, an object shows positive phototaxis, whereas it reacts negatively in bright light. At an intermediate intensity range, no phototactic reaction may occur at all.

Apart from the above classification, which is based on the description of motion, one may distinguish between kinds of phototaxis according to the nature of the photoreceptive system. There are systems of widely differing types, among which, strange as it seems, are a visual and a photosynthetic one.

2 The phototactic pigments

The pigments active in phototaxis belong to various classes. Phototactic action spectra have been established, but these have not always led to identification of the pigments. In most cases these pigments only represent a minor fraction of the total of coloured compounds present in the object, and so isolation and accumulation is often difficult. Consequently one has to rely upon action spectra as a tool for obtaining information about the pigments. The following pigments are known, or believed to participate in phototaxis.

Chlorophyll-a. This pigment (see fig. 16) is active for instance in the phobophototaxis of Cyanophyceae, (see NULTSCH [1962a, b]).

Biliproteins. C-phycocyanin and B-(C)-phycoerythrin, (fig. 36) according to the same author, operate in both topophototaxis and phobophototaxis of Cyanophyceae.

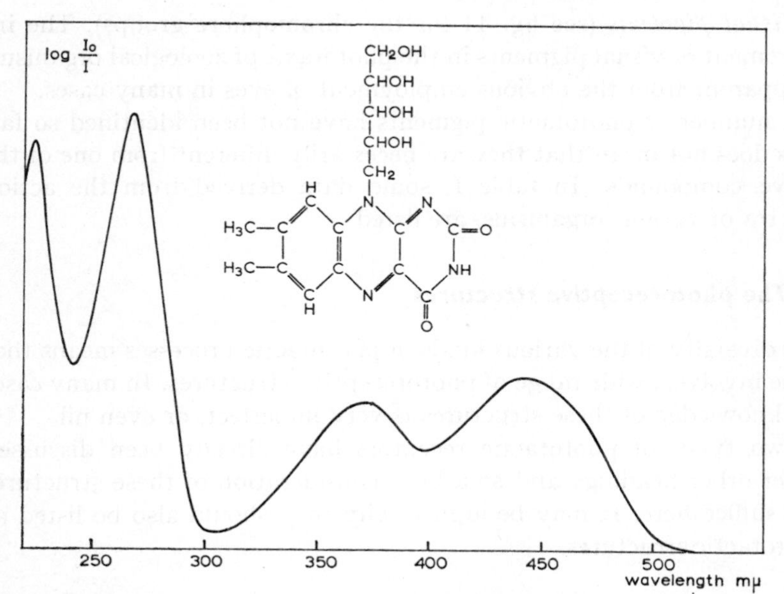

Fig. 64. Riboflavin. Structural formula and absorption spectrum in distilled water

Carotenoids (fig. 31). A carotenoprotein was observed to function in the topophototaxis of *Platymonas subcordiformis* by HALLDAL [1961a]. As a possible active carotenoid, hydroxy-echinenone was mentioned by this author. β-carotene was suggested to function as a phototactic pigment in the eye-spot of *Euglena* by WOLKEN [1961b]. On the other hand, NULTSCH [1962a] stated that the activity of carotenoids is not clearly established in the phobophototaxis of Cyanophyceae.

Riboflavin. This pigment, $C_{17}H_{20}N_4O_6$, (fig. 64) is most probably the mediator of the negative phobophototaxis in bright light of chloroplasts in the alga *Vaucheria sessilis*. This conclusion was reached by HAUPT and SCHÖNFELD [1962] and is based on the very close resemblance of the phototactic action spectrum with the absorption spectrum of riboflavin.

Phytochrome. According to HAUPT [see 1960] this pigment is responsible for the dim-light phobophototaxis of *Mougeotia* chloroplasts. Some of the properties of this largely unknown pigment will be discussed under photomorphogenesis.

Bacteriochlorophyll (fig. 18) according to MANTEN [1948] is active in the phobophototaxis of purple bacteria.

Visual pigments (see fig. 44 for the chromophore groups). The involvement of visual pigments in the phototaxis of zoological organisms is apparent from the obvious employment of eyes in many cases.

A number of phototactic pigments have not been identified so far. This does not mean that they are necessarily different from one of the above compounds. In table I, some data derived from the action spectra of various organisms, are listed.

3 The photoreceptive structures

The diversity of the various kinds of phototactic processes means that these involve a wide range of photoreceptive structures. In many cases our knowledge of these structures is very imperfect, or even nil.

Two types of phototactic receptors have already been discussed under other headings and so a brief consideration of these structures will suffice here. It may be argued why they should also be listed as phototactic structures.

3.1 The eye

For structural data, see fig. 59. In some cases the eye functions in a phototactic process. One may wonder why a distinction should be made between seeing and phototaxis since both types of process make use of the eye. The answer is that the interplay of light perception and physiological processes differs in the two kinds of phenomenon. If, for instance, a bird sees his meal, he will approach and pick it up. It does not matter from which side he looks at it. This is vision, or rather, seeing. On the other hand, supposing that the same bird is a migrating one, his navigation when he migrates depends on at least two phenomena: (1) light perception, and (2) the so-called "chronometer factor" (see MATTHEWS [1955]). This factor has the function of an internal physiological

TABLE 1

Some approximate data on non-identified phototactic pigments*

absorption		half-width value of action region (mμ)	sign of photo taxis	type of photo taxis	source	reference
major maximum (mμ)	shoulder or minor maximum (mμ)					
495	425 450 480	...	+	topo	*Euglena gracilis*, green	BÜNNING and SCHNEIDERHÖHN [1956]
415	450 480 510	...	–	phobo	*Euglena gracilis*, green	BÜNNING and SCHNEIDERHÖHN [1956]
480	420 610	...	+	topo	*Euglena gracilis*, green	WOLKEN and SHIN [1958]
410	425	...	+	topo	*Euglena*, chlorophyll-free	GÖSSEL [1957]
410	449 476	10	–	phobo	*Euglena*, chlorophyll-free	GÖSSEL [1957]
493	435	115	+, –	topo	*Platymonas subcordiformis*	HALLDAL [1958b]
493	435	100	+, –	topo	*Dunaliella salina*	HALLDAL [1958b]
493	435	105	+, –	topo	*Stephanoptera gracilis*	HALLDAL [1958b]
485	435	85	+	topo	*Ulva* gametes	HALLDAL [1958b]
475	...	65	+	topo	*Peridinium trochoideum*	HALLDAL [1958b]
475	...	65	+	topo	*Goniaulax catenella*	HALLDAL [1958b]
570	...	45	+	topo	*Provocentrum micans*	HALLDAL [1958b]
385	?	90 ?	+	topo	*Phormidium spec.*	NULTSCH [1962b]
450	380 485	105	all strophes	phobo	*Lemna trisulca*, chloroplasts	ZURZYCKI [1962a]
483	425	65	–	phobo	*Mougeotia*, chloroplasts	HAUPT and SCHÖNBOHM [1962]

* Major and minor maxima may refer to different pigments.

"clock" which enables the bird to adjust the direction of flying in such a way that, although the sun or the stars are observed at continuously changing positions, the migratory track is still followed. Since the direction of flight is ultimately determined relative to a light source, this phenomenon should be classified as phototaxis.

Another type of phototaxis is found in arthropods. Certain species are capable of orientation with the aid of the polarization direction of the incident light (see STOCKHAMMER [1959]). For example, bees are able to orient themselves relative to the polarization pattern of the sky, (see VON FRISCH *et al.* [1960]). The polarization of the incident light is analyzed by the anisotropic rhabdome in which rhodopsin molecules are supposed to be arranged symmetrically in a radial way. Such an analyzing capacity was demonstrated by means of an electrophysiological technique by BURKHARDT and WENDLER [1960]. These authors inserted micro-electrodes into retinula cells of *Calliphora,* and observed that rotation of the polarization plane of the incident light resulted in changes of the light-induced potentials of these cells. Since the polarization pattern of the incident light is ultimately "translated" into intensity differences in the photoreceptive compounds, this type of orientation should be considered to be phototaxis.

3.2 *Chloroplasts and related structures*

For chloroplasts and related structures see fig. 40. In cases in which the phototaxis action spectrum coincides with the absorption spectrum of chlorophylls, the photosynthetic structures are taken to be the photoreceptive organelles of phototaxis as well. In this respect it would be interesting to know whether the structure of the photosynthetic apparatus found in purple bacteria has any effect on the phototactic behaviour. This is because these organisms have chromatophores, free grana, or a combination of these organelles.

The photoreceptor for certain phototactic movements of chloroplasts appears to be located outside of the chloroplasts. As such receptors are found to be distributed throughout the cell, they may be tentatively termed:

3.3 *Dispersed phototactic receptors*

These were studied in cells of the alga *Mougeotia* which contain a single large flat chloroplast. The dimensions of such a chloroplast are slightly less than the length and the diameter of the cylindrical algal cell. HAUPT [1959a] concluded that the photoreceptive pigment, responsible for the "dim-light" or positive phototaxis of these chloroplasts is identical with phytochrome. By illuminating only a small spot of either the chloroplast or the cytoplasm, HAUPT [1962] demonstrated that the phototactic pigment is localized in the cytoplasm. HAUPT and BOCK [1962] obtained evidence that the phytochrome molecules are oriented in a spiral pattern in the rather viscous cytoplasmic layer adjoining the cell wall. The slope of the spiral lies at 45 °C to the long axis of the cell. More data about the structure of this spiral are not available as yet. According to HAUPT and THIELE [1961], the same type of chloroplast is encountered in the alga *Mesotaenium*.

3.4 *The eyespot*

Many forms of eyespots, also termed "stigmata", occur among flagellates. The stigma is a pigment organelle consisting of coloured globules which contain carotenoids, as far as known, for example, β-carotene was observed in the *Euglena* eyespot (see WOLKEN [1961b]). MAST [1928] described a number of eyespots of different shape. In some cases, for example in *Chlamydomonas*, the stigma is accompanied by a lens-like body. A schematic picture of the phototactic organelle in *Euglena* is shown in fig. 65. The stigma is located near to a gullet which is in contact with the environment. It encloses the lower part of the flagellum. At the basal end the flagellum is swollen and it is anchored by one or more roots which are connected to the bottom of the gullet. The interior part of the gullet is broadened to the so-called "reservoir". Such details, however, have never been recorded in other phototactic flagellates.

The structure of the *Euglena* stigma was extensively studied by WOLKEN [1961b, c]. The orange-red globules which compose the stigma are packed closely, but at random. Their diameter ranges from 100 to 300 mμ. Electron microscopical observations give a slight indication that the globules contain lamellae. Between the layer of globules and the membrane of the flagellum-containing structure, fibrillae are found. As the phototactic action spectrum more or less resembled the absorption spectrum of the stigma carotenoids, the eyespot was considered to be the phototactic receptor. On the other hand, GÖSSEL [1957] arrived at the conclusion that the negative phobophototaxis of *Euglena* does not require the presence of an eyespot. This author worked with two chlorophyll-free mutants, one in which the stigma was present and in the other one it was absent. Both of them were negatively phototactic. Under the phase-contrast microscope the flagellum showed a swelling at its base. As a related flagellate, *Astasia longa*, is not capable of phototaxis and its flagellum does not show a swollen base, Gössel suggested, in agreement with earlier authors, (for example HALLDAL [1958b]), that the phototactic receptor is located in the basal swelling of the flagellum. It was also observed by this author that light of wavelengths longer than 530 mμ is unable to evoke phototaxis in *Euglena*, though it is absorbed by the stigmal pigments. Therefore he suggested that the function of the stigma is restricted to periodically shading the photoreceptor, the periodicity of the shading being a result of the rotatory motion of the organism.

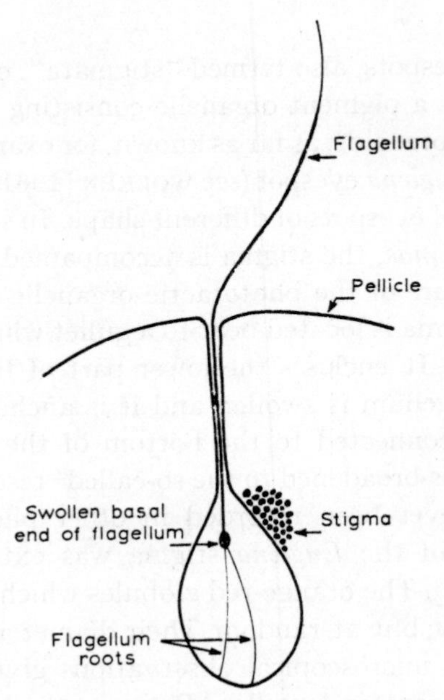

Fig. 65. Schematic picture of the phototropic organelle of the flagellate *Euglena*

This seems to be contradictory to the fact that WOLKEN [1961b] observed a resemblance between the absorption spectrum of the stigma and the phototactic action spectrum. However, this action spectrum referred to positive phototaxis and the possibility that positive and negative phototaxis may be different processes will be discussed in the next section.

3.5 The paraflagellar body

There is little information about the structure of the swollen base of the flagellum in which the photoreceptor is possibly located. CHADEFAUD and PROVASOLI [1938–1939] suggested that in a *Euglena* strain, this photoreceptor is not actually located within the flagellar base, but in a separate structure, the "paraflagellar body" which is in rather close contact with the flagellum. According to them this body consists of two parts, a greyish "chromophobic" and a black "chromophilic" one. These authors also assumed that the paraflagellar body is connected with the eyespot by cytoplasmatic strands. However, it seems more likely that such a connection would link the paraflagellar body and the membrane of the reservoir.

Since the flagellum is the phototactic effector in flagellate organisms, a few words may be added about its structure. Further details for the *Euglena* flagellum are given in WOLKEN [1961b]. In this alga, two flagella of different lengths occur. The longer one serves the purpose of locomotion and its diameter ranges from 250 to 400 mμ. It is built up of eleven pairs of axonemata, or filaments. Nine of these pairs are arranged peripherically and the remaining two pairs occur centrally. The filaments are surrounded by a matrix substance which, in its turn, is enclosed by a membrane. From this membrane, thin fibrils called mastigonemata emerge. These fibrils may function in enlarging the effect of the flagellar sweep.

4 The nature of the process

What has been said of the divergent nature of the phototactic structures can also be said of that of the various phototactic reactions. In addition, most of the concepts of the primary phototactic processes are based on hypotheses rather than direct evidence.

Phototactic reactions initiated by visual processes, such as the orientation of birds and arthropods in light fields, will not be discussed here since the photoreaction involved is the visual one already described under Vision. The factors that make a phototactic reaction out of it are neural processes and belong under neurophysiology or even psychology. When considering other types of phototactic processes, one may distinguish:

4.1 Bacterial phototaxis

This taxis, first observed by ENGELMANN [1888], is of the phobic type.

MANTEN [1948] concluded that the phototactic shock reaction of the bipolarly flagellated purple bacterium *Rhodospirillum rubrum* is very likely to be mediated by a sudden decrease of the rate of photosynthesis. CLAYTON [1953a, b] arrived at the same conclusion. CLAYTON [1953c] also studied various features of bacterial phototaxis, such as all-or-none response, refractoriness, recovery, summation, accomodation, and rhythmicity. The results agreed fairly well with such features of other irritable, for instance, neural systems. He therefore put forward the hypothesis that a common mechanism for irritability underlies all excitable systems. LINKS [1955] was the first to find a possible mechanism. He inferred that a tactic response would result from a sudden decrease in concentration of the energy-supplying substance in the motor apparatus. HOFFMAN-BERLING [1954, 1955] stated that ATP functions as the energy source for rhythmic contraction of isolated spermatozoan flagella as well as for the contractility of trypanosomes, and so Links suggested that this substance, which also acts in muscle contraction, is the energy source for phototaxis.

This hypothesis is supported by the results of a number of other studies, of which only that by TIBBS [1957] will be mentioned. This author measured the rate of the disappearance of ATP in suspensions of *Polytoma* flagella. He found that in a system with two flagella, the energy released by this process per second is 15 times that needed to move a spherical cell with a diameter of 10 μ at a speed of 100 μ/sec. in water at 20 °C.

This proposal by Links considers only a peripherically located process and does not take into account the occurrence of a possible "central agency" for coordinating tactic responses. CLAYTON [1958] pointed out the necessity for such a mechanism. He argued that in the bipolarly flagellated bacteria a central coordination of the activities of both flagella is needed to prevent the organism from getting "stuck", instead of carrying out a phototactic response. Moreover he concluded from experiments on the suppression of phototaxis by thiol inhibitors that the cooperation of sulfhydryl groups is required for the synthesis of the energy-yielding compound.

4.2 *Phototaxis of flagellates*

Particularly in the case of these organisms, it has become clear that positive and negative phototaxes are different processes. BÜNNING and SCHNEIDERHÖHN [1956] and BÜNNING and TAZAWA [1957] observed that constant illumination of the *Euglena* photoreceptor results in the establishment of negative phobic phototaxis, and this reaction becomes positive only on periodical shading of the photoreceptive structure. This shading results from the presence of the eyespot and its periodicity is due to the rotatory motion of the organism. According to HALLDAL [1958b], the action spectra for positive and negative phototaxis of the same species of Volvocales, and most probably of Dinophyceae, are identical.

Bünning, in BÜNNING and GÖSSEL [1959], disagreed with this conclusion for *Euglena* and said that the action spectra for negative phototaxis of light- and dark-adapted *Euglenas* are different from each other. Therefore environmental conditions may affect the phototactic pigment systems or their composition.

The chemical composition of the medium is of considerable importance to phototaxis. HALLDAL [1957] found that in *Platymonas subcordiformis*, the sign of phototaxis can be reversed by a change of the Ca^{++}/Mg^{++} ratio of the medium. Ca^{++} causes a negative phototaxis and Mg^{++} a positive one in light of the same intensity. HALLDAL [1959] established that the K^{+} ion also takes part in this balance and stated that the effects of Mg^{++} and Ca^{++} differ from those of K^{+}. Mg^{++} and Ca^{++} are required for motion, while K^{+} affects the motility, the phototactic activity, and the mode of response. The presence of carbon dioxide, oxygen or the total gas pressure have no influence on phototaxis.

The antagonistic effects of these divalent metal ions are known to occur with ATP-ase activity (see NEEDHAM [1952]). Therefore HALLDAL [1958b] suggested that the hypothesis of Links which was discussed above, also holds for the phototaxis of motile algae. There is, however, a basic difference between the two conceptions of the mechanism: Links assumed that phototaxis is mediated by a sudden decrease of the ATP concentration in the flagellum, whereas Halldal proposed that the ATP-ase activity is changed. It is evident that if the ATP concentration is below optimum, a concentration dependency of the process will occur. In this case, photosynthesis being an ATP producer will influence phototaxis. If photosynthesis cannot be involved, as is the case with chlorophyll-free mutants of *Euglena* (GÖSSEL [1957]), the required ATP has to be generated by other metabolic processes. It should be added that the reversal of the phototactic sign seen in the brine alga *Platymonas* and other salt water forms, could not be obtained with *Chlamydomonas moewisii*.

This disagreement between the ideas of Bünning, see also BÜNNING and SCHNEIDERHÖHN [1956], and HALLDAL [1958b] concerning the coincidence of the action spectra of positive and negative phototaxis is explained by the latter author in terms of distortion of Bünning's results on negative phototaxis by photosynthesis. HALLDAL [1961b] obtained an indication that two light processes are involved in inducing phototactic response changes in *Platymonas*. One of these is most probably photosynthesis while a pigment system resembling phytochrome may be active in the other.

Brief mention should be made of the two types of phototaxis. HALLDAL [1960] and NULTSCH [1962a] stated that topo- and phobophototaxis are two different processes which are possibly operated along different metabolic pathways. Since no data about differences in the mechanism are available, this problem will not be dealt with here, except by mentioning two statements by Nultsch. He pointed to the fact that the reactions differ in (1) energy requirement, and (2) spectral sensitivity. The two types of phototaxis may interfere with each other.

In certain cases, for example in *Euglena,* and under adequate light conditions, a phobotaxis is seen which causes orientation of the organism according to the direction of the light beam. This effect is due to the fact that summation of periodic intensity changes occurs at a single site in the cell, namely the photoreceptor. Such a phenomenon is termed "pseudotopophototaxis". As the mechanism of this process is identical with that of the phobophototaxis, it will not be considered any further here.

4.3 Phototaxis of chloroplasts

In this type of phototaxis the arrangement of chloroplasts in the cell is changed by the action of light. In cells with chloroplasts which are small compared with the dimensions of the cell, this rearrangement means a search for the position which coincides with the locus of favourable, or less unfavourable, light intensity. The positions of such chloroplasts are given terms such as "parastrophe" – arrangement along the cell walls parallel with the light beam – and other "-strophes". However the optical condition of the cell may render such morphological terms unsuitable for physiological considerations. HAUPT [1959b] therefore proposed to use the terms "bright-light arrangement", "dim-light arrangement" and "dark arrangement" with regard to the phototactic reactions of chloroplasts. Such a nomenclature has another advantage by also covering reactions of the large single chloroplast in algal cells like those of *Mougeotia*. In such cells, the phototactic reaction consists of a rotation of the chloroplast around its long axis. In dim light, the chloroplast orients itself perpendicularly to the incident beam, while in bright light a parallel orientation occurs.

Although much research on chloroplast movements has been done, the nature of the process still is far from clear. ZURZYCKI [1962b] reviewed the hypotheses on the mechanism of the chloroplast reactions. He emphasized the highly hypothetical and incomplete character of these theories. For a critical survey, reference is made to Zurzycki's paper. At present it will suffice to list the various proposed mechanisms in order to demonstrate the divergency of opinions. The following agents are considered to be possibly responsible for the phototactic motion of chloroplasts: (1) reaction of the peristromium, (2) differences in surface tension along the chloroplasts, (3) electrokinetic forces, (4) pulling of cytoplasmic fibres, (5) plasmatic impulses, and (6) passive transport due to cytoplasmic streaming. Thus some of the theories suggest that the driving force is produced within the chloroplast, and others that this force originates in the cytoplasm. In fact it is true that light may bring about changes in both structures. For instance, MOHR [1956] observed that blue light induced an increase of the chloroplast volume in the protonemata of the fern *Dryopteris filix mas* while red light caused a decrease of this volume. Evidence of light effects in the cytoplasm has been obtained by various authors. As an example, ZURZYCKI [1960] observed in centrifugation experiments with *Lemna* cells that the viscosity of the cytoplasm depends on the light condition. Such effects will be considered in some more detail under photodinesis.

It may be that the driving force is produced in both the cytoplasm and the chloroplast. If this is true, a duality in the phototaxis of chloroplasts would occur. A dual character in this reaction was noticed by ZURZYCKI and ZURZYCKA [1955] who studied the influence of some catalyst poisons. They concluded that in *Lemna trisulca* two types of phototactic reactions can be distinguished. One of these seems to depend on photosynthesis in a direct way, whereas the other is related to the "capability for photosynthesis" rather than photosynthesis proper. According to HAUPT and SCHÖNBOHM [1962], the difference in action spectra for positive and negative phototaxis of *Mougeotia* chloroplasts as well as the difference in the after-effects of irradiation demonstrate that two different mechanisms may operate in these processes. It should be stressed however that the present discussion does not intend to suggest that the two reactions take place at different loci in the cell.

ZURZYCKI [1962b] gave a general statement of the problem by saying that each motion of a chloroplast reflects a disturbance of the equilibrium of forces acting between the plastid and its surroundings. Such a disturbance is caused by a change in the energy distribution in the cell. Since ATP is the most important energy "distributor" in the living cell, this compound may be the major, and possibly exclusive, mediator of chloroplast phototaxis. As ATP is produced in photosynthesis and may leak through the plastid membrane, the relation between chloroplast phototaxis and photosynthesis is understandable. However, if the ATP hypothesis, which is still highly speculative, were right, it seems to explain only part of the phototactic processes in the chloroplast. For as HAUPT [see 1962] stated, phytochrome acts as the photoreceptor for positive phototaxis of the *Mougeotia* chloroplast, but is located in the cytoplasm. In which way, and even whether, the reaction initiated by the excitation of this pigment can be related with the ATP hypothesis is far from clear at the present time.

Much more research is needed for the understanding of the phototactic reactions. For more detailed reviews of the numerous phototaxis studies, see CLAYTON [1959], HAUPT [1959b, c] and ZURZYCKI [1962b].

7

Photokinesis

1 *Introduction*

Photokinesis is generally defined as the light-induced change of motility of an organism. If such a change consists of a motility increase, the photokinesis is called positive while negative photokinesis means a decrease of motility below the dark value.

According to MAST [1926] who studied photokinesis with *Volvox*, this reaction consists of a change in rate, amplitude and vibrational mode of the flagellar sweep. The direction of the sweep is not affected.

Photokinesis only deals with the rate of motility. The spatial distribution of a population of photokinetically active organisms will therefore not be changed by light action as it is in phototaxis, although the two phenomena may be related. LUNTZ [1931] found that the threshold values of photokinesis and phototaxis of the motile algae *Eudorina*, *Volvox* and *Chlamydomonas* are intimately related and the action spectra have proved to be nearly identical.

2 *The photokinetic pigments*

Chlorophyll-a. According to NULTSCH [1962b, c], this pigment is active in photokinesis in some species of the Cyanophycea *Phormidium*. WOLKEN and SHIN [1958] noticed a band in the photokinetic action spectrum for *Euglena gracilis* at 630 mμ. According to WOLKEN [1961b], the presence of this band suggests that a porphyrin-like molecule – perhaps chlorophyll – is active in photokinesis. As no measurements were performed between 630 and 700 mμ, it may quite well be that chlorophyll is involved, the actual band peak occuring around 680 mμ.

Carotenoids? The photokinetic action spectrum for *Euglena gracilis*, established by WOLKEN and SHIN [1958], shows a band at 465 mμ. The authors suggested that this band is due to carotenoid activity and speculated that the carotenoid could be β-carotene. The identification of this pigment, however, has not yet been accomplished. The shape of the band in question was determined only by measurements at four wavelengths with spacings of about 20 mμ. NULTSCH [1962c], on the other hand, denied the involvement of carotenoids, or stated that carotenoid activity, if any, is very low [1962b]. On consideration of these action spectra, the present author is inclined to prefer the latter conclusion.

Biliproteins? NULTSCH [1962b, c] came to the same conclusion for phycobilin action on the rate of swimming as he did for carotenoids. Three species of *Phormidium* showed a minor band in the action spectrum around 620 mμ and this was ascribed to the vibrational band of chlorophyll-a. It does seem that in the case of *Phormidium autumnale* the intensity of the 620 mμ band exceeds that of the minor chlorophyll-a maximum. It seems more likely that phycocyanin is involved in photokinesis to some degree. This conclusion is also suggested in one of NULTSCH's papers [1962c), though it is rejected in a second one [1962b]. Actually, with *Phormidium* "spec." the phycocyanin activity is only extremely small, if present at all.

A non-identified pigment. With the same three species of *Phormidium*, NULTSCH [1962b, c] observed a pronounced photokinetic effect in the far-blue and UV region. A distinct maximum of the action spectrum was found at 390 mμ. The pigment, or pigment mixture, was not identified.

3 The photokinetic structures and the nature of the process

No actual data on these topics are available. The effectors are the same as those in phototaxis but there is no evidence of the receptor structures. One may even wonder whether a photoreceptor in the conventional sense occurs. Chlorophyll-a was found to be involved in the photokinesis of some organisms. As soon as light is absorbed by this pigment, photosynthesis starts. However, at least in some cases, a delay was observed between the onset of illumination and the change of motility which might be interpreted in terms of a diffusion of photosynthetically formed mediating agents from the photosynthetic apparatus towards the photokinetic effector. Such an agent might be photosynthetically generated oxygen. NULTSCH [1956] stated that in diatoms the photokinetic activity is due in part to oxygen liberated in photosynthesis, and thus part of the motility phenomenon is "aerokinesis" rather than true photokinesis. However it was not possible to replace the light effect entirely by saturating the suspension with air. Therefore could another photosynthetically produced compound, perhaps ATP, also be involved? If this is the case, photokinesis would be mediated by a change in the cell metabolism rather than the excitation of a typical photokinesis receptor. On the other hand, the shape of the photokinetic action spectra made NULTSCH [1962c] doubt whether photosynthesis is the only process involved in photokinesis. Unfortunately, the motility action spectra were only compared with absorption spectra. Comparison with photosynthesis action spectra might help to form conclusions in this respect.

LUNTZ [1932] proposed a duplicity theory for photokinesis. He suggested that the change from positive to negative photokinesis, and *vice versa,* can be explained by assuming the occurrence of two simultaneous processes, each with a different intensity dependency. No proposal was made as to the actual nature of these processes.

Many studies have been made in this field, though the majority of these are descriptive rather than informative about the basic nature of the process. References, giving access to these investigations will be found in the papers discussed.

8

Photodinesis

1 Introduction

Photodinesis is defined as the effect of light on protoplasmic streaming. Such an effect may be of a two-fold nature: the rate of streaming as well as the "intensity of streaming", that is the amount of protoplasm transported per unit area and time, can be changed by light action. Moreover, two types of cytoplasmic response may occur. The reaction to illumination may be only temporary, or alternatively it is permanent. In the first case, the effect is of a stimulatory character, and in the second case it is "tonic" (see HAUPT [1959d]).

Light may accelerate or retard protoplasmic streaming, that is cause positive or negative photodinesis. Protoplasmic streaming is measured by determining the displacement of cytoplasmic inclusions, such as chloroplasts and mitochondria. For a discussion on protoplasmic streaming as such, reference is made to a review by KAMIYA [1960].

A discussion of the early studies on photodinesis is given by BOTTELIER [1934]. HAUPT [1959d] also reviewed the more recent papers. The evaluation and comparison of some of these papers is difficult because of differences in the conditions before and during the measurements, the intensity and purity of the light, and the use of several organisms. In some cases the results with one and the same plant species obtained by two investigators are contradictory. Only a few papers yield information which is of particular interest with regard to the present discussion and only these will be considered.

According to ZURZYCKI [1951], under adequate conditions, the rate of protoplasmic streaming in green leaves of *Elodea densa* is oxygen-dependent. If these leaves were kept anaerobically and in the dark, the protoplasm ceased to flow. Subsequent introduction of air resulted in re-establishment of this streaming in the dark. However, the re-establishment could also be effected by illumination under anaerobic conditions. Therefore, the oxygen evolved in photosynthesis may well re-animate the protoplasmic streaming. If this conclusion is correct, such effect is an aerodinetic, rather than a photodinetic phenomenon, and will not be discussed further.

2 The photodinetic pigments

If for this reason chlorophyll and its accessory pigments active in photosynthesis are not regarded under the present heading, it can be stated that all suggestions concerning the nature of the photodinetic pigments are only speculative. BOTTELIER [1934] established the spectral sensitivity at six wavelengths for the protoplasmic streaming in epidermis cells of *Avena* coleoptiles. In order to avoid photosynthetic effects, etiolated seedlings were used. The data on wavelength dependency, however, are too scanty to yield a reliable action spectrum. Bottelier replotted the action spectrum for phototropism established by BLAAUW [1909], and showed that the data for photodinesis fitted reasonably well with this action spectrum. The values obtained by Bottelier were obtained with epidermis cells situated at distances up to 15 mm from the apex. According to BÜNNING [1955], the carotenoid lutein occurs as the major pigment in the apical region of the *Avena* coleoptile. However, this pigment is believed to function purely as a light screen (see also THORNING [1955]). For the reasons discussed under Phototropism, the function of the actual photoreceptor was ascribed to *riboflavin*.

According to BEIKIRCH [1925], infra-red and near ultraviolet radiation are inactive in effecting photodinesis. SCHWEIKERDT [1928] also stated that infra-red is without any effect and made the interesting observation that spectral regions in the red, green and blue induced protoplasmic streaming in cells of *Vallisneria spiralis*. However the reactions to red and green were only temporary. There was also a temporary reaction in the blue, but in addition in this spectral range a permanent tonic change was observed. The temporary reaction might be due to photosynthesis since the red was most effective while the green was least effective. One may wonder why the effect is only temporary. Might it be that the oxygen gush at the onset of photosynthesis is responsible for its temporary character? In any case, it seems that the tonic reaction in blue light is mediated by a true photodinetic pigment.

3 *The photodinetic structures and the nature of the process*

The structures which are responsible for photodinesis are likely to be located in the cytoplasm, or even to be a part of it. The cytoplasm, even when flowing, displays a certain structure (see FREY-WYSSLING [1957]). It shows both plastic and elastic properties. The relatively thin outer cytoplasmic layer is highly viscous or nearly rigid, while the viscosity of the remaining part of the cytoplasm is lower, and transitions from the gel to the sol state take place. VIRGIN [1949] stated that the rate of the protoplasmic streaming in *Elodea* cells is inversely proportional to the viscosity of the cytoplasm. This relationship is of interest with regard to photodinesis, especially since according to VIRGIN [1951], the cytoplasmic viscosity in *Elodea* cells is instantaneously changed on illumination. The sign of the change depends on the light intensity. At both high and low intensities the viscosity decreases, whereas at medium intensity it increases. The same author [1952, 1954] established the action spectra for the light-induced viscosity changes. This spectrum is located in the blue and there appear to be two peaks, at about 460 and 490 respectively though the author [1954] stated that the two-peaked shape of the action spectrum is still questionable. In fig. 66, Virgin's data are replotted on a different scale together with the data on wavelength dependency established by BOTTELIER [1934]. When considering the fact that both sets of measurements were performed with different objects, namely *Elodea*, and *Avena* coleoptiles, it seems justifiable to conclude that both processes may well be mediated by the same photoreceptor. If this conclusion were right, it would fit nicely into Virgin's conception about the relationship between viscosity and streaming of the cytoplasm. However, even if it were established beyond doubt that a change of viscosity is required to establish cytoplasmic streaming, the nature of the motive force is still unknown.

The data on physics and chemistry of the cytoplasmic streaming were reviewed by KAMIYA [1960]. He found that the general trend in the various assumptions is to consider the boundary between the outer cortical cytoplasmic layer and the inner cytoplasm, the endoplasm, as the site of the driving force. JAROSCH [1957] when studying isolated drops of protoplasm obtained from Characeae under the microscope with dark-field illumination, observed fibrillar structures in the protoplasm. These structures were highly dynamic and appeared and vanished continuously. These fibrils may associate with each other to bundles which, if sufficiently thick, exhibited a wave-like motion. Free fibrils moved along a straight line. The author suggested that cell inclusions, such as chloroplasts and mitochondria, are able to move with the aid of plasmic fibrils attached to their surface. A protoplasmic streaming might be effected by the motion of fibrils more or less aligned along the cortical cytoplasmic layer. VIRGIN [1952] speculated on a possible role of phytohormones in the protoplasmic streaming in

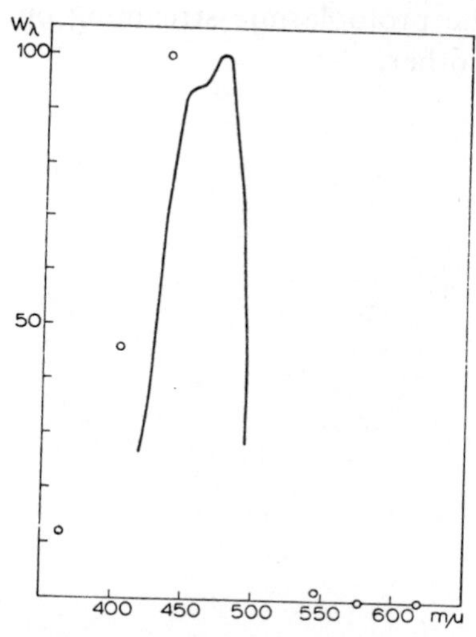

Fig. 66. Wavelength-dependency of protoplasmic streaming (open circles) in epidermis cells of the *Avena sativa* coleoptile, data replotted from BOTTELIER [1934], and protoplasmic viscosity in *Elodea* cells (drawn curve), replotted from the data of VIRGIN [1954]

plant cells. It might be that these compounds act *via* a change of the sol-gel interfaces in the cytoplasm. However the nature of the phytohormone effect is far from clear.

The results obtained by a number of Japanese investigators, also reviewed by KAMIYA [1960], made it clear that (1) ATP in adequate concentration evokes motion in isolated cytoplasmic drops, (2) ATP-dephosphorylating activity is found in *Nitella* protoplasm, and (3) blocking of SH-groups by p-chloromercuribenzoate results in halting the protoplasmic streaming in various objects. WEBER [1958] proposed an hypothesis in which both ATP-dephosphorylation and SH-groups play a role in the chemical processes which might cause the relative shifting of two kinds of filaments, namely actin and L-myosin structures, in the muscle fibres. It was suggested that in this way, muscle contraction can be explained. According to KAMIYA [1960], it is an attractive working hypothesis that the gliding of the cytoplasmic fibrils in plant cells might be due to a shifting force produced in the same way.

The nature of the mechanism underlying protoplasmic streaming is too far removed from photobiological phenomena to be considered in any detail here. The above discussion demonstrates the complete lack of understanding of the link between what is known about the physics and chemistry of the protoplasmic streaming on the one hand, and photodinesis on the other.

9

Phototropism

1 *Introduction*

Phototropism is related to phototaxis in the same way as photodinesis to photokinesis. That is, phototropism deals with the movement of part of an organism, whereas phototaxis is concerned with the motion of the entire organism. Phototropism is thus defined as the light-induced bending of plants or plant organs. The bending may occur towards or away from the light source, or to form a certain angle to the incident beam. These three cases are indicated as positive phototropism, negative phototropism and diaphototropism respectively. Phototropism is mainly encountered in plants, but its occurrence is not restricted to them. This phenomenon has also been observed in sessile lower zoological organisms, such as Bryozoa, see KAISSLING [1962].

Usually, phototropism is due to a difference in growth rate of two opposed sides of a tissue when they are illuminated with light of unequal intensities. This means that such phototropic tissues must be capable of growth, and so only young parts are able to show this type of phototropism. This kind of phototropism is based on a light growth reaction. However fully grown plant tissues may also respond phototropically to light. In this case, the underlying mechanism consists of light-induced turgor changes. In the majority of the latter cases the direction of the light-induced bending is not determined by the light gradient, but by the structure of the reacting tissue, for example, the pulvini of many leguminous leaves. The latter phenomenon is termed "photonasty". As photonasty is to be regarded a special case of phototropism, it will also be dealt with under the present heading.

When discussing phototropism, a few words should first be said about the basic processes because the phototropic reactions may depend on the two entirely different phenomena, growth or turgor. As phototropism is mostly found in plants and has been extensively studied in these organisms, the following discussion is confined to plant phototropism. The following processes can be distinguished.

Light growth reaction. The growth rate of plants is affected by light. This phenomenon shows up most clearly when comparing the lengths of shoots of potatoes sprouted in a dark storage room or grown under daylight conditions. Growth, at least in higher plants depends on two processes, namely (1) cell multiplication, and (2) cell elongation. Basically, the first process does not yield a macroscopical change of the plant shape, but the latter one does. Since the elongation phenomenon is responsible for phototropism, cell division is left out of further consideration here.

Cell elongation is brought about by water intake which depends on osmotic processes. Whether or not these processes are able to produce any change of the dimensions of the cell is determined by the plastic properties of the cell wall. These mechanical features of the cell walls are probably controlled by the action of growth hormones, the auxins. Therefore, the effect of light on the auxin content should be considered.

Light turgor reaction. In contradistinction to the light growth reaction, the turgor phenomena are usually reversible. The tropic movements are brought about by asymmetric turgor changes in the pulvini. One may think of two possible basic processes for producing these light-induced changes, namely variations of (1) the osmotic values of the cells, and (2) permeability. BRAUNER [1959] summarized the reasons, based on experiments concerning phototropic responses of pulvini of *Robinia pseudacacia* in either air or water, favouring the idea that permeability changes are mainly responsible for the light turgor reaction.

For more detailed information on phototropism and photonasty, reference is made to the following elaborate reviews: SCHRANK [1950], BRAUNER [1954, 1959], WENT [1956], GALSTON [1959a], BANBURY [1959], REINERT [1959], PAGE [1962], BRIGGS [1963] and SHROPSHIRE [1963].

2 The phototropic pigments

The nature of the phototropic pigment(s) in most cases has not yet been established beyond doubt. The candidate compounds are considered below.

2.1 Riboflavin and related compounds

Synonyms for riboflavin are: lactoflavin and vitamin B_2. For structural formula and absorption spectrum of riboflavin in aqueous solution see fig. 64. This pigment is considered to be active in phototropism for

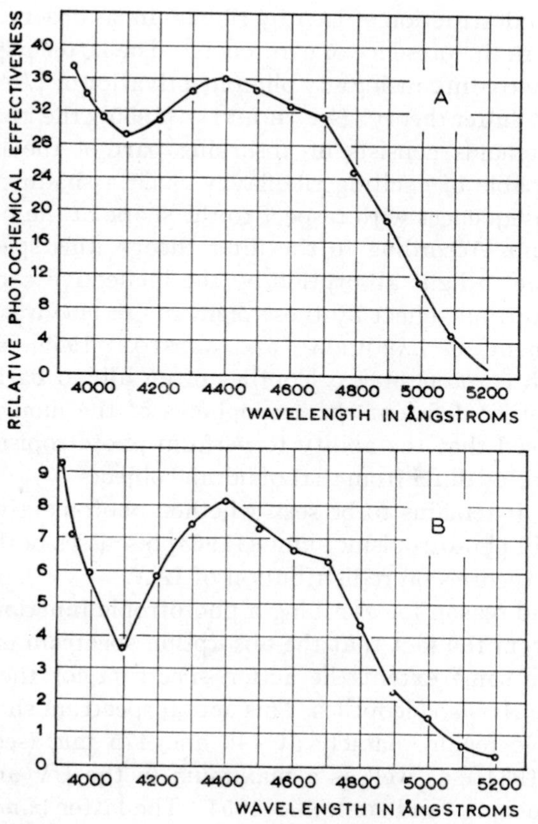

Fig. 67. Action spectra of riboflavin-sensitized photooxidation of indoleacetic acid *in vitro* (A), and photoinactivation of this compound by a brei of etiolated pea epicotyls (B). From: GALSTON and BAKER [1949]. By permission of the American Journal of Botany

mainly two reasons. The first reason for considering excited riboflavin responsible for initiating the first step in the phototropic reaction chain is suggested by experiments performed by GALSTON [1949] and GALSTON and BAKER [1949], on the mediation of photooxidation of the auxin indoleacetic acid (IAA) by this pigment. The latter authors also established action spectra of photoinactivation of this auxin *in vitro* in the presence of either riboflavin or a brei of etiolated pea epicotyls. The action spectra (fig. 67), resemble each other fairly well. It is noteworthy that no shift of the "brei spectrum" is seen. Support for flavin participation was gained by many other studies. REINERT [1953] demonstrated that the *in vitro* photodestruction of IAA by riboflavin, as observed by Galston, is decreased in the presence of carotenoids. The latter pigments are not likely to be active in causing any photoinactivation of IAA. According to the so-called "filter theory" (see THORNING [1955]), the protective action of the carotenoids consists of absorbing part of the blue radiation which is capable of exciting riboflavin. Such a shading effect should have its consequences with respect to the shape of the phototropic action spectrum. According to the filter theory, this spectrum will be distorted due to light absorption by the ineffective carotenoids. The lack of phototropic effect by these pigments *in vivo* was confirmed by the experiments of LABOURIAU and GALSTON [1955]. These authors worked with carotene-free coleoptiles of an albino barley mutant as well as carotene-deficient sporangiophores of the mould *Phycomyces*. They observed that the ability to perform phototropism in these did not considerably differ from that of normal objects.

However, it remains to be seen whether photoinactivation of IAA is involved in phototropism. BRIGGS [1963] discusses both this and also the various theories on redistribution of IAA.

The second reason for ascribing a phototropic function to riboflavin is derived from the fact that the absorption spectrum of this pigment resembles to some extent the action spectrum for the first positive curvature in *Avena* coleoptiles. This action spectrum shows two bands in the visible region, namely at 440 and 475 mμ, (see for example JOHNSTON [1934]), as well as a maximum in the UV around 380 mμ according to MILLS and SCHRANK [1954]. The latter band could not be observed by CURRY *et al.* [1956] in the phototropic responses of the base of *Avena* coleoptiles. Therefore, there is some uncertainty in this respect. GALSTON [1959a], when referring to a number of studies suggested that the mentioned discrepancy might be due to different action spectra for the apex and base phototropic curvatures of the oat coleoptiles. However, as BRIGGS [1963] remarked, the UV-induced curvature is essentially different from the "true" base curvature.

Riboflavin displays only a single absorption maximum at 440 mμ

with a weak shoulder around 470 mμ in the visible region. The phototropic action spectrum shows two distinct bands in this spectral region (fig. 68) though the obvious 475 mμ band of the latter spectrum might be an artifact due to screening of the photocatalyst by ineffective carotenoids.

The belief that riboflavin and possibly other flavins as well, functions as the principal phototropic pigment is widely accepted though a definite proof of this function has yet to be found. According to

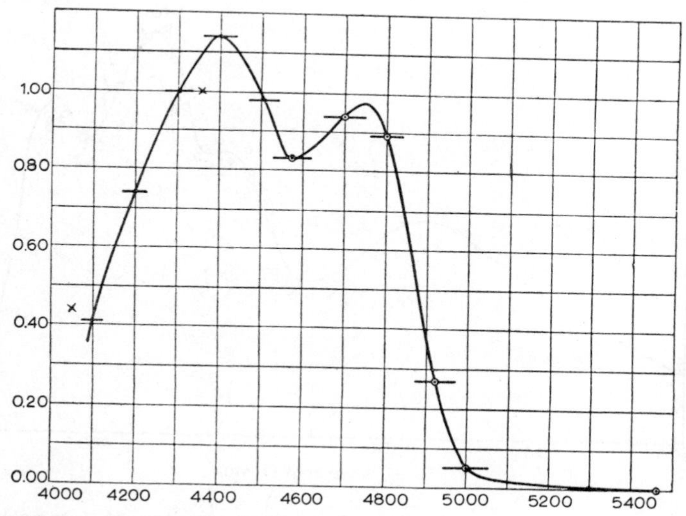

Fig. 68. Action spectrum of the first positive curvature of *Avena* coleoptiles. From: JOHNSTON [1934]

GALSTON [1959a] further investigations on the phototropic action spectra, in particular in the UV region, may solve the problem. For in the blue part of the visible spectrum other compounds, such as carotenoids, vitamin K, folic acid and certain flavonoids absorb as well.

A different hypothesis concerning the action of riboflavin was suggested by WAYGOOD and MACLAGHLAN [1956]. According to these authors, free riboflavin or its phosphate, flavin mononucleotide (FMN), reacts with IAA oxidase rather than the auxin itself. They observed that, *in vitro*, this pigment inhibits the enzyme activity, and found that this inhibitory effect is reversed in blue light. These results lead the authors to suggest that riboflavin or another flavin also controls IAA destruction *in vivo*, the extent of this control being dependent on the photo-excitation of the pigment.

Doubt has been cast on the riboflavin hypothesis in a paper of MER [1957]. This author, who worked with both wheat and oat coleoptiles, was unable to reproduce the results obtained by GALSTON and BAKER [1949] on the elongation of pea stem sections in media containing IAA with or without riboflavin, in the dark as well as in the light. Since

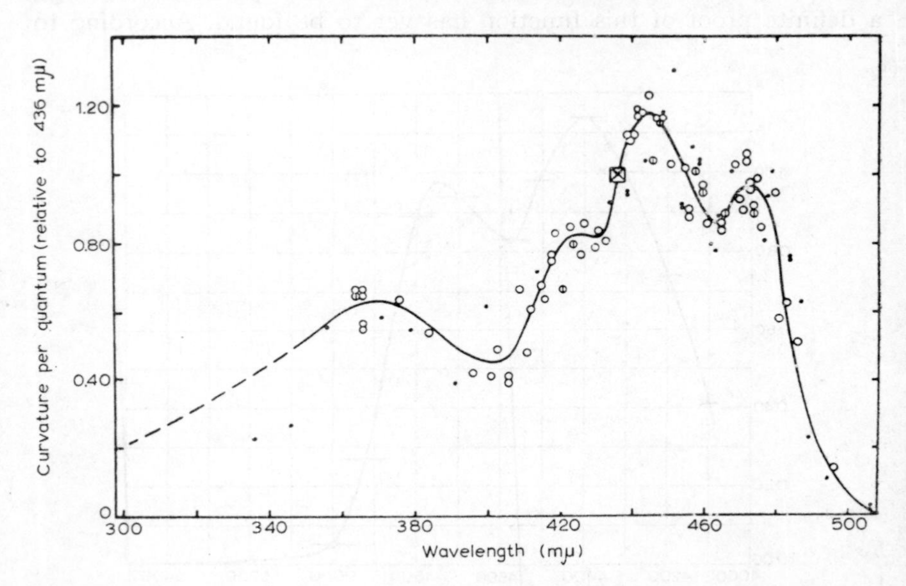

Fig. 69. Action spectrum of the low-intensity positive curvature of *Avena* coleoptiles. From: THIMANN and CURRY [1961]

Mer did not find significant differences in his experimental series, he concluded that either the riboflavin was not taken up by the cells, or this compound when excited did not affect IAA in its *in vivo* state. Therefore, according to him, though the *in vitro* photodestruction of IAA by riboflavin was clearly established, it remains to be seen whether this pigment functions as the phototropic mediator in the cell. Since the publication of Mer's paper, results supporting Galston's theory have been communicated. For a detailed discussion, reference is made to GALSTON [1959a] and REINERT [1959].

A different criticism was offered by THIMANN and CURRY [1961]. Their main objection is based on the fact that (1) the absorption spectrum of an aqueous solution of riboflavin shows only a single maximum in the visible region, whereas in the *Avena* tip phototropic action spectrum two or possibly three bands occur, and (2) the intensity of the UV maximum at 365 mμ of such a solution is only slightly less than that of the 440 mμ band, whereas in the action spectrum the height of the 365 mμ band is roughly 50% of that of the 400 mμ peak (see fig. 69). Thimann and Curry referred to a paper by HARBURY *et al.* [1959] who showed that water and other hydrogen-bonding solvents tend to flatten the flavin absorption spectrum in the visible in such a way that the three-peaked absorption spectrum seen in benzene solutions becomes a single band, while the UV maximum shifts from 340 to 365 mμ. Consequently when riboflavin is in an aqueous solvent it shows a single band in the visible and the UV maximum coincides with that of the phototropic action spectrum. However, if the riboflavin is in a solvent in which more than one peak in the visible spectrum occur, as in the case of benzene, its UV maximum no longer coincides with that of the action spectrum. Hence Thimann and Curry consider the phototropic function of riboflavin to be rather questionable.

2.2 *Carotenoids*

The main reasons for considering carotenoids to be the sensitizers for phototropism, as advocated for example by Thimann and coworkers (THIMANN and CURRY [1961]), are derived from the fact that (1) a rather satisfactory matching of the absorption spectra of these pigments with the phototropic action spectrum occurs in the visible (see also SHROPSHIRE and WITHROW [1958]), and (2) the carotenoid distribution and the phototropic sensitivity approximately coincide in the *Avena* coleoptile. Shropshire and Withrow concluded from experiments on the quantum requirement in the UV that in this region there is no maximum of the action spectrum due to the presence of the photocatalyst. CURRY and GRUEN [1961], on the other hand, were not successful in reproducing these results.

According to BÜNNING [1955] the highest carotenoid concentration occurs just below the tip of the *Avena* coleoptile, while the maximum phototropic sensitivity is located in the tip itself (see LANGE [1928]) Another objection is based on the fact that carotenoids extracted with hexane from coleoptile tips by Thimann and Curry are in their *trans*-configuration and do not absorb in the near-UV. To this these authors added that, according to INHOFFEN *et al.* [1951], 9-9′ *cis*-mono-β carotene shows a near-UV absorption maximum of the same intensity ratio with the bands in the visible as is seen in the phototropic action spectra. However, a *cis*-carotenoid has never been extracted from *Avena* coleoptiles. Moreover, as Thimann and Curry remarked, the location of the UV absorption band of this carotenoid is too far off towards the short-wave side, being at 340 mμ, to coincide reasonably well with that of the 365 mμ band of the action spectra. Other carotenoids in the *cis*-configuration might be different in this respect, and

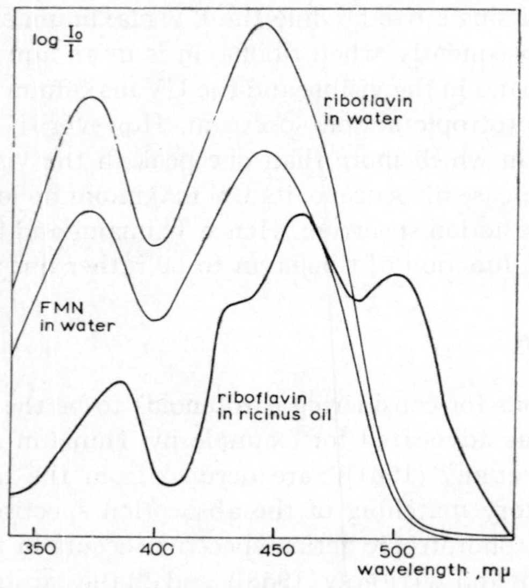

Fig. 70. Absorption spectra of riboflavin and FMN in aqueous solution as well as that of riboflavin in ricinus oil

complex formation with proteins might shift the absorption bands of the carotenoids so as to make them coincide with those of the action spectra.

While there is no direct evidence for, and a certain amount against either flavins or carotenoids acting as the phototropic pigment, they still seem to be candidates. GALSTON [1959a] commented that the state in which flavins occur in the living cell is still unknown and so the argument based on the discrepancy of both types of the near-UV spectra cannot be used to discount their phototropic function.

Another explanation of the three-peaked spectrum apparently shown by the flavins in the visible makes use of the "filter theory" (see REI-

NERT [1953]). However THIMANN and CURRY [1960] treated the screening effect mathematically, and decided that this explanation is not likely to be true. In any case, it seems worthwhile to keep in mind the suggestion of Galston about the effect of the *in vivo* state on the spectrum of riboflavin. Fig. 70 illustrates the considerable influence of the solvent on the absorption of riboflavin by comparing the spectra of this compound and FMN in aqueous solution with that of riboflavin in ricinus oil. Apparently in this medium three absorption bands occur in the visible, while the maximum in the near-UV is not shifted to the short-wave side as it is in benzene. On the contrary, all the maxima are shifted to the long-wave side by about 10 mμ, and the relative distances between the various bands approximately correspond with those of the action spectra. As a consequence, it is clear that the effect of the *in vivo* state on the riboflavin absorption should be examined thoroughly.

There are more data *pro* as well as *contra* the conception that either carotenoids or flavins are sensitizers for phototropism. The respective studies were extensively discussed in the reviews cited earlier. A mention should be made that REINERT [1953], when confirming Galston's finding that riboflavin acts as a sensitizer in the *in vitro* photodestruction of IAA, observed that β-carotene is not active in mediating this photolysis.

The possibility that two pigments instead of a single one operate in phototropism has also been considered. It might be that both of these pigments function independently of each other, one of them being active in the visible and the other one in the near-UV. According to THIMANN and CURRY [1960], the similarity of the dosage-response curves at both spectral regions does not favour such a possibility. SHROPSHIRE and WITHROW [1958] observed that irradiation with 365 mμ light excites a blue fluorescence in the near-apical zones of coleoptiles. They suggested that a pigment absorbing in the near-UV may transfer its excitation energy by emission of quanta which can be absorbed by the phototropic pigment in the visible. This method of energy transfer would be extremely inefficient. If energy transfer were to take place, the present author prefers to think of the transfer by resonance which was discussed under photosynthesis. The results of BRIGGS [see 1963], who found the blue fluorescence of a buffer extract of oat coleoptiles to be located at 450 mμ, favour this possibility. The transfer of electronic energy by inductive resonance requires a good overlap of the emission spectrum of the transferring pigment with the absorption spectrum of the receiving one. However, a fluorescence in this region is often observed in living cells and may be due to several compounds, perhaps $NADH_2$. We should not consider the occurrence of two phototropic pigments at these wavelength regions until we have exhausted the possibility of a single one explaining the observed phenomena.

2.3 *Chlorophyll derivatives*

Chlorophylls were considered to be the probable precursors of a growth inhibitor by BLAAUW-JANSEN [1954]. She observed that irradiation of chromatograms of extracts from *Chlorella* cells gave rise to an inhibitor of the growth of *Staphylococcus aureus* at exactly the same location as the chlorophyllides. However BLAAUW-JANSEN [1964] decided that the inhibitory phenomenon was most likely due to a direct photoinactivation of the bacteria rather than *via* the formation of a growth inhibitor. ASOMANING and GALSTON [1961], on the other hand, observed that the flavin and carotenoid content of the coleoptile tips of oat and barley increased upon irradiation with red light. The same is true for carotenoids in corn seedlings (COHEN and GOODWIN [1962]). This phenomenon might explain how light can induce changes in the phototropic sensitivity.

2.4 *Phytochrome*

A number of effects of red light have been found to be at least partially reversible by the action of far-red light, namely: (1) increase in tissue sensitivity towards applied IAA (see LIVERMAN and BONNER [1953]), (2) change in the type of growth response to IAA concentration (see BLAAUW-JANSEN [1959]), (3) increase in carotenoid content in corn seedlings (see COHEN and GOODWIN [1962]) and (4) shift of the dosage response to higher intensities for the first positive and negative curvatures in oat coleoptiles (see BRIGGS [1963]). The reversibility of the red light effect was suggested by BORTHWICK and HENDRICKS [1960] to be due to the activity of the morphogenetic pigment phytochrome.

Red light may reduce the amount of diffusible or extractable auxin in *Avena* coleoptiles (for example BLAAUW-JANSEN [1959] and BRIGGS [1963]). According to BLAAUW-JANSEN [1959], 740 mμ light is as effective as 660 mμ light in this respect.

2.5 *Unknown pigment*

It is possibly responsible for the "true" base curvature of the *Avena* coleoptile. BÜNNING [1955] determined the absorption spectrum of a pigment extracted from coleoptile bases. This spectrum coincided with the action spectrum for the base curvatures established by HAIG [1934]. The pigment showed an absorption maximum around 410 mμ which was not very pronounced and the absorption fell to zero between 500 and 550 mμ. The nature of this pigment is still unknown. Bünning remarked that it might possibly be a flavone.

2.6 *Indoleacetic acid*

Though it is not a sensitizer for phototropism in the usual sense, this auxin should also be mentioned since CURRY *et al.* [1956], who established the action spectrum for the base curvatures of *Avena* coleoptiles induced by irradiation with UV, observed that this spectrum, apart from a 12 mμ shift towards the long-wave side, fitted the absorption spectrum of IAA reasonably well. This shift was suggested to be due to a conversion of IAA to some derivative in the living cell. One may wonder whether complex formation with proteins might be responsible for this phenomenon. If the base curvature in question were actually due to direct photodestruction of auxin, this does not constitute a true sensitizing role by IAA in phototropism. In any case, the evidence of the action spectrum excludes carotenoids and flavins from taking part in the UV phototropic responses of the coleoptile base.

Carotenoids and flavins have been mentioned as possible sensitizers of phototropism based on growth processes. The same pigments (see BRAUNER [1948, 1959]), stand as candidates for phototropism due to light turgor reactions. In addition to this, red an far-red light beyond 680 mμ can induce movements in pulvini, for example in *Phaseolus multiflorus*. The active pigment in the red may be tetrapyrrole compounds such as the chlorophylls and their derivatives. These pigments do not function by causing the curvatures in growth-dependent phototropism, although they may affect the phototropic sensitivity.

2.7 *Retinal-opsin complexes*

The phototropic action spectrum of zoological organs, namely the zooids of the Bryozoa *Bugula avicularia*, was established by KAISSLING [1962]. It closely resembled the absorption spectra of the retinal-opsin complexes in vision.

3 The phototropic structures

In general, two types of phototropic structures can be distinguished. which may be designated (1) the growth type, and (2) the turgor type.

3.1 Growth-type structures

These can be subdivided into two classes, namely (a) tissues, and (b) single cells. Phototropic tissues are encountered in higher as well as in lower plants. In higher plants, these tissues appear in the growing parts of stems, petioles, leaves and coleoptiles. In lower plants, they are observed in protenemata of mosses which are positive phototropic, while their rhizoids react negatively, fern prothalli and certain algae. At the present time there are no data regarding the molecular organization of the phototropic apparatus in these tissues.

Phototropic cells are less complex and so may be studied more readily. This is particularly true of experiments on phototropic response to polarized light. Such cells as the germinating spores of certain fungi, mosses and ferns have been examined by BÜNNING and ETZOLD [1958]. They observed that (1) conidia of the fungus *Botrytis cinerea* germinate parallel to the vibration plane of polarized blue light, (2) spores of the fern *Dryopteris filix-mas* germinate in polarized red light in such a way that the chloronemata grow perpendicular and the rhizoids grow parallel to the plane. The growth direction of the chloronemata could be changed by rotating the polarization plane but the direction of the rhizoids could not. This indicates that the rhizoids of these cells are nonphototropic, their growth direction being determined by the first cleavage of the cell. This cleavage plane is determined by the polarization plane. Finally, (3) spores of the moss *Funaria hygrometrica* reacted in the same way as those of the fern as far as the chloronemata were concerned, while the growth direction of the rhizoids was random.

The molecular organization of the phototropic structures in germinating spores was extensively studied by Jaffe (for example JAFFE and ETZOLD [1962]). This paper describes experiments on the germination of *Botrytis cinerea* conidia and spores of the fern *Osmunda cinnamomea* in polarized blue light. The phototropic receptor molecules were found to be highly dichroic and oriented. Both *Botrytis* and *Osmunda* spores germinated parallel to the vibration plane of the incident polarized light. However they differed in the site of the start of growth. This became evident by irradiating with non-polarized light and by shading part of the individual spores with opaque chromium bands 40 mμ wide. The more brightly illuminated parts of the *Botrytis* cells germinated, while the *Osmunda* cells grew out from the darker parts. It was found that an intensity difference approaching 100% is required to completely orientate growth as was found with polarized light. The authors concluded that the effect of polarized light is due to the fact that in part of the cell no light is absorbed at all, which is equivalent to a "100% difference" with those parts where the radiation can be ab-

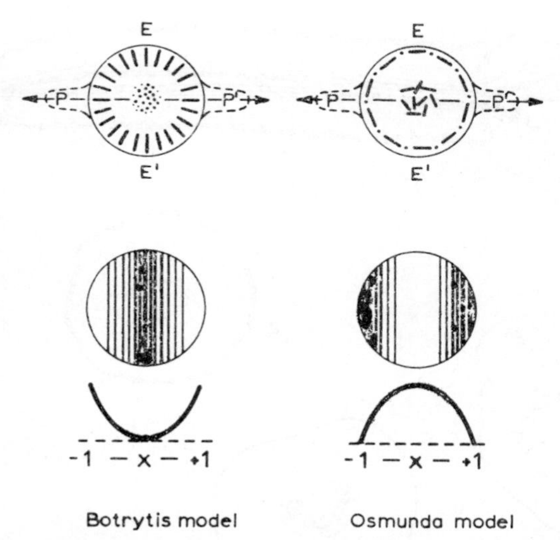

Fig. 71. Diagrams of the molecular orientation of the photoreceptive pigments in *Osmunda* and *Botrytis* spores, and the patterns of the relative rates of light absorption across the cell due to these molecules. P and P′ are the poles of the model cell diameter in the vibration direction and E-E′ is the "equator", defined by the "vibration poles". From JAFFE and ETZOLD [1962] by courtesy of the Journal of Cell Biology

sorbed. In other words, the photoreceptive molecules are highly dichroic as well as highly oriented. The authors deduced the orientation of the photoreceptive molecules which are shown in fig. 71. With *Fucus* zygotes the situation corresponds with that of the *Osmunda* model (JAFFE [1958]). In the periclinical *Osmunda* model, absorption is maximum at the "vibration equator" and zero at the "vibration poles". The reverse is true of the anticlinical *Botrytis* model. With the aid of these models, and assuming that the *Botrytis* and *Osmunda* spores grow in the regions where respectively most and least light is absorbed, it can be explained why the spores of both species germinate in the vibration plane of polarized light, but will only start growing under different light conditions.

The structure of the phototropically reactive part may influence the light distribution in the plant, and hence its phototropism. Such is the case with the *Avena* coleoptile (see BÜNNING *et al.* [1953]), and more notably in the sporangiophore of the mould *Phycomyces* (see BLAAUW [1918]). In the first case, the illuminated side and the first leaf screens the opposite side of the coleoptile, whereas in the second case, a "lens effect" of

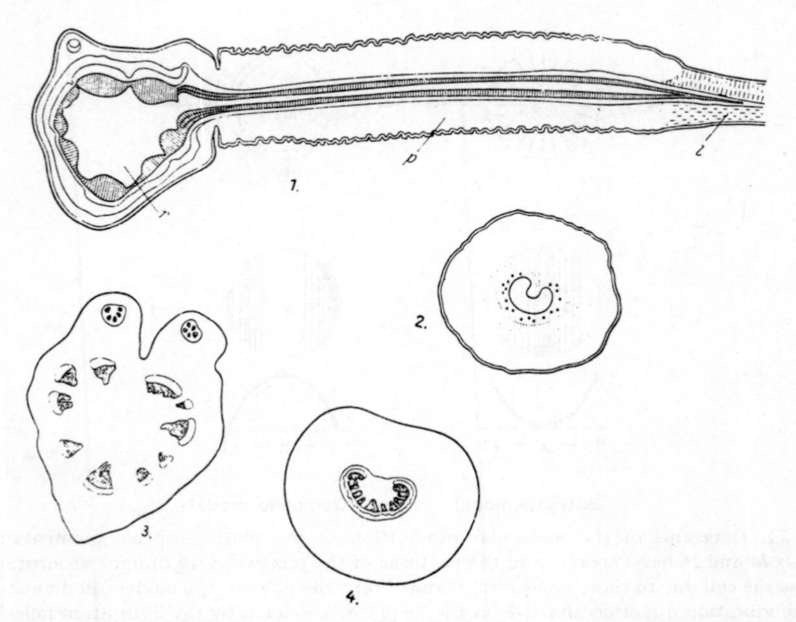

Fig. 72. Pulvinus of *Robinia pseudacacia* (1 and 2), and cross-sections through petiole (3) and pulvinus (4) of *Phaseolus multiflorus*. r, rachis; p, pulvinus; l, lamina. From: BRAUNER [1959]

the transparent upper region of the sporangiophore focusses the light on the distal cell wall. Although a number of papers, adequately reviewed by BANBURY [1959], on the phototropic reactions of such sporangiophores have been published, the phototropic structure is not yet understood. The fact that not all phototropic organisms respond to the polarization direction of the incident light leads one to conclude that the organization of the photoreceptor molecules differs for various species.

3.2 Turgor-type structures

These or at least the effector organs, are easier to distinguish from the adjacent tissues than the growth-type ones. Fig. 72 shows a schematic representation of *Robinia* and *Phaseolus* pulvini. In the moving part, the "rigid" transport elements are located centrally and are surrounded by thin-walled parenchymatic cells which allow considerable changes in their volume. This enables the upper or lower side to be shortened while the opposite side stretches in an accordion-like way, thus making the leaf execute an upward or downward movement. In these species, light perception also occurs in the pulvinus though in others, for example Malvaceae, this process is located in the leaf. The stimulus is then transmitted towards the remotely located effector.

According to THIMANN and CURRY [1961], the perception of the light stimulus in leaves might be correlated with the phototaxis of their chloroplasts. This suggestion is however, highly speculative and is still without an experimental basis.

4 The nature of the process

The phototropic phenomena based on growth reactions are found in a wide range of species and have been studied in higher plants, algae, liverworts, mosses, ferns, and fungi. As far as they are known, their action spectra resemble one another fairly well. There are exceptions such as the *Avena* coleoptile "true" base curvature which shows a wavelength dependency clearly different from the more general type found in the coleoptile tips (see HAIG [1934]). Consequently more than one phototropic system may operate in one object, and in the *Avena* coleoptile four of such systems have been distinguished. Zimmerman and Briggs (see BRIGGS [1963]) termed these systems I–IV. Systems I, II, and III represent the first positive, first negative and second positive curvature mechanisms respectively. These systems occur in succession with increasing doses of light and their mechanisms differ. Firstly, according to these authors, systems I and II obey the Bunsen-Roscoe reciprocity law which holds that a photochemical effect is proportional with the product of light intensity and exposure time. System III, however, was supposed to follow the exposure time and to be independent of light intensity for the ranges checked. Furthermore the log dosage-response curves of systems I and II proved to be shifted towards larger doses by pretreatment with phototropically inactive red light, whereas it was the slope of this curve for system III which was increased. On the other hand, BLAAUW-JANSEN [1959] did not observe such a shift for the system I curve, but an increase of its maximum. According to BLAAUW [1964], this shift can be clearly observed only after a lag time of at least 30 min. between the red light irradiation and the phototropic induction though the rise of the maximum of the curve took place instantaneously. Blaauw supposed that this rise escaped Briggs' attention because his safelight was a green light of relatively high intensity, while Blaauw-Jansen worked in complete darkness. HUISINGA [1964] found that light doses as low as 20 erg/cm^2 are sufficient to affect both the growth of excised coleoptile cylinders and the geotropism of intact coleoptiles. Therefore Blaauw thought it quite possible that green light can also affect phototropic phenomena.

The fact that systems I and II are separate mechanisms is proven by the finding that species equipped with both types show S-shaped curvatures. Zimmerman and Briggs classed as system IV the phototropic reactions in the far-UV, studied by CURRY *et al.* [1956]. Only positive curvatures are known with this system. The reciprocity law holds and red light induces a reduction of the curvature.

From kinetic considerations, Zimmerman and Briggs decided upon the following mechanisms. In system I and II an "unactivated" photoreceptor, different for the two systems, is "activated" by light, and subsequently "inactivated" by a second photoact. The suggested scheme for system III is completely different. A precursor is reversibly changed to an intermediate compound by light action to form an equilibrium concentration of both substances. The intermediate compound is then transformed into the phototropic agent by a thermal reaction. In Briggs' laboratory, unpublished experiments with corn (BRIGGS [1963]) were carried out to determine the temperature dependency of the systems. The results fit the proposed schemes in that systems I and II were found to be insensitive towards temperature and system III, the only one in which a dark reaction is involved, proved to be temperature-dependent. Finally, as mentioned earlier, system IV is likely to be a direct photoinactivation of IAA.

A number of theories concerning the nature of the processes mediated by the excited phototropic agent have been proposed. The hypothesis of BLAAUW [see 1919], that phototropism is based on local differences in growth rate due to uneven light distribution was explained in terms of unequal distribution of growth hormones resulting from light intensity gradients in the plant. Such a redistribution has been demonstrated by WENT [1928] who collected the auxin diffusing out of tips of illuminated as well as non-illuminated coleoptiles. He compared the amounts of auxin diffusing from the illuminated and the dark sides of *Avena* coleoptiles by placing the tips on two small agar blocks which were separated from each other by mica platelets. He observed that (1) 16% less auxin diffused out of the illuminated tips than out of the dark controls, and (2) the illuminated half released about 50% less auxin than the opposite half of one and the same coleoptile tip after an initial 90-minutes' unilaterial illumination period in incandescent light of 1000 m.c./sec. BRIGGS [1963], however, ascribed the reduction of the amount of diffusable auxin to the activity of the red light component.

These data refer to the first positive curvature. ASANA [1938] showed that more auxin is released by the illuminated side than by the opposite one in the case of the operation of the negative curvature, and BURKHOLDER and JOHNSTON [1937] obtained adequate results for the third positive curvature. The redistribution of auxin is thus mediated by the excited phototropic pigment. There are several theories on the way in which this redistribution is effected:

(1) Light-induced lateral transport of auxin; the Cholodny-Went theory. CHOLODNY [1927] and WENT [1928], independently of each other, concluded that auxin is redistributed under unilateral illumination because of a light-induced lateral shift of the growth hormone diffusing downwards from the coleoptile tip.

(2) Photodestruction of auxin. STEWART and WENT [1939] deduced from extraction experiments that a small amount of auxin is inactivated by light. This photodestruction may proceed either *via* sensitizers (see GALSTON [1959]), or, at least in the far-UV, by direct light action (see CURRY *et al.* [1956]).

(3) Light-induced decrease of auxin production. This possibility was suggested by OPPENOORTH [1941]. GALSTON [1959], who proposed such a decrease, (see [1950]), discussed the possibility in terms of photoinactivation of enzymes or cofactors involved in auxin synthesis.

(4) Reduced sensitivity or the cells towards growth hormones due to light action. From experiments with *Raphanus* hypocotyls, VAN OVERBEEK [1933] concluded that half of the phototropic curvature is due

to unequal distribution of auxin, and half is effected by a decrease of the response of the cells to the growth hormone.

According to BRIGGS [1963], cases 2, 3 and 4 are likely to be induced by red rather than blue light.

These theories need not exclude one another. On the contrary, it seems likely (see WENT [1956] and BRIGGS [1963]) that the various systems operate *via* different mechanisms or combinations of them. A considerable amount of supporting evidence for these processes has been published which has been adequately discussed in the reviews already referred to. Many problems must be solved before a clear insight into the situation can be obtained.

The above data and hypotheses mainly refer to phototropism in *Avena* coleoptiles and it is not certain that they are generally applicable to green plants, the lower ones included. It is even less certain whether they apply to fungi. CURRY and GRUEN [1959] established the action spectrum for the positive curvature of *Phycomyces* sporangiophores. This spectrum lead the authors to suggest that the photoreceptors for *Avena* and *Phycomyces* are identical. However the mechanisms which effectuate the bending phenomena may well be different for both objects. For example, BLAAUW [1914] claims that contrary to the behaviour of *Avena* coleoptiles, the growth of *Phycomyces* is first accelerated in weak light, and subsequently retarded. Even now the role of the light growth reaction in phototropism is far from elucidated (see BRIGGS [1963]). BANBURY [1952] studied the effect of IAA on the growth of sporangiophores of this mould, and concluded that no clear evidence in favour of a growth-regulating function of IAA could be obtained. The walls of fungi consist of chitin and it is possible (BANBURY [1959]) that growth in these hyphae is regulated in a different way from that in cells with cellulose walls. Opinions differ widely in this respect. For instance, GENTILE and KLEIN [1955] stated that IAA is required for the growth of *Diplodia*. The possibility remains that various fungi regulate their growth in different ways. Since no uniform concept has been established, there will be no further discussion of this problem here.

The curious phototropic orientation of *Pilobolus* sporangiophores should be mentioned. This reaction has been described by a number of authors, (*e.g.* VAN DER WEY [1929]). When mature, this sporangiophore discharges its content suddenly and vigorously. If a point light source is in the environment, the sporangiophore aims the discharge very accurately towards it. In case of two such sources, placed at an angle smaller than 10°, the sporangia are shot exactly in between, while at angles greater than 10°, one of the sources is selected to be aimed at. At the base of the swollen head of the sporangiophore a carotenoid-rich ring is developed though the function of this ring is not understood (BANBURRY [1959]).

The idea that turgor-type phototropism is effectuated by auxin is based on experiments in which the growth substance was externally applied. Application of an auxin paste to one side of the object resulted in a negative curvature, that is, the pasted side became concave. This phenomenon was observed with *Mimosa pudica* by BURKHOLDER and PRATT [1936], and with different species of *Phaseolus* by VON GUTTENBERG and KRÖPELIN [1948] and BRAUNER and ARSLAN [1951]. The latter authors demonstrated by experiments using vital staining, that the transport system from either the sides or the central part of the lamina occupy corresponding locations in the pulvinus. It was suggested that under unequal illumination of the leaf, auxin is unequally distributed in the pulvinus *via* the transport systems, and thus brings about a curvature to adjust the leaf relative to the incident light. The stretching of the side to which the auxin paste was applied indicates that this substance causes a reversible enlargement of the volumes of the parenchymatic pulvinus cells. It was suggested that this phenomenon is due to auxin-induced permeability changes. For electrophysiological reasons, THOMAS [1939] concluded that IAA actually affects the permeability properties of the membranes of adult *Coleus* cells.

The mechanism of phototropism has not yet been explained beyond doubt. It seems likely that a number of systems operate, or co-operate, in this process. In most, if not all, cases, the role of effecting agent is played by auxin, and inactivation of this substance by photodynamic action is likely to occur in at least one of the phototropic systems. Candidates for the photodynamically active phototropic pigment are either carotenoids or flavins and most of the available evidence seems to be in favour of the latter compounds.

10

Photomorphogenesis

1 *Introduction*

Photomorphogenesis is defined as a light-controlled formative effect. This definition is rather vague, but seems to be the best way to put it since photomorphogenesis covers such a wide field of phenomena, ranging from seed germination to bird migration. The former process depends on growth and development, while the latter is governed by activity of secretory tissues.

Treatment of so many phenomena of widely diverging nature under one and the same heading hardly seems justifiable. However, when viewed from the standpoint of investigators studying the action of light in biology, such a combination becomes permissible. In this case emphasis is laid upon the general formative function of light rather than on each process in particular. The vague outline of photomorphogenesis means for instance, that phototropism which is based on the light growth reaction, belongs to this field. On the other hand, in the cases in which this tropism depends on the completely different process of the light turgor reaction, it is clearly related with non-formative phototaxis phenomena. For this reason phototropism was discussed separately and will not be considered in this section.

One may distinguish between two kinds of photomorphogenetic processes, namely reactions in which the response is effected by (1) light stimulation alone, and (2) an interplay between light and dark periods, often combined with endogenous rhythms in the organism. For the latter type, the term "photoperiodicity" is used.

These rhythms are seen in many animals and plants, but a discussion on their nature would carry too far from the basic consideration of photoprocesses. For adequate reviews of the rhythmic phenomena see for example, CLOUDSLEY-THOMPSON [1961] and BÜNNING [1964].

An impressive amount of literature on photomorphogenesis has been published, though it contains little information on the basic photoprocesses. General information concerning the various photomorphogenic phenomena can be obtained from the following: PARKER and BORTHWICK [1950], BORTHWICK *et al.* [1956], DOORENBOS and WELLENSIEK [1959], SALISBURY [1961], BORTHWICK and HENDRICKS [1961], NAYLOR [1961], FARNER [1961], ASCHOFF and WEVER [1962a, b], MOHR [1962] and DE WILDE [1962].

2 The photomorphogenetic pigments

2.1 Phytochrome

Many light-dependent developmental processes in plants are controlled by this pigment. It was first detected *in vivo*, and partially purified from etiolated 3-day-old maize seedlings by BUTLER *et al.* [1959]. The pigment is a soluble protein which according to BUTLER [1961b], does not sediment at 173000 g after two hours of centrifugation. Nothing is known of the nature of the chromophore group.

Phytochrome occurs in two forms, as can be seen from the location of the absorption bands shown in fig. 73. These forms are designated, after the wavelength of maximum absorption, "P_{660}" and "P_{730}" or more generally: "P_R" and "P_{FR}". According to BERTSCH [1963], phytochrome also absorbs in the blue. In solution the two forms are interconvertible by light action. SIEGELMAN *et al.* [1962] succeeded in concentrating and purifying phytochrome to such an extent that a clear blue solution resulted. Upon irradiation, this preparation visibly changed colour. However opinions differ as to whether photoreversibility of the pigment *in vivo* can occur to any considerable extent. NAKAYAMA *et al.* [1960] and DE LINT and SPRUIT [1963] could observe *in vivo* only the photoconversion of P_{660} to P_{730}, and were unsuccessful in demonstrating conversion in the opposite direction. According to them, P_{730} is likely to be enzymically destroyed in the plant cell. BUTLER and DOWNS [1960] stated that part of the convertibility is lost upon irradiation. HENDRICKS *et al.* [1962] mentioned that the pigment *in vivo* is photoconvertible, although there is a net loss of reversibility on the $P_{730} \rightarrow P_{660}$ reaction.

In darkness, only the red-absorbing form is found. Upon irradiation with red light, this form bleaches and P_{730} is produced. In maize seedlings, irradiation with far-red light converts P_{730} into P_{660}. However the latter authors stated that with extracts from barley the amount of total phytochrome decreased, while at the same time, there was a decrease of solubility. Therefore they concluded that denaturation of the protein moiety is responsible for the loss of P_{730}.

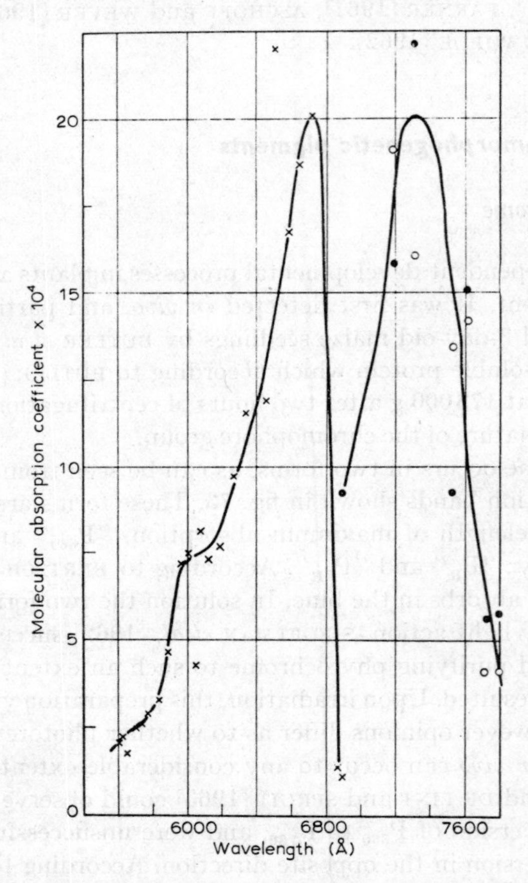

Fig. 73. Absorption spectra of the P_{660} and P_{730} forms of phytochrome. From: BORTHWICK and HENDRICKS [1961]

They also found that down to −20 °C, the reversibility is temperature-independent. At −196 °C no photoreaction was observed, though warming restored the reversibility.

This is to some extent reminiscent of the behaviour of visual pigments when irradiated at liquid nitrogen temperature. However even at this temperature a photoreaction was still observed, namely the transformation of rhodopsin into pre-lumirhodopsin. In vision, the true photoact consists of a *cis-trans* isomerization. As a consequence of this isomerization, thermal reactions, ultimately leading to a disruption of the chromophore–opsin link take place at higher temperatures. With phytochrome, on the other hand, no change at all was observed in the low-temperature range upon irradiation.

There are two possible reasons for the failure to observe a change: (1) the determination of the absorption spectra was not sufficiently accurate to see the relatively small shift or change in the spectral shape on the structural changes due to, for example, stereoisomerization or the formation of metastable states, and (2) phytochrome in its first excited singlet state is capable of performing the reactions, but these can occur only at higher temperatures. Which of these two possibilities holds is not clear as yet. Also in this respect it would be most helpful to know the nature of the chromophore group in question, but only a suggestion by HENDRICKS *et al.* [1962] can be considered. According to these authors, the absorption spectra of P_{660} and allophycocyanin suggest a similarity of structure, whereas the extreme weakness of the Soret band in both forms of phytochrome argues against the possibility of the chromophore being found in cyclic tetrapyrroles such as chlorophylls and hemins. The authors also pointed to the fact that open-chain tetrapyrroles, such as phycobilins, can isomerize at the methene bridges, and the terminal rings can be lactams or lactims. If the four pyrrole rings are arranged in such a way that the molecule approximates to a porphin structure, it might be stabilized by hydrogen bonding with a protein carrier. However Hendricks *et al.* pointed out that there are two facts not in favour of the allophycocyanin suggestion. Phycocyanins are not known (1) to occur in green plants, except for blue-green and red algae, and (2) to be involved in enzymic reactions. Because of the probably enzymic activity of phytochrome, the latter fact is of importance.

The authors remarked that this enzymic character is suggested by physiological observations, for example the light-dependent germination starts as soon as P_{660} is converted to P_{730}. The latter form may be the enzymically active compound controlling the germination process. According to Hendricks *et al.* the enzymic action of phytochrome, beyond seed germination, also controls many kinds of phenomena such as bud dormancy, leaf expansion, plastid formation, stem elongation and flowering, and so it should appear at a "metabolic crossing point" from which many reactions can start. As examples of such central processes, redox reactions with pyridine nucleotides, and coenzyme-A-induced acyl activation were mentioned, although it should be emphasized that such statements are purely hypothetical and the actual mechanism of phytochrome action is still obscure.

HENDRICKS *et al.* [1962] noticed a slow dark conversion of P_{730} to P_{660} in the plant as well as in extracts from barley seedlings. This conversion is temperature-dependent and requires the presence of oxygen. They also stated that fluorescence could only be observed with P_{660}, the emission maximum occurring around 690 mμ. BONNER [1962], however claims that the dark-conversion product of P_{730} resembles P_{660} but is not identical with it. This product absorbs at slightly longer wavelengths than P_{660}, with a maximum at 665 mμ. Irradiation with far-red light is needed to convert this compound into P_{660}.

HENDRICKS *et al.* [1960] when studying seed germination and radicle elongation, concluded that the photocontrol in these cases is exerted by simultaneous excitation of both forms of the photomorphogenetic pigment. They further suggested that this pigment also mediates the response to blue light. This conclusion was critisized by MOHR [1962] who believed that a different pigment is responsible for the short-wave reaction.

According to HENDRICKS *et al.* [1956], the photoreaction probably involves the formation of a triplet state free radical. This suggestion is merely hypothetical and is neither contradicted nor supported by experimental evidence.

2.2 *Copper flavoproteins*

These possibly contain an adenine dinucleotide group. MAHLER [1954] suggested that this might be butyryl coenzyme-A dehydrogenase, which may function as a cytochrome-c reductase. For example the shape of the action spectra for anthocyanin synthesis and for hypocotyl lengthening (shown in fig. 74), the effects of copper enzyme inhibitors and correlations with the distribution of copper lead MOHR [1957] and SIEGELMAN and HENDRICKS [1957, 1958] to suggest that the photoreceptive pigment is one of these flavoproteins.

2.3 *Other flavoproteins, riboflavin*

As far as these compounds are involved in the light growth reaction of Phototropism, they should also be listed here.

2.4 *Carotenoids*

The same holds for these pigments. References to information on these two categories are given in the corresponding section under Phototropism.

2.5 *Visual pigments?*

As it has been shown, for example by BENOIT and OTT [1944] (see also BURGER [1949]) that in some animals with photoperiodic reactions, the eye functions as the perceptive organ, the pigments described under Vision should be included.

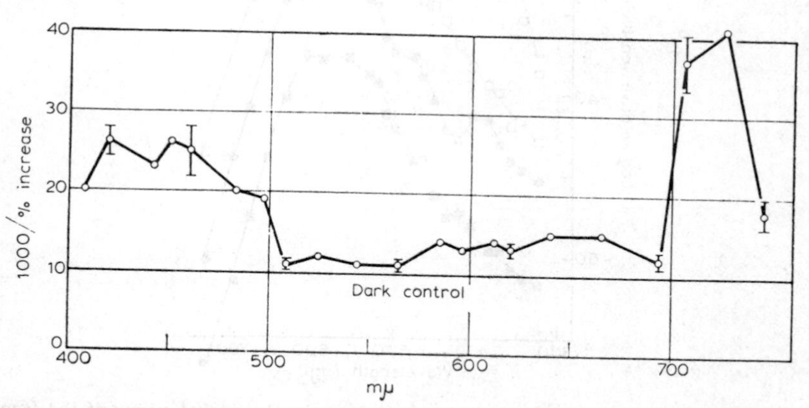

Fig. 74. Action spectrum for control of hypocotyl growth in seedlings of *Lactucasativa* L., var. Grand Rapids. From: MOHR and WEHRUNG [1960]

However it is rather puzzling that the spectral effectiveness distribution does not coincide with the absorption spectra of rhodopsin or iodopsin. For instance, BURGER [1943] stated that in the male starling the most effective wavelength region in provoking sexual activity is located between 580 and 680 mμ. Similarly, with some mammals, for example the ferret studied by MARSHALL and BOWDEN [1934], there is no coincidence. Apart from the visible wavelengths, UV light of 365 mμ is also highly efficient in producing recurrence of oestrus in the female ferret.

If visual pigments are involved in stimulating this process, one is inclined to consider the possibility of erythrolabe and chlorolabe as the pigments active in photomorphogenesis in the starling, while cyanolabe might be active in the case of the ferret. However, it could also be that one or more photomorphogenetically receptive compounds, different from the visual pigments and not yet identified, occur in the eye.

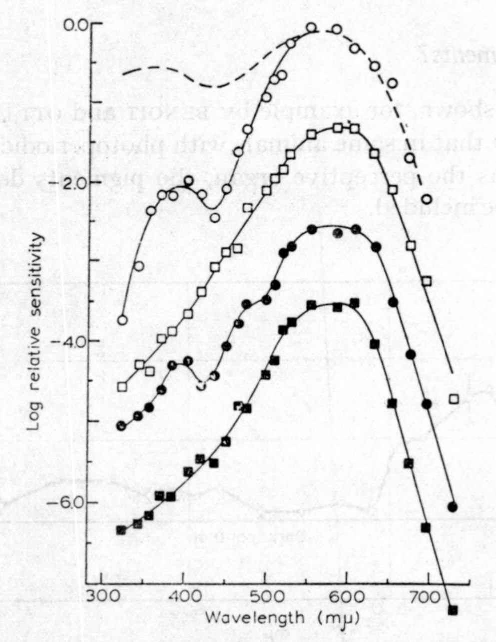

Fig. 75. Action spectra for the impulse frequency in the pineal nerve of the frog's frontal organ. Symbols refer to different animals. Broken line, absorption curve for iodopsin. From: DODT and HEERD [1962]

2.6 *Pigments from encephalic photoreceptors*

Photomorphogenetic phenomena in certain light-sensitive animals are controlled by encephalic receptors in addition to the retinal ones. According to BENOIT and OTT [1944], BENOIT *et al.* [1950], (see also BENOIT [1951]), direct photostimulation of the hypothalamus or the pituitary region affects their humoral secretory function (see HANKE and GIERSBERG [1963]) and in this way produces photoperiodic responses of the gonads. Benoit and coworkers found that the encephalic parts in question are highly sensitive towards violet, blue and yellow light. If the hypothalamo-hypophysial system is stimulated only by irradiation of the retina, red and orange light are highly effective while green and blue

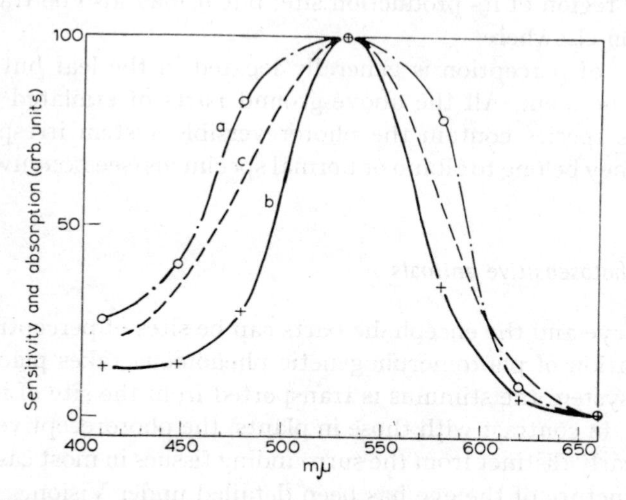

Fig. 76. Action spectra for light-feeding reaction (a) and reaction time (b) with *Phoxinus laevis*, as well as (c) absorption spectrum of a porphyropsin. From: DE LA MOTTE [1963]

are less active. Therefore they concluded that a pigment system, different from the retinal pigments, operates in the encephalic receptors. No information about the nature of this encephalic pigment system is available at present.

In another encephalic photoreceptor, the pineal organ, the receptive pigments may be identical with the visual ones. Action spectra established by DODT and HEERD [1962] indicate that iodopsin may function as the photoreceptive compound in the frog pineal organ, see fig. 75, whereas DE LA MOTTE [1963], working with the fish *Phoxinus laevis*, obtained indication that in this case (fig. 76), porphyropsin may be the active pigment in the organ in question.

3 *The photomorphogenetic structures*

3.1 *In plants*

It is only possible to locate the site where the photomorphogenetic perception occurs and the stimulating agent is formed. This agent may react in the region of its production site, but it may also be transported to function elsewhere.

The site of perception is generally located in the leaf but can also occur in the stem. All the above-ground parts of etiolated seedlings of various species contain the photoreversible system irrespective of whether they belong to albino or normal specimens (see BORTHWICK *et al.* [1952]).

3.2 *In photosensitive animals*

Both the eye and the encephalic parts can be sites of perception. Since the regulation of photomorphogenetic phenomena takes place *via* the humoral system the stimulus is transported from the site of its formation. Still, in contrast with those in plants, the photoreceptive structures are clearly distinct from the surrounding tissues in most cases.

The structure of the eye has been detailed under Vision.

Much work has been done on the structure of the hypothalamo-hypophysial system in birds by Benoit and coworkers, which is reviewed by BENOIT [1951], and FARNER [1961]. The photoreceptive cells however, have not yet been identified beyond doubt. The presence of neurosecretory cells of the supraoptico-paraventricular nuclear complex of the hypothalamus as well as the neurosecretion-carrying axons belonging to them seem to be essential for establishment of the photoperiodic phenomena (ASSENMACHER [1957]).

In fish, photostimulation results in activating the pituitary which controls the sexual organs by means of the gonadotropin level in the blood (HARRINGTON [1959]).

In insects the photoperiodic control of the diapause depends on an antagonism between the *corpora allata* and the subesophageal ganglion, (see DE WILDE and STEGWEE [1960]).

Distinct photoreceptive cells have been found in the pineal organ of fishes, amphibians, and reptiles (see VAN DE KAMER [1964]). Apart from ganglion cells and supportive elements, the organ situated on top of the

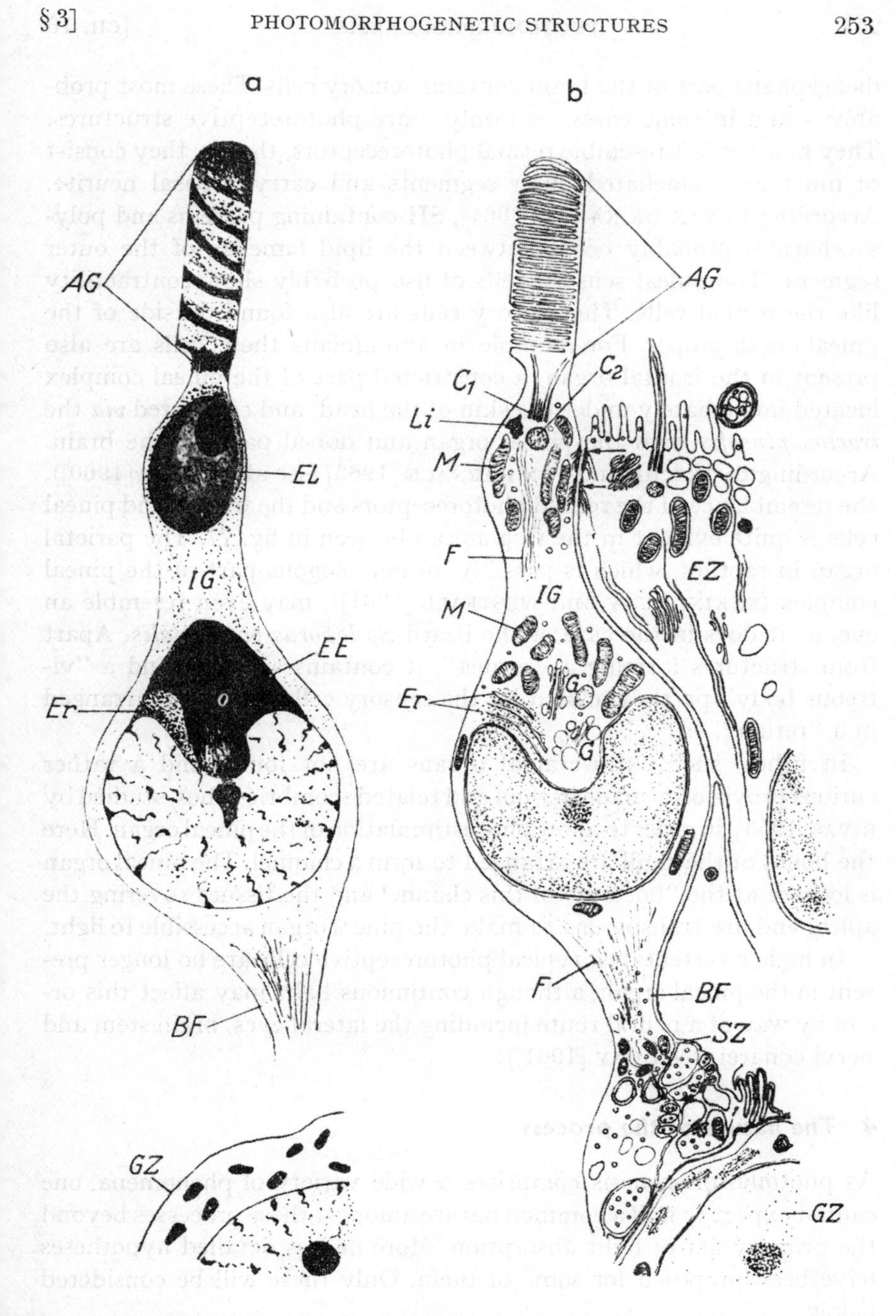

Fig. 77. Photo- and electron-micrographs of sensory cells from the frontal organ of *Rana temporaria*. From: OKSCHE and VON HARNACK [1963]

diencephalic part of the brain contains sensory cells. These most probably – and in some cases, certainly – are photoreceptive structures. They more or less resemble retinal photoreceptors, that is, they consist of inner and lamellated outer segments and carry a basal neurite. According to VAN DE KAMER [1964], SH-containing proteins and polysaccharides probably occur between the lipid lamellae of the outer segment. The pineal sensory cells of fish probably show contractility like the retinal cells. The sensory cells are also found outside of the pineal organ proper. For example in amphibians these cells are also present in the frontal organ, a constricted part of the pineal complex located immediately under the skin of the head, and connected *via* the *tractus pinealis* with the pineal organ and dorsal parts of the brain. According to OKSCHE and VON HARNACK [1963] (see also STEYN [1960]), the resemblance of the retinal photoreceptors and the frontal and pineal cells is quite evident in the frog as can be seen in fig. 77. The parietal organ in reptiles, which is possibly an homologous part of the pineal complex (EAKIN, QUAY and WESTFALL [1961]), may even resemble an eye, as it does in the case of the lizard *Sceloporus occidentalis*. Apart from structures forming a "cornea", it contains a "lens" and a "vitreous body" partly enclosed by the sensory cells which are arranged in a "retina".

In fishes, such extra-cranial organs are not found and a rather curious provision is made in tuna and related scombric fishes, studied by RIVAS [1953], in order to allow photostimulation of the pineal organ. Here the bones of the skull are arranged to form a channel. The pineal organ is located at the "bottom" of this channel and the tissues covering the apical end are transparent to make the pineal organ accessible to light.

In higher vertebrates, typical photoreceptive cells are no longer present in the pineal organ, although continuous light may affect this organ by way of a neural route including the lateral eyes, brain stem and nervi conarei (see QUAY [1961]).

4 *The nature of the process*

As photomorphogenesis comprises a wide variety of phenomena, one cannot expect to find a common nature amongst these processes beyond the primary act of light absorption. More or less detailed hypotheses have been proposed for some of them. Only these will be considered below.

4.1 *In plants*

Two classes of photomorphogenetic reactions can be distinguished. The first, termed the "low energy reaction", functions at a relatively low light level, whereas the second, called the "high energy reaction", requires a relatively large amount of radiation. As an example of a low energy reaction, the leaf and stem growth of etiolated pea seedlings, studied by PARKER *et al.* [1949], reacts to only a few ergs/cm². The high energy reaction is seen for example in the inhibition of the lengthening of the hypocotyl of etiolated white mustard seedlings examined by MOHR [1957], which requires irradiation for 16 hours on two consecutive days with 0.35 milliwatt/cm².

The low energy reaction involves phytochrome and the very first photoprocess runs as follows:

$$P_{660} \underset{\substack{h\nu_{730} \\ \text{(dark)}}}{\overset{h\nu_{660}}{\rightleftharpoons}} P_{730}.$$

It has been suggested (see BORTHWICK and HENDRICKS [1961]), that as a consequence of this conversion, redox couples are forced into action. These authors, referring to a paper of PLATT [1956], suggested that an increase in the number of double bonds in the molecule explains the shift of the absorption to the long-wave side. The difference between the locations of the red and the far-red absorption bands of the two forms of phytochrome may be indicative of a difference of about three conjugate double bonds. They therefore assigned the following location to the hydrogen acceptor and donor in their reaction mechanism:

$$P_{660} + \text{H acceptor} \underset{\substack{h\nu_{730} \\ \text{(dark)}}}{\overset{h\nu_{660}}{\rightleftharpoons}} P_{730} + \text{H donor}.$$

The hypothetical character of this reaction scheme should be emphasized. Although it requires confirmation, the idea is an attractive one.

Whether such a reaction initiates any other processes common to all the low-energy photomorphogenetic processes is not known. One may think of phosphorylation in connection with this and in fact some effect of the phytochrome system on oxidative phosphorylation was observed by GORDON and SURREY [1960]. However there is no clear-cut evidence for this effect being a direct or an indirect one. According to SISLER and KLEIN [1961], it is very unlikely that the ATP content is affected by irradiation with red or far-red light. MARCUS [1960] found that phytochrome regulates the formation of the NADP-linked triose phosphate dehydrogenase. Once again it is still obscure whether or not the relation is a direct one.

According to GALSTON [1959b], phytochrome controls the production of an inhibitor for the IAA oxidase in pea buds, which explains how the phytochrome system can interfere in growth. However, this process need not be common to all the phytochrome-controlled phenomena and its relation with the pigment conversion may well be an indirect one.

Three types of plants can be distinguished on the basis of their photoperiodism, namely "long-day", "short-day", and "day-neutral" (see DOORENBOS and WELLENSIEK [1959]). The types are genetically determined. In some cases, such as the flower formation in *Pharbitis nil*, which is a short-day species studied by NAKAYAMA *et al.* [1960], the periodism apparently interferes with the reversibility of the phytochrome. Though explanations have been offered, these have been reviewed by MOHR [1962] and will not be discussed here. These mechanisms are probably without relation to the photoact, and certainly are not common to all photomorphogenetic processes.

The high energy reaction involves a pigment different from phytochrome which is probably a flavoprotein. Both reactions may act synergistically, as in the case of, for example, the mustard seedling (see MOHR [1957]). A considerable difference between the high energy reaction and the phytochrome system lies in the fact that there is no reversibility of the former system. MOHR [1957] and SIEGELMAN and HENDRICKS [1957, 1958] suggest that the photoreceptive pigment may be butyryl coenzyme-A or a related compound. If this is true, the primary reaction is again an electron or hydrogen transfer.

A large number of papers are dedicated to the effect of various compounds on the light reaction in photomorphogenesis. It was hoped that this would yield information regarding the identity of the photomorphogenetic effector. As a serious candidate for such a function, gibberellic acid was proposed. However evidence, and consequently opinions, are rather contradictory in this respect. Arguments *pro* and *contra* the relation of this substance and photomorphogenesis have been reviewed by MOHR [1962] and KANDELER [1962]. LOCKHARDT [1962] concluded that the natural gibberellin synthesis is not affected by light, though whether light interferes in gibberellin destruction remains to be seen. No general photomorphogenetic effector has yet been found beyond doubt.

4.2 *In animals*

Photomorphogenesis also includes a variety of reactions in animals. Therefore the problem of identifying a basic photoprocess which is common to all types of such widely divergent reactions is also found here. The problem is even more difficult since the variety of animal photoreceptors is much larger than that in plants. One may even wonder whether there is a common process in animal photomorphogenesis at all. Unfortunately information about this problem is even more sparse with animals than with plants. The following discussion will be restricted to the best-understood phenomena.

The hypothalamo-hypophysial system can be stimulated by various factors including temperature and light. See for example HENDERSON [1963] who studied the photoperiodicity of the trout reproductive cycle. The stimuli originate in the various sensory end-organs which in case of photostimulation are the photoreceptive cells of the eye and possibly some elements of the hypothalamo-hypophysial system proper. According to DONOVAN and HARRIS [1955], one or more humoral agents are produced upon stimulation by neurosecretory cells of the hypothalamus. These compounds regulate the production of gonadotropins by the pituitary, and so bring about the photoperiodic control of the reproductive cycle. In migratory birds, migration activity and the fat cycle are controlled by the same system (see WOLFSON [1959]) the stimulation being transmitted from the photoreceptors *via* nerve impulses. Whether the photoprocesses leading to initiation of these impulses are equivalent to those in vision is still unknown. For a review of the extensive work on this topic by Benoit and associates, see FARNER [1959].

The pineal system may act differently. According to DODT and HEERD [1962], light of short wavelengths as well as visible light inhibits pineal nerve impulses, while they are stimulated by light of longer wavelengths and darkness. Apart from this chromatic response, there is also an achromatic one, with a sensitivity maximum at about 560–580 mμ. The photopigment which mediates the chromatic response of the pineal nerve in frogs contains retinal as its chromophore. The authors suggested that inhibition and excitation could be due to two kinds of secretory compounds produced upon illumination, one of which may be released by orange and red light while the other is formed by UV. Evidence about the secretory products and in particular about the processes leading to their formation is still meagre.

QUAY [1963a] found that in adult rats a day-night rhythm occurs in the amount of pineal serotonin or 5-hydroxytryptamine. This compound functions, at least partly, as the precursor of the pineal-specific, and possibly humoral, melatonin. QUAY [1963b] also observed that continuous irradiation of rats with white light from incandescent or fluorescent lamps reduced the weight of the pineal organ. The results suggested that this reduction is primarily due to inhibition of the citric acid cycle, and the accumulation of certain metabolites and lipids, as well as protein synthesis. The pineal complex probably functions in controlling animal activity and, in lower vertebrates, melanophore reactions.

Though a considerable amount of work has been done on the photoperiodicity in insects, information about the primary photoprocess in these organisms also is very meagre. KATO [1959] suggested that the production of diapause eggs may be mediated by excitation of riboflavin derivatives. If this were the case, this kind of photoperiodicity might depend on the photodynamic oxidizing action of riboflavin-related compounds, already discussed under Phototropism.

The impressive amount of research on various kinds of photoperiodicity in different animal species, adequately reviewed by FARNER [1961], principally deals with responses of the photoperiodic effectors. The nature of the primary reactions both in plants and animals are still far from understood.

11

Bioluminescence

1 *Introduction*

The processes considered so far depend on light absorption. Bioluminescence is an emission of visible light by a living organism and so light is a product rather than an agent. The production of light has been discussed in the chapter on the basic processes. A brief survey of bioluminescent species is given below. Chlorophyll luminescence, which was considered under Photosynthesis, will not be dealt with in this discussion.

Though bioluminescence is not seen very often – which according to HARVEY [1940] is because man is so fundamentally diurnal that he rarely notices faint luminescence – the phenomenon is rather wide-spread and occurs in many different plant and animal species. For a detailed survey of luminous organisms, reference should be made to HARVEY [1940].

Organisms may luminesce for two reasons: either they are luminous themselves or they carry symbiotic luminescent species, often in complicated luminous organs adapted to accommodate these species such as those of squids and fishes. Such luminous "hotels" have nothing to do with luminescence as such, and will not be considered here. HARVEY [1955] classified self-luminescent species in representatives of the plant and the animal world. In luminous plants, light is continuously emitted and requires no stimulation, whereas, as a rule, luminous animals require excitation and the duration of the emission is only relatively short. The occurrence of bioluminescence in plants is restricted to certain fungi and bacteria. In the animal world, this phenomenon has been observed in more than 40 genera which are listed in the latter paper of Harvey. The light emission has been studied only in a small percentage of those various species and so bioluminescence of only a very restricted number of animals is considered below. Other types of this process may also occur. For relevant reviews, see HARVEY [1940, 1952], JOHNSON [1955] and MCELROY and SELIGER [1961, 1963].

2 The emitting systems

The emitting compound is given the general term "luciferin". In general bioluminescence is an enzymic reaction and the enzyme systems are designated "luciferases". The reaction is rather specific so that the luciferin and luciferase from different species will not produce light upon mixing. In any case, the emitting compounds are different for various species. This statement is based on the diversity of the colour of the emitted light. For instance, the luminescences of bacteria, fungi, hydroids and Coleoptera are blue to green, white, yellowish, and orange respectively. The railroad worm, *Phrixothrix,* emits both yellow light and, from its cephalic luminous organ, a bright red luminescence. The following systems have been studied.

2.1 Bacterial luminescence

The examination of the bacterial emitting system was considerably facilitated by the development of a technique for extracting the components. This was done most successfully by STREHLER [1953] who prepared acetonized powders from the luminous bacterium *Achromobacter fisheri*. Upon dissolving this powder in water, light emission occurred which faded within a few minutes. STREHLER and CORMIER [1953] studied various factors affecting the luminescence of cell- and particle-free extracts from the acetonized powders. It was found that NAD, or $NADH_2$, was the primary factor which limited the light production of non-dialyzed extracts. In dialyzed preparations however, only $NADH_2$ was able to bring about luminescence. If in addition to NAD, substrates such as malate were added, light was also produced by the dialyzed extracts.

MCELROY *et al.* [1953] prepared active extracts by HCl- and $(NH_4)_2SO_4$-precipitation of cell-free bacterial lysates. They found that FMN is essential for $NADH_2$ to function in initiating light emission by bacterial extracts.

In addition to $NADH_2$ and FMN, a third factor obtained from kidney cortex powders, was shown to participate in the light reaction by

CORMIER and STREHLER [1953]. They identified this compound as palmitaldehyde and found that other fatty aldehydes with chains of 7 or more carbon atoms are also active in the luminescent process. Consequently, they concluded that long-chain aldehydes play a role in the bacterial light reaction. The requirement of such aldehydes was confirmed by MCELROY and GREEN [1955]. These authors studied the light production reaction in a mixture of "highly purified" bacterial luciferase, $FMNH_2$, a long-chain fatty aldehyde and oxygen. They noticed that FMN in a reduced state is essential for luminescence. The kinetics of the light reaction suggested that two $FMNH_2$ molecules interact with the luciferase. McElroy and Green hypothesized that one of these flavin molecules in the reduced form reacts with the aldehyde, while the other functions in the formation of an organic peroxide. This peroxide would act as an oxidant for the FMN-aldehyde complex. The subsequent aldehyde peroxidation to form acid and water would then yield the energy required for light emission. According to TOTTER and CORMIER [1955], one of the flavin molecules which is normally in the oxidized state is tightly bound to the luciferase, while the other one either oxidized or reduced, may also occupy a site in the enzyme, but its dissociation constant is far lower than that of the first flavin. The latter authors speculated that the long-chain aldehyde, or a derivative of it, may function in binding both flavins, and so facilitate the hydrogen or electron transfer required for light production. The emission-linked oxidation was suggested to remove the hydrogen atoms from the loosely bound $FMNH_2$ and the resulting FMN then dissociates from the enzyme. Consequently it was suggested that light may be produced by the oxidation of a luciferase-FMN-$FMNH_2$ complex.

HASTINGS and GIBSON [1963], working with extracts from the luminous bacterium *Achromobacter fisheri*, suggested that the enzyme first reacts with $FMNH_2$, to form a product, termed "Intermediate I", with a half-life of 10 sec. at 10 °C. A reaction between this product and oxygen yields "Intermediate II". What happens next will depend on the presence or absence of long-chain aldehydes. If these compounds are absent, a light reaction occurs with a low quantum yield for each $FMNH_2$ oxidized, whereas considerably stronger light is emitted in the presence of aldehydes. This would mean that without aldehydes, a spontaneous dissipation of intermediate II, coupled with a very dim light emission takes place, while with aldehyde added a third compound, "Intermediate III", is formed. The decay of the latter compound leads to an aldehyde-free excited enzyme complex which, on returning to its ground state emits light. From kinetic evidence, Hastings and Gibson deemed it likely that several intermediate steps occur upon the addition of aldehyde and prior to the formation of the excited species.

The authors suggested that Intermediate I is the reduced luciferase. Tentatively, they proposed the enzyme to be a disulfide containing protein, represented here as: Enz-$(S)_{2n}$. Intermediate I, then may be written: Enz-$(SH)_{2n}$. Intermediate II, formed upon the reaction with oxygen, will be Enz-$(SH)_n(SOOH)_n$. In the presence of aldehyde, intermediate III is formed, and may be represented as: Enz*-$(SH)_n(SOOH)_n$-$(RCHO)_n$. The final excited species, Enz-$(S)_{2n}$, will be produced by liberation of an acid, RCOOH, and water. Indication that luciferase is a sulfhydryl enzyme was procured by CORMIER *et al.* [1956].

The role of the long-chain aliphatic aldehyde is not yet clear. HASTINGS *et al.* [1963] stated that the light production in the luminescence reaction is maximum in the presence of such compounds with chain lengths of 12, 13 and 14 carbons. The authors concluded that the action of aldehydes proceeds *via* the chemical steps involved in the production and decay of the excited state in the luminescent molecule. Aldehyde oxidation to form acid simultaneously with light-emission was proposed by MCELROY and GREEN [1955], but has not yet been proved.

As a matter of fact, STREHLER [1955] and TERPSTRA [1960, see also 1958] concluded that no aldehyde is consumed in the light reaction. TERPSTRA [1960] suggested that long-chain aldehydes function as binding agents between protein and $FMNH_2$. Acccording to TERPSTRA [1964], it should be emphasized that the activity of aldehydes in the *in vivo* bacterial luminescence has not been established beyond doubt. Aldehyde might only be essential in luminescence *in vitro* for satisfying certain spatial requirements of the light reaction. After completion of this manuscript, experiments by Hastings and Gibson (see HASTINGS [1964]) which are in agreement with this suggestion, became known to the author. In these experiments, luciferase mixed with $FMNH_2$ was quickly frozen in liquid nitrogen. Luminescence was then obtained upon warming the ice to about —20 °C. The amount of light emitted from the frozen state was fully equal to the yield which would have been obtained had the reaction been allowed to continue its course in the liquid state. Significantly this yield was the same with or without added aldehyde.

Experiments on the influence of FMN concentration on the light reaction suggest a two-point attachment of $FMNH_2$ (TERPSTRA [1960]). TERPSTRA and VAN EIJK [1961] concluded from ionic effects on the light reaction that the phosphate group of the $FMNH_2$ is not likely to participate in a direct bond with the enzyme. The complex formation may proceed *via* the iso-alloxazine ring system or the ribityl group of $FMNH_2$. The authors also found that in enzyme preparations, Ca^{++} ions prevented the oxidation of free as well as enzyme-bound reduced flavin mononucleotide. The factor responsible for this oxidation proved to be unaffected by heat. This factor, called "substance X", generally accompanying the enzyme in preparations from *Photobacterium phosphoreum*, was found to be not essential to the light reaction. It was suggested that the protective activity of the calcium ions takes place by screening the free phosphate group of $FMNH_2$.

Evidence of the presence of a dissociable enzyme activator, termed "U", which is also necessary for the light reaction in this bacterium was procured by TERPSTRA [1962, 1963]. This factor is not stable to heat. It was suggested that emission of luminescence requires the presence of $FMNH_2$ and a complex formed by the enzyme with both U and aldehyde. It was also found that U exerts a protective function against luciferase inactivation, perhaps by preventing the oxidation of SH-groups.

TERPSTRA [1963] and TERPSTRA and STEENBERGEN [1964] suggested that the $FMNH_2$-oxidizing substance "X" may be identical with the activator "U" in its dissociated form. The nature of the light-emitting molecule has not yet been elucidated. As it is both highly fluorescent and essential in the light reaction, FMN was supposed to be the emitting species until recently (see MCELROY and STREHLER [1954]). However, the peaks of the bacterial luminescence spectra lie between about 470 and 490 mμ as shown in fig. 78, and are considerably removed from the fluorescence maximum of FMN in aqueous solution which is at 530 mμ. TERPSTRA [1962, 1963] and TERPSTRA and STEENBERGEN [1964] tried to identify the light-emitting molecule. The original suggestion that the dissociable enzyme activator "U" might function as the light emitter was not supported by subsequent gel-filtration experiments. In these the active non-protein fraction did not show a distinct fluorescence maximum at 470 mμ. However, a fluorescence increase at 470 mμ was actually obtained upon adding $FMNH_2$ to the enzyme preparations and pre-irradiating the mixture with the 366 mμ mercury line for a few minutes. Fig. 79 shows the resulting fluorescence spectrum. In

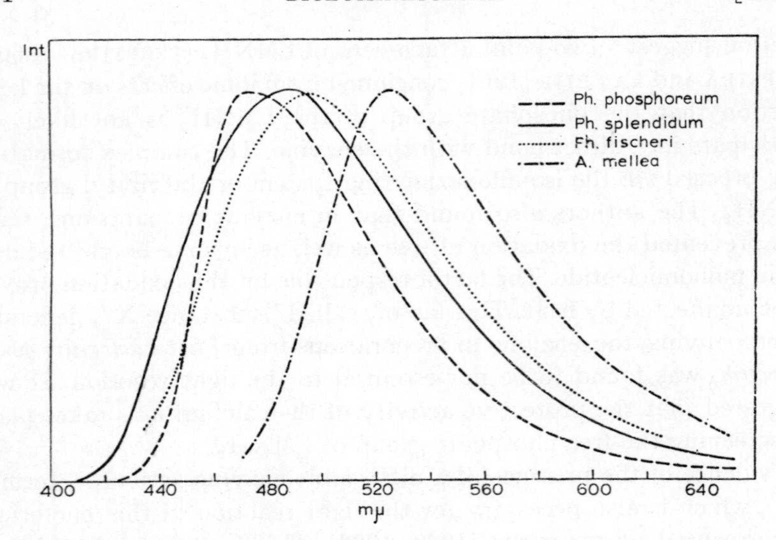

Fig. 78. Emission spectra of three *Photobacterium* species as well as the fungus *Armillaria mellea*. From: SPRUIT-VAN DER BURG [1950]

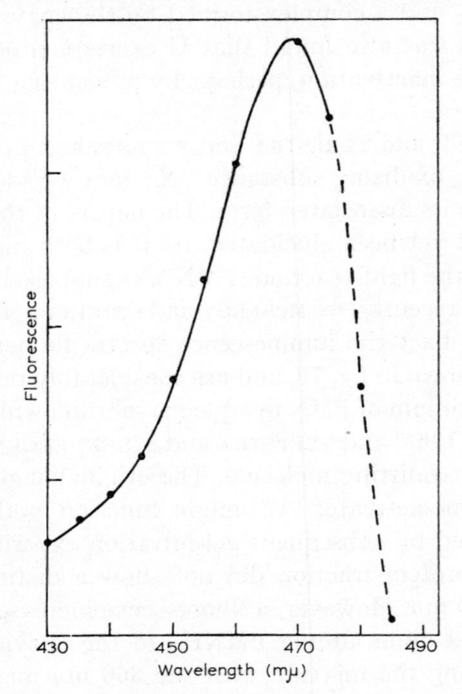

Fig. 79. Fluorescence spectrum of the compound produced by UV-irradiation of a luciferase preparation from *Photobacterium phosphoreum* in the presence of $FMNH_2$. From: TERPSTRA [1963]

other words, the compound fluorescing around 470 mμ was not present in the original enzyme preparation but had to be formed. The author suggested that the reduced flavin combined with a thermostable compound, termed "C", to form a precursor of the fluorescent species. Upon UV-irradiation this precursor may be oxidized by excited FMN, which leads to the formation of the fluorescent complex FMNC. This compound was suggested to be responsible for light emission. Support

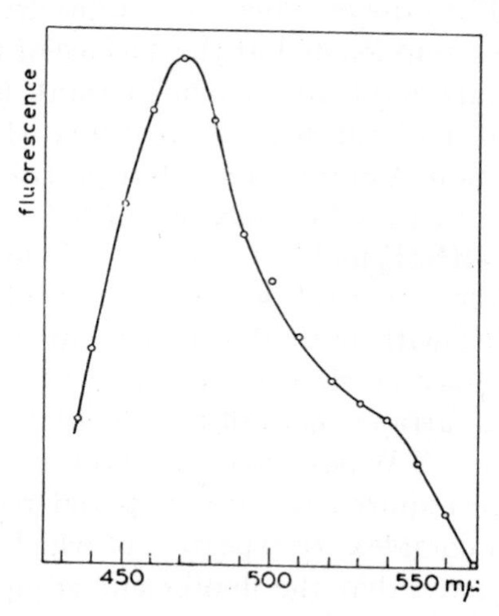

Fig. 80. Fluorescence spectrum of the compound produced by adding H_2O_2 to a luciferase preparation from *Photobacterium phosphoreum*, by courtesy of Dr. W. TERPSTRA

for the oxidative formation of such a luminescent complex was gained by TERPSTRA and STEENBERGEN [1964] from experiments in which the addition of H_2O_2 to luciferase preparations was shown to result in the formation of a compound with a fluorescence spectrum probably identical with that of the substance formed upon UV irradiation, as can be seen in fig. 80. The fact that the long-wave side of this spectrum does not closely resemble that of the fluorescence band depicted in fig. 79 need not be relevant. The accuracy of this part of the latter spectrum is considerably reduced by the overlap of a relatively high base of the fluorescence band of FMN present in the mixture.

Originally, TERPSTRA [1963] suggested that the FMN-part of the FMNC complex is responsible for the 470 mμ fluorescence and luminescence. However a further study of the action of some inhibitory and activating agents on the light reaction lead TERPSTRA and STEENBER-

GEN [1964] to conclude that the C-part of the mentioned complex rather than the FMN moiety is likely to be the seat of the production of both fluorescence and bioluminescence. The results fitted the following hypothesis. The light reaction consists of two consecutive reactions, namely (1) oxidation of a fluorescent group, and (2) subsequent reduction of this group at a reduced site of the enzyme. This reduced site may be formed by the reduction of the active group U which is supposed to be "linked" to the enzyme *via* a sulfhydryl group. Near to a reduced fluorescent group located at the surface of the luciferase complex, an SH-group carrying U in the oxidized state is fixed, and there is a long-chain aldehyde molecule in close proximity which is arranged in a particular configuration. A number of such tripartite combinations may occur at the enzyme surface, but only one of them will be considered.

Addition of two $FMNH_2$ molecules to such a combination will result in the reduction of the oxidized U group by one of these while the other one forms a complex with both the fluorescent group and the long-chain aldehyde. It may be that a certain carbon chain length is required for the proper arrangement of the aldehyde at the enzyme surface by way of Van Der Waals forces. A certain length of the carbon chain might also be required to satisfy spatial requirements for the formation of such a complex. Irrespective of which of these is correct, Terpstra next suggested that the fluorescent group-$FMNH_2$-aldehyde complex is capable of incorporating two oxygen molecules. The oxidized complex then disintegrates into FMN and a peroxide, presumably hydrogen peroxide, both of them in a free state, leaving the unchanged aldehyde and the excited fluorescent group still bound to the enzyme surface. This group releases its energy by the emission of luminescence, and is subsequently reduced by the reduced sulfhydryl-U complex which is thus oxidized and so completes the cycle. In this scheme, the intermediates I and II postulated by HASTINGS and GIBSON [1963] are replaced by a single intermediate, namely the complex: reduced fluorescent group-$FMNH_2$-aldehyde. According to the ideas of TERPSTRA and STEENBERGEN [1964], intermediate III is identical with this complex after the uptake of two oxygen molecules. In any case, further research is needed to confirm these theories.

The blue-green light quanta emitted in bacterial bioluminescence, represent an energy of about 65 kcal/einstein. According to MCELROY and GREEN [1955], peroxidation of aldehyde might furnish sufficient energy to cover this light emission. Nothing can be said of the energy relations in the reaction scheme proposed by TERPSTRA and STEENBERGEN [1964] as yet.

2.2 Fungal luminescence

A survey of 34 luminous fungi, together with 17 species in which the luminescence is still doubtful, has been given by WASSINK [1948]. It seems that luminescence occurs throughout all of the cells, and BERLINER and HOVNANIA [1963], working with cultures of *Panus stipticus* and *Armillaria mellea* noticed that growing hyphae are especially capable of light emission. Aerial rhizomorphs were "dark" and only surface and submerged mycelia emitted luminescence. The emission spectrum of *Armillaria mellea* is shown in fig. 78. AIRTH and MCELROY [1959] were the first to prepare cell-free luciferase extracts. They obtained *in vitro* luminescence by adding a cold-water extract from *Collybia velutipes* which contains luciferase, to a hot-water extract from *Armillaria mellea* which contains luciferin or oxyluciferin, and supplying $NADH_2$ or $NADPH_2$ in the presence of oxygen. AIRTH [1961] concluded that an inhibitor is present in the enzyme preparations. Its inhibiting action could be overcome by addition of bovine plasma albumin. It was found that neither flavins nor long-chain aldehydes can stimulate the fungal luminescence. This reaction therefore differs from that in bacteria. At least two enzymes seem to operate in the crude light reaction system. AIRTH and FOERSTER [1962] isolated two fractions from the same species that AIRTH [1961] had worked with. Both fractions were enzymic. One of them was suggested to catalyze an electron-transfer reaction consisting of the oxidation of $NADH_2$ and the reduction of an unknown compound which is then utilized in the light reaction proper. The other fraction contained luciferase. Indication was obtained that the latter enzyme catalyzes the oxidation of the reduced form of the unknown compound. The luciferase is insoluble in water. BERLINER and BRAND [1962] studied the effect of UV irradiation on the luminous reaction in *Panus stipticus*. BERLINER [1963] found that the responses towards UV irradiation of *Armillaria mellea* are considerably different from those in *Panus stipticus*. From these experiments, she concluded that the fungal luminescent systems are not likely to be the same for all species.

Turning now to light emission by animals, the luminescence of Coleoptera which has been extensively studied, will be considered first.

2.3 *Firefly luminescence*

This most spectacular bioluminescence has been studied both *in vivo* and *in vitro*. According to SELIGER and MCELROY [1960], the spectral distribution of *in vivo* bioluminescence of the firefly *Photinus pyralis* is identical with that of the *in vitro* light emission given in fig. 81. The luminescence colour is green and shows a maximum at 562 mμ. Both luciferin and luciferase have been prepared in a crystalline state. GREEN and MCELROY [1956] obtained needle- or rod-shaped luciferase crystals. The enzyme

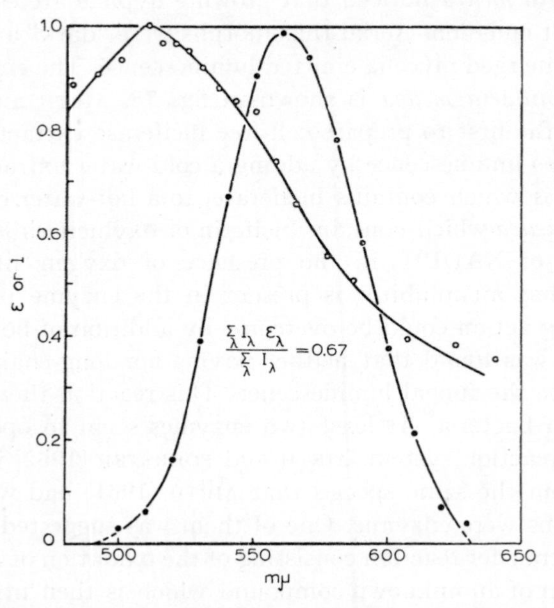

Fig. 81. Emission spectrum (solid dots) of the bioluminescence of an extract of the firefly *Photinus pyralis* in glycylglycine buffer at pH 7.6. Open circles, the phototube spectral sensitivity. From: SELIGER and MCELROY [1960]

is a euglobulin: it is a protein insoluble in water. Its isoelectric point occurs in between pH 6.2 and 6.3, and its molecular weight is likely to be about 100000. BITLER and MCELROY [1957] prepared luciferin crystals, which are anisotropic needles. The molecular weight of luciferin was found to be 308, and the empirical formula was suggested to be $C_{13}H_{12}N_2S_2O_3$. WHITE *et al.* [1961] succeeded in synthesizing firefly luciferin. They worked out the structural formula and found that the luciferin molecule contains 11 instead of 13 carbons. They also synthesized the oxidation product dehydroluciferin. They prepared both D- and L-luciferin, the structural formula of the D-isomer being shown in fig. 82. SELIGER *et al.* [1961] found that the D- and L-isomers reacted in exactly the same way as natural luciferin, except for the fact that the D-form produced light upon oxidation, whereas no luminescence is emitted by the L-isomer. MCELROY and SELIGER [1963] observed that oxygen was consumed by the D-isomer but not by the L-isomer. It is the D-isomer which is found *in vivo*. SELIGER and MCELROY [1962] obtained chemiluminescence with firefly luciferin in the absence of luciferase by the addition of a strong base to synthetic luciferyl-adenylate dissolved in dimethylsulfoxide. In this case no stereospecificity of the luciferin isomers for the light emission was observed.

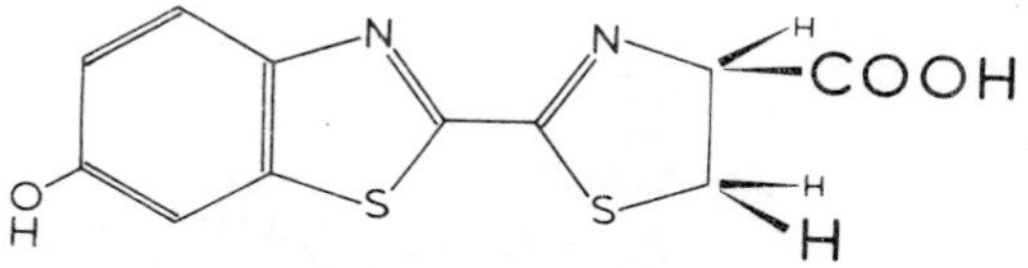

Fig. 82. Structural formula of the D-isomer of firefly luciferin. According to WHITE *et al.* [1961]

The reaction mechanism has been elucidated by McElroy and associates. MCELROY [1947] found that ATP participates in the light reaction. The enzyme luciferase (E) catalyzes a reaction between ATP and luciferin (LH_2) in such a way that a complex enzyme-luciferin-adenosinemonophosphate (E-LH_2-AMP) is formed, while inorganic pyrophosphate (PP) is released (MCELROY and GREEN [1956]). This process was supposed to be the transfer of an adenyl group to the carboxyl group of luciferin. The presence of magnesium ions is required for this reaction. The oxidation product of luciferin formed in the light reaction is called "oxyluciferin". According to MCELROY and SELIGER [1963], light is emitted upon the oxidation of E-LH_2-AMP to

$$\mathrm{E{-}\overset{\overset{\large O}{/\!\!/}}{L}{-}AMP},$$

standing for the "oxyluciferin" complex in the presence of oxygen. They found that one mole of D-luciferin consumes one mole of atmospheric oxygen on oxidation. Since the oxygen consumption is not affected by catalase, it was concluded that the light reaction does not result in the production of free hydrogen peroxide. The authors suggested that the nature of the excitation process may consist of the formation of an organic hydroperoxide out of the E-LH_2-AMP complex, followed by a dehydration reaction. The latter reaction may leave one of the oxygen atoms bound to the complex while the other may be used in the formation of a water molecule. The dehydration reaction may result in producing an excited enzyme-oxyluciferyl-adenylate complex which then returns to its ground state under emission of a light quantum. SELIGER and MCELROY [1959] found an average value of 0.88 ± 0.25 for the number of light quanta emitted per luciferin molecule oxidized. They therefore concluded that one quantum is emitted per oxyluciferin molecule produced. The oxidation reaction outlined above, would produce 100 kcal. This amount of energy is amply sufficient for the emission of a "blue" quantum by an excited luciferin molecule.

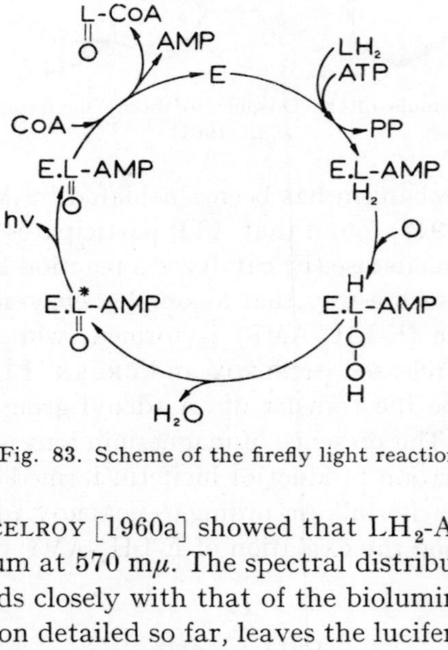

Fig. 83. Scheme of the firefly light reaction

SELIGER and MCELROY [1960a] showed that LH_2-AMP "acid" fluorescence is maximum at 570 mμ. The spectral distribution of this fluorescence corresponds closely with that of the bioluminescence.

The light reaction detailed so far, leaves the luciferase still bound to oxyluciferin and AMP after the quantum emission. Since oxyluciferin is a potent inhibitor of the luciferase activity, AIRTH *et al.* [1958] searched for the way in which the enzyme is freed from this inhibiting compound. They found that coenzyme A is capable of removing oxyluciferin from the enzyme surface by the formation of oxyluciferyl-CoA. It was also found that CoA occurs in considerable quantities in firefly lanterns. This scheme for the firefly light reaction and the cyclic regeneration of the free enzyme is summarized in fig. 83.

2.4 *Other bioluminescences*

A considerable number of other animal bioluminescent organisms have been studied. The mechanisms of these light reactions are not so well understood as those discussed above. A brief enumeration of some data of particular interest will suffice here.

The marine ostracod crustacean *Cypridina hilgendorfii* emits a blue luminescence with the maximum at 460 mμ. In the submaxillary gland, the luciferin and the luciferase are found in granules (HARVEY [1952]). Luciferin is contained in granules with a diameter of 10 μ and the luciferase in granules of 2 μ diameter. When they are secreted, these granules dissolve in the sea water and luminescence results. The light production takes place outside the organism though as the light emis-

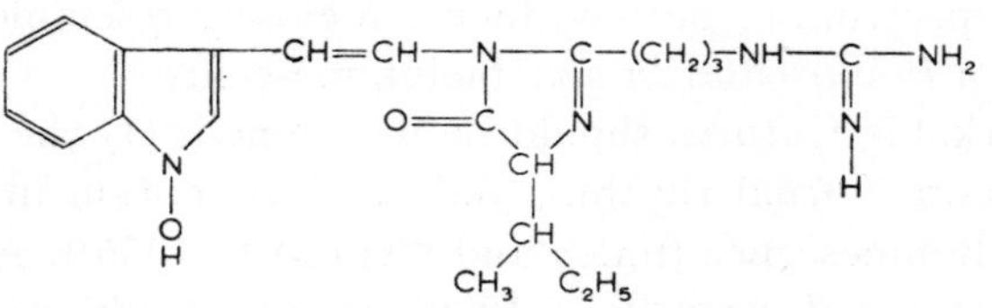

Fig. 84. Structural formula of *Cypridina* luciferin as proposed by HIRATA *et al.* [1959]

sion depends on the presence of an enzyme, the oxygen-dependent reaction is true bioluminescence. WEIR *et al.* [1955] determined an iso-electric point of about 3.3 for luciferase, whereas SHIMOMURA *et al.* [1961] found this point to be about 4.4. The figures for the molecular weight range from 80000 to 45000. For instance, TSUJI and SOWINSKI [1961] decided that the molecular weight amounts to 79650, while SHIMOMURA *et al.* [1961] obtained a value of about 50000. The luciferase may be a metallo-protein.

Luciferin has been prepared in the crystalline state (SHIMOMURA *et al.* [1957] and HENEDA *et al.* [1961]) in the form of orange-red needles. HIRATA *et al.* [1959] found the empirical formula to be $C_{21}H_{28}O_2N_6$, and suggested the provisional structural formula shown in fig. 84.

The *Cypridina* light reaction is much simpler than those discussed previously. Light emission occurs upon the luciferase-catalyzed oxidation of luciferin in the presence of oxygen. This reaction was studied by CHASE [1949], and can be written:

$$2LH_2 + O_2 \xrightarrow{E} 2L + 2H_2O + h\nu.$$

The reaction also takes place in the absence of the enzyme although in this case, no light is emitted (CHASE *et al.* [1961]). SIE *et al.* [1961] established a cross-reaction between luciferins and luciferases of both *Cypridina* and *Apogon*. The bioluminescence of this fish seems to be based on the same system as that of *Cypridina*. The emission spectra were identical for all possible combinations.

The marine photosynthetic dinoflagellate *Gonyaulax polyedra* emits a blue luminescence with a major maximum around 470 mμ on mechanical stimulation. HASTINGS and SWEENEY [1957] studied the luminescence of cell-free extracts and found that, in addition to luciferin, luciferase and oxygen, a relatively high salt concentration is required for light emission. BODE and HASTINGS [1963] purified *Gonyaulax* luciferin. They found it to be a small, readily oxidizable molecule. The fluorescence spectrum of purified luciferin closely resembled the emission spectra of *in vitro* and *in vivo* bioluminescence.

Two remarkable features should be mentioned: (1) the bioluminescence exhibits a diurnal rhythm, and (2) illumination influences the capacity for luminescence (HAXO and SWEENEY [1955]). According to SWEENEY, HAXO and HASTINGS [1959], photoactivation and photoinhibition of this bioluminescence are attributable to light absorbed by the photosynthetic pigments. In addition, some far-red absorbing pigment may act as a sensitizer for photoinhibition. HASTINGS and SWEENEY [1960] determined the action spectrum for shifting the phase of the luminescence rhythm. This spectrum showed two narrow maxima at 650 mμ and 475 mμ. No evidence of a far-red reversibility of the phase shift was found to occur. BODE *et al.* [1963] observed that the luciferin activity also displays a diurnal rhythm, closely corresponding to that of the light emission.

DE SA *et al.* [1963] described the occurrence and isolation of intracellular particles which emit light upon addition of dilute acid in the presence of oxygen. The particles look like crystals under the electron microscope, and are highly birefringent. These "crystalline" bodies were termed "scintillons". They are rhombohedral or twinned rhombohedral. The long axis is 0.3 μ on the average, but ranges from 0.1 to 0.6 μ. Both the width and thickness range from 0.1 to 0.3 μ. There is a quantitative relationship between *in vitro* luminescence and particle number. The particles are found throughout the cell, but their concentration is highest towards the periphery. The possible relationship between these particles and the soluble luminescence system, isolated from *Gonyaulax,* is still obscure. DE SA *et al.* [1963] did not succeed in isolating any soluble enzyme or substrate from the purified particles, and could not detect any effect of the soluble system on the activity of these particles. In more recent studies, De Sa and Hastings (see HASTINGS [1964]) have identified guanine as a major component of the crystals; indeed crystals having a similar birhombohedral structure are found in authentic crystalline guanine. However the luminescent system is believed to be an additional component and small, though measurable, quantities of *Gonyaulax* luciferase have been extracted from scintillons in a weakly acid medium.

The sea pansy, *Renilla reniformis,* is a colony of zooids on a stalk. When excited, it emits blue-green light with a maximum at 485 mμ (CORMIER and ECKROADE [1962]). CORMIER [1960] prepared cell-free extracts and found that the light reaction requires the presence of luciferase, luciferin, molecular oxygen and an adenine-containing nucleotide. Originally ADP or AMP were thought to represent this nucleotide. However, CORMIER [1962] obtained evidence that it is 3′,5′-diphosphoadenosine (DPA) which is involved in the emission process. It was suggested that the DPA takes part in a luciferase-catalyzed reaction with luciferin to form an intermediate which emits light upon oxidation by molecular oxygen. The system is activated by divalent metal ions.

The balanoglossid *Balanoglossus biminiensis,* a worm-like marine animal, secretes a bluish-luminescent slime over its whole body. CORMIER and DURE [1963] prepared luciferin and luciferase out of this species. They found that the luminescent system does not require oxygen, but does need hydrogen peroxide. DURE and CORMIER [1963] presented evidence that balanoglossid luciferase is a peroxidase. It can even be replaced by horseradish peroxidase in the bioluminescent reaction.

The polychaete annelid *Chaetopterus variopedatus* was studied by JOHNSON [1959]. This marine worm displays bioluminescence in two ways: (1) by secreting a luminous slime, and (2) by secreting non-slime material from gland cells containing granules. A study of the luminescent slime suggested that the reactants in this also occur in particles.

The luminescence system of the "marine fireworm" *Odontosyllis enopla*, a syllid worm, was studied by SHIMOMURA *et al.* [1963a] who established partial purification of both luciferin and luciferase. Luciferase was found to catalyze the oxidation of luciferin in the presence of molecular oxygen to give a blue-green luminescence with a maximum at 507 mμ.

A luminous protein, termed "aequorin", was extracted from the hydromedusan *Aequorea aequorea* by SHIMOMURA *et al.* [1962, 1963b]. This protein was found to emit light in the presence of calcium ions, and to a lesser extent in the presence of strontium ions. The luminous system was actually found to consist only of aequorin and Ca^{++} ions, and is probably the simplest bioluminescent system. Neither a luciferin nor a luciferase participate in the light reaction, and the presence of oxygen or peroxides is not necessary. The overall reaction is believed to proceed according to the equation

$$\text{aequorin} + Ca^{++} \rightarrow \text{products} + Ca^{++} + h\nu.$$

The emission maximum occurs at 460 mμ. The molecular weight of aequorin was calculated to be 35000. The close similarity between both the excitation and the emission spectra of this system and those observed with $NADH_2$ lead the authors to suggest that chemical excitation of a pyridinium group is involved in the bioluminescence of *Aequorea*.

A luminescent protein named "halistaurin" from another hydromedusan, *Halistaura*, was also extracted and purified by SHIMOMURA *et al.* [1963c]. The properties were found to be the same as those of aequorin with regard to Ca^{++} requirement and oxygen-independency of the light reaction, and the emission spectrum also showed a maximum at 460 mμ. Sr^{++} ions also activate light emission, but, as in the case of aequorin, to a much smaller degree. The authors obtained indications that the halistaurin molecule is larger than the aequorin one though they suggested that the active groups of both proteins may be identical.

The luminous organs of many animals have been described but since these structures differ greatly and do not appreciably contribute to the knowledge of the emission mechanism, a discussion of these organs will not be entered into. A number of interesting pictures have been collected by HARVEY [1940] who also listed an impressive number of luminous organisms.

In conclusion it can be stated that while only a few of the bioluminescent mechanisms are fully understood, it is clear that the various systems operate in basically different ways.

12

Concluding remarks

Many photoprocesses take place in biology without belonging to the regular light-dependent reactions which are required for maintaining the living organism. An example of this is sunburn which is due to photodynamic activity arising from excitation by UV light. Since this book deals primarily with the effects of visible radiation, it seems reasonable to refrain from a discussion of such UV-induced phenomena. Some sensitizers are also capable of causing photodynamic damage in visible light, but in any case, the most photodynamic processes belong under the heading of "stress biology", a field quite different from "normal" photobiology. Still, some of the photodynamic phenomena are of regular importance to the organism, but these again depend on irradiation with UV rather than visible light, for example the conversion of pro-vitamin D into vitamin D. For this reason, photodynamics have not been dealt with under a separate heading, and so if the discussion of a photobiological process included photodynamic action, this was considered at the same time. Such was the case with the riboflavin-catalyzed photooxidation of indoleacetic acid *in vitro*, and probably *in vivo*. It is not claimed that all photobiological processes other than photodynamics have been considered in this book. For instance, melanophore reactions induced by direct light action were not considered. Only the major fields were dealt with.

When considering the photoreactions, the diversity of the various processes is quite evident. The key substance involved in all photoreactions is the light absorbing pigment and a study of these compounds may be the best basis for a comparison of the various photobiological processes. A survey of the major pigments involved in these processes, their occurrence and their function is given in table 2.

In this table, only the compounds essential for light absorption are listed: cytochromes and related substances which act as cofactors in photosynthesis rather than as light absorbers, are not included. Upon

TABLE 2

Survey of the major photobiologically active pigments and their functions

photoreceptive pigment	approximate location of major absorption bands *in vivo* (mμ)	active in	photo-receptor structure	photo-induced reaction	"primary" result	end product of photo-reaction	ultima result
chlorophyll-a	680, 440	photo-synthesis	chloroplasts, chromatoplasm	generation of free electrons	oxidation and reduction	$NAD(P)H_2$ ATP	carbohydrat synthesis
chlorophylls b-e	680–650, 470–400	,,		energy transfer			
chlorobium chlorophylls	810, 740, 450	,,	granules free grana	generation of free electrons	,,	,,	,,
bacterio-chlorophyll	890, 850 800, 590, 370	,,	chromatophores, free grana	,,	,,		,,
chlorophyll-a and bacterio-chlorophyll (at least)		phototaxis	photosynthetic organelles			ATP?	direction of locomotion
		photokinesis	photosynthetic organelles			ATP?	motility
retinal-opsin complexes	600–500	vision	rods, cones, cells	stereo-isomer-ization	exposure of active groups	stimulus	information
		phototaxis	rods, cones, cells				direction of locomotion
		phototropism	cells				curvature
		photo-morphogenesis	sensory cells encephalic parts, rods, cones				various morphologica effects
carotenoids	550–350	photo-synthesis	all photo-synthetic organelles	energy transfer			excitation of chlorophyll
		phototaxis	photosynthetic organelles, eyespots?			ATP?	direction of locomotion

TABLE 2 *(Continued)*

Survey of the major photobiologically active pigments and their functions

otoreceptive pigment	approximate location of major absorption bands *in vivo* (mμ)	active in	photo-receptor structure	photo-induced reaction	"primary" result	end product of photo-reaction	ultimate result
tenoids	550–350	phototaxis	paraflagellar body?				
		photokinesis?	same?			ATP?	motility
		photo-tropism?	cells			photo-dynamic agent	curvature
		photo-morpho-genesis	cells			photo-dynamic agent?	various morphological effects
		protection against radiation?	photosynthetic organelles				
roteins	650–550	photosynthesis	chloroplasts, chromatoplasm	energy transfer			excitation of chlorophylls
		phototaxis	chromatoplasm			ATP?	direction of locomotion
		photokinesis	chromatoplasm			ATP?	motility
flavin related pounds	450, 365	phototaxis	chloroplasts			ATP?	orientation
		photodinesis	cytoplasm			ATP? –SH?	protoplasmic streaming
		phototropism	cells			photo-dynamic agent?	curvature
		photomorpho-genesis?	cells			photo-dynamic agent?	various morphological effects
tochrome	730 or 660	photomorpho-genesis	cytoplasm			active enzyme	various morphological effects
		phototropism?	cytoplasm				sensitivity control
		phototaxis	cytoplasm				orientation of chloroplasts
		photosynthesis?					inhibition by P_{730}?

consideration of the table, two facts become evident. First, the knowledge about many processes is still incomplete, and second, each photoreceptive pigment functions as a catalyst for a number of reactions.

As far as known, the nature of the photopigments is very varied. Three classes are of greatest importance, namely (1) pyrrole derivatives – the chlorophylls and biliproteins – (2) carotenoids, including haplocarotenoids which constitute the chromophore groups of the visual pigments, and (3) flavins. The nature of phytochrome has not yet been elucidated and it will be recalled that HENDRICKS *et al.* [1962] suggested that the active group of phytochrome might be related to allophycocyanin, and thus be a pyrrole derivative. However this suggestion is merely hypothetical, and the authors also mentioned some objections to their own suggestion.

Table 2 illustrates that a limited class of pigments is active in the photocatalysis of a large number of biological phenomena. The open spaces in the table show that in most cases the way in which such a catalysis occurs is still obscure. In conclusion, it can be said that an impressive number of unsolved problems await elucidation and photobiology remains a most exciting field for those who are interested in the problems of light and life.

References

ABRAHAMSON, E. W., R. G. ADAMS and V. WULFF, 1959, Reversible spectral changes in retinene solutions following flash illumination. *J. Phys. Chem.* **63**, 441–443.

ADAMSON, A. W., 1960, Physical chemistry of surfaces. Interscience Publishers, Inc., New York, London.

AIRTH, R. L., 1961, Characteristics of cell-free fungal bioluminescence. *In*: W. D. McElroy and B. Glass, eds., Light and Life, The Johns Hopkins Press, Baltimore. pp. 262–273.

AIRTH, R. L. and G. E. FOERSTER, 1962, The isolation of catalytic components required for cell-free fungal bioluminescence. *Arch. Biochem. Biophys.* **97**, 567–573.

AIRTH, R. L. and W. D. MCELROY, 1959, Light emission from extracts of luminous fungi. *J. Bacteriol.* **77**, 249–250.

AIRTH, R. L., W. C. RHODES and W. D. MCELROY, 1958, The function of coenzyme A in luminescence. *Biochim. Biophys. Acta* **27**, 519–532.

ALLEN, M. B., C. S. FRENCH and J. S. BROWN, 1960, Native and extractable forms of chlorophyll in various algal groups. *In*: M. B. Allen, ed., Symp. Comp. Biol., **1**: Comparative Biochemistry of Photoreactive Systems. Academic Press, New York, London. pp. 33–51.

ALLEN, M. B., L. R. PIETTE and J. C. MURCHIO, 1962, Free radicals in photosynthetic reactions. I. Electron paramagnetic resonance signals from illuminated *Chlorella pyrenoidosa*. *Biochim. Biophys. Acta* **60**, 539–547.

AMESZ, J. and L. N. M. DUYSENS, 1962, Action spectrum, kinetics and quantum requirement of phosphopyridine nucleotide reduction and cytochrome oxidation in the blue-green alga *Anacystis nidulans*. *Biochim. Biophys. Acta* **64**, 261–278.

ANDERSON, J. M., U. BLASS and M. CALVIN, 1960, Biosynthesis and possible relations among the carotenoids and between chlorophyll *a* and *b*. *In*: M. B. Allen, ed., Comparative Biochemistry of Photoreactive Systems. Academic Press, New York, London. pp. 215–224.

ANDROES, G. M., M. F. SINGLETON and M. CALVIN, 1962, EPR in chromatophores from *Rhodospirillum rubrum* and in quantasomes from spinach chloroplasts. *Proc. Natl. Acad. Sci.* **48,** 1022–1031.

ARDEN, G. B. and K. TANSLEY, 1955a, The spectral sensitivity of the pure-cone retina of the grey squirrel (*Sciurus carolinensis leucotis*). *J. Physiol.* **127,** 592–602.

ARDEN, G. B. and K. TANSLEY, 1955b, The spectral sensitivity of the pure-cone retina of the souslik (*Citellus citellus*). *J. Physiol.* **130,** 225–232.

ARNOLD, W. and H. K. MACLAY, 1959, Chloroplasts and chloroplast pigments as semiconductors. *In*: The Photochemical Apparatus. Its Structure and Function. Brookhaven Symp. Biol., **11**. Brookhaven National Laboratory, Upton. pp. 1–8.

ARNOLD, W. and H. K. SHERWOOD, 1957, Are chloroplasts semiconductors? *Proc. Natl Acad. Sci.* **43,** 105–114.

ARNON, D. I. 1951, Extracellular photosynthetic reactions. *Nature*, **167**, 1008–1010.

ARNON, D. I., 1960, The chloroplast as a functional unit in photosynthesis. *In*: W. Ruhland, ed., Encyclopedia of Plant Physiology **5**, Pt. 1. Springer-Verlag, Berlin, Göttingen, Heidelberg. pp. 773–829.

ARNON, D. I., 1961, Cell-free photosynthesis and the energy conversion process. *In*: W. D. McElroy and B. Glass, eds., Light and Life. The Johns Hopkins Press, Baltimore. pp. 489–565.

ARNON, D. L., M. B. ALLEN and F. R. WHATLEY, 1954, Photosynthesis by isolated chloroplasts. *Nature* **174**, 394–396.

ARNON, D. I., F. R. WHATLEY and M. B. ALLEN, 1957, Triphosphopyridine nucleotide as a catalyst of photosynthetic phosphorylation. *Nature* **180**, 182–185.

ARNON, D. I., F. R. WHATLEY and M. B. ALLEN, 1958, Assimilatory power in photosynthesis. Photosynthetic phosphorylation by isolated chloroplasts is coupled with TPN reduction. *Science* **127**, 1026–1034.

ARONOFF, S., 1960, The chemistry of chlorophyll. *In*: W. Ruhland, ed., Encyclopedia of Plant Physiology **5**, Pt. 1. Springer-Verlag, Berlin, Göttingen, Heidelberg. pp. 234–251.

ASANA, R. D., 1938, On the relation between the distribution of auxin in the tip of the *Avena* coleoptile and the first negative phototropic curvature. *Ann. Bot.* N.S. **2**, 955–957.

ASCHOFF, J. and R. WEVER, 1962a, Über Phasenbeziehungen zwischen biologischer Tagesperiodik und Zeitgeberperiodik. *Zs. Vergl. Physiol.* **46**, 115–128.

ASCHOFF, J. and R. WEVER, 1962b, Resynchronisation der Tagesperiodik von Vögeln nach Phasensprung des Zeitgebers. *Zs. Vergl. Physiol.* **46**, 249–275.

ASOMANING, E. J. A. and A. W. GALSTON, 1961, Comparative study of phototropic response and pigment content in oat and barley coleoptiles. *Plant Physiol.* **36**, 453–464.

ASSENMACHER, I., 1957, Répercussions de lésions hypothalamiques sur le conditionnement génital du canard domestique. *Compt. Rend.* **245**, 210–213.

AUBERT, J. P., G. MILHAUD and J. MILLET, 1957, L'assimilation de l'anhydride carbonique par des bactéries chimiautotrophes. *Ann. Inst. Pasteur* **92**, 515–528.

BALL, S., F. D. COLLINS, P. D. DALVI and R. A. MORTON, 1949, Studies on vitamin A. 11. Reactions of $retinene_1$ with amino compounds. *Biochem. J.* **45**, 304–307.

BALL, S., T. W. GOODWIN and R. A. MORTON, 1948, Studies on vitamin A. 5. The preparation of $retinene_1$-vitamin A aldehyde. *Biochem J.* **42**, 516–523.

BANBURY, G. H., 1952, Physiological studies in the Mucorales. I. The phototropism of sporangiophores of *Phycomyces Blakesleeanus*. *J. Exptl. Bot.* **3**, 77–94.

BANBURY, G. H., 1959, Phototropism of lower plants. *In*: W. Ruhland, ed., Encyclopedia of Plant Physiology, **17**, Pt. 1. Springer-Verlag, Berlin, Göttingen, Heidelberg. pp. 530–578.

BANNISTER, T. T., 1960, The photoreduction of chlorophyll a. *In*: L. J. Heidt, R. S. Livingston, E. Rabinowitch and F. Daniels, eds., Photochemistry in the Liquid and Solid States. John Wiley and Sons, Inc., New York, London. pp. 110–121.

BANNISTER, T. T. and J. E. BERNARDINI, 1962, The photoreduction of chlorophyll in the presence of diphosphopyridine nucleotide in pyridine solutions. *Biochim. Biophys. Acta* **59**, 188–201.

BASSHAM, J. A., 1963, Energy capture and conversion by photosynthesis. *J. Theoret. Biol.* **4**, 52–72.

BASSHAM, J. A. and M. CALVIN, 1957, The path of carbon in photosynthesis. Prentice Hall, Inc., Englewood Cliffs.

BAUMGARDT, E., 1959, Visual spatial and temporal summation. *Nature* **184**, 1951–1952.

BEIKIRCH, H., 1925, Die Abhängigkeit der Protoplasma-Strömung vom Licht und Temperatur und ihre Bedingtheit durch andere Faktoren. *Bot. Arch.* **12**, 389–445.

BEINERT, H., B. KOK and G. HOCH, 1962, The light induced electron paramagnetic resonance signal of photocatalyst P700. *Biochem. Biophys. Res. Comm.* **7**, 209–212.

BENOIT, J., 1951, Titres et travaux scientifiques. Imprimerie des dernières nouvelles de Strasbourg.

BENOIT, J. and L. OTT, 1944, External and internal factors in sexual activity. Effect of irradiation with different wave-lengths on the mechanisms of photostimulation of the hypophysis and on testicular growth in the immature duck. *Yale J. Biol. Med.* **17**, 27–46.

BENOIT, J., F. X. WALTER and I. ASSENMACHER, 1950, Contribution à l'étude du réflexe opto-hypophysaire gonadostimulant chez le canard soumis à des radiations lumineuses de diverses longueurs d'onde. *J. Physiol.* (Paris) **42**, 537–541.

BENSON, A. A. and M. CALVIN, 1950, Carbon dioxide fixation by green plants. *Ann. Rev. Plant Physiol.* **1**, 25–42.

BERGERON, J. A., 1959, The bacterial chromatophore.: *In*: Brookhaven Symp. Biol., **11**. The Photochemical Apparatus. Its Structure and Function. Biology Department, Brookhaven National Laboratory, Upton. pp. 118–129.

BERLINER, M. D., 1963, The action of monochromatic ultraviolet radiation on luminescence in *Armillaria mellea. Radiation Research* **19**, 392–401.

BERLINER, M. D. and P. B. BRAND, 1962, Effects of monochromatic ultraviolet light on luminescence of *Panus stipticus. Mycologia* **54**, 415–421.

BERLINER, M. D. and H. P. HOVNANIAN, 1963, Autophotography of luminescent fungi. *J. Bacteriol.* **86**, 339–341.

BERTSCH, W. F., 1962, Two photoreactions in photosynthesis: evidence from the delayed light emission of *Chlorella. Proc. Natl. Acad. Sci.* **48**, 2000–2004.

BERTSCH, W. F., 1963, The photoinhibition of growth in etiolated stem segments. III. Far-red reversibility of blue light effects in *Pisum. Am. J. Bot.* **50**, 754–760.

BICKOFF, E. M., A. L. LIVINGSTON, G. F. BAILEY and C. R. THOMPSON, 1954, Alfalfa carotenoids. Xanthophylls in fresh and dehydrated alfalfa. *Agric. Food Chem.* **2**, 563–567.

BISHOP, P. M. and C. P. WHITTINGHAM, 1963, Emerson effect in isolated chloroplasts. *Nature* **197**, 1225–1226.

BITLER, B. and W. D. MCELROY, 1957, The preparation and properties of crystalline firefly luciferin. *Arch. Biochem. Biophys.* **72**, 358–368.

BLAAUW, A. H., 1909, Die Perzeption des Lichtes. *Rec. Trav. Bot. Néerl.* **5**, 209–372.

BLAAUW, A. H., 1919, Licht und Wachstum. III. *Meded. Landbouwhoogeschool Wageningen* **15**, 87–204.

BLAAUW, O. H. 1964, Personal communication.

BLAAUW-JANSEN, G., 1954, Chlorophyllide, the probable precursor of a growth inhibitor. *Nature* **174**, 312–313.

BLAAUW-JANSEN, G., 1959, The influence of red and far red light on growth and phototropism of the *Avena* seedling. *Rec. Trav. Bot. Néerl.* **8**, 1–39.

BLAAUW-JANSEN, G., 1964, Personal communication.

BLINKS, L. R., 1954, The photosynthetic function of pigments other than chlorophyll. *Ann. Rev. Plant Physiol.* **5**, 93–114.

BLINKS, L. R., 1960, Chromatic transients in the photosynthesis of green, brown, and red algae. *In*: M. B. Allen, ed., Comparative Biochemistry of Photoreactive Systems. Academic Press, New York, London. pp. 367–375.

BODE, V. C., R. DE SA and J. W. HASTINGS, 1963, Daily rhythm of luciferin activity in *Gonyaulax polyedra. Science* **141**, 913–915.

BODE, V. C. and J. W. HASTINGS, 1963, The purification and properties of the bioluminescent system in *Gonyaulax polyedra. Arch. Biochem. Biophys.* **103**, 488–499.

BOGORAD, L., 1960, The biosynthesis of protochlorophyll. *In:* M. B. Allen, ed., Comparative Biochemistry of Photoreactive Systems. Academic Press, New York, London. pp. 227–256.

BOLL, F., 1876, Zur Anatomie und Physiologie der Retina. *Monatsber. Kön. Preuss. Akad. Wiss. Berlin* **41**, 783–787.

BONNER, B. A., 1962, *In vitro* dark conversion and other properties of phytochrome. *Plant Physiol.* **37**, Suppl. XXVII.

BORTHWICK, H. A. and S. B. HENDRICKS, 1960, Photoperiodism in plants. *Science* **132**, 1223–1228.

BORTHWICK, H. A. and S. B. HENDRICKS, 1961, Effects of radiation on growth and development. *In*: W. Ruhland, ed., Encyclopedia of Plant Physiology, **16**. Springer-Verlag, Berlin, Göttingen, Heidelberg. pp. 299–330.

BORTHWICK, H. A., S. B. HENDRICKS and M. W. PARKER, 1952, Action spectrum for inhibition of stem growth in dark-grown seedlings of albino and non-albino barley (*Hordeum vulgare*). *Bot. Gaz.* **113**, 95–105.

BORTWICK, H. A., S. B. HENDRICKS and M. W. PARKER, 1956, Photoperiodism. *In*: A. Hollaender, ed., Radiation Biology, III. McGraw-Hill Book Company, Inc., New York, Toronto, London. pp. 479–517.

BOTTELIER, H. P., 1934, Über den Einfluss äusserer Faktoren auf die Protoplasmaströmung in der *Avena*-Koleoptile. *Rec. Trav. Bot. Néerl.* **31**, 474–582.

BOUMAN, M. A., 1949, On the quanta explanation of vision. Doctoral thesis, State University, Utrecht.

BOUMAN, M. A., 1961, History and present status of quantum theory in vision. *In:* W. A. Rosenblith, ed., Sensory Communication. The M. I. T. Press and John Wiley and Sons, New York, London. pp. 377–401.

BOUMAN, M. A. and H. A. VAN DER VELDEN, 1947, The two-quanta explanation of the dependence of the threshold values and visual acuity on the visual angle and the time of observation. *J. Opt. Soc. Am.* **37**, 908–919.

BOUMAN, M. A. and H. A. VAN DER VELDEN, 1948, The two-quanta hypothesis as a general explanation for the behaviour of threshold values and visual acuity for the several receptors of the human eye. *J. Opt. Soc. Am.* **38**, 570–581.

BOWEN, E. J., 1946, The chemical aspects of light. Clarendon Press, Oxford.

BRAUNER, L., 1948, Untersuchungen über die phototropischen Reaktionen des Primärblattgelenks von *Phaseolus multiflorus* in weissem und in farbigem Licht. *Rev. Fac. Sci. Univ. Istanbul.* Sér. B **13**, 211–267.

BRAUNER, L., 1954, Tropisms and nastic movements. *Ann. Rev. Plant Physiol.* **5**, 163–182.

BRAUNER, L., 1959, Phototropismus und Photonastie der Laubblätter. *In*: W. Ruhland, ed., Encyclopedia of Plant Physiology, **17**, Pt. 1. Springer-Verlag, Berlin, Göttingen, Heidelberg. pp. 472–491.

BRAUNER, L. and N. ARSLAN, 1951, Experiments on the auxin reactions of the pulvinus of *Phaseolus multiflorus. Rev. Fac. Sci. Univ. Istanbul*, Sér. B **16**, 257–300.

BRIGGS, W. R., 1963, The phototropic responses of higher plants. *Ann. Rev. Plant Physiol.* **14**, 311–352.

BRIL, C., 1958, Action of a non-ionic detergent on chromatophores of *Rhodopseudomonas spheroides. Biochim. Biophys. Acta* **29**, 458.

BRIL, C., 1960a, Personal communication.

BRIL, C., 1960b, Studies on bacterial chromatophores. I. Reversible disturbance of transfer of electronic excitation energy between bacteriochlorophyll-types in *Chromatium. Biochim. Biophys. Acta* **39**, 296–303.

BRINDLEY, G. S., 1954, The order of coincidence required for visual threshold. *Proc. Phys. Soc.*, B **67**, 673–676.

BRODY, M. and R. EMERSON, 1959, The effect of wavelength and intensity of light on the proportion of pigments in *Porphyridium cruentum. Am. J. Bot.* **46**, 433–440.

BRODY, S. S., 1958, New excited state of chlorophyll. *Science* **128**, 838–839.

BRODY, S. S. and M. BRODY, 1961, Action spectra for sensitization of light emission from monomeric and aggregated chlorophyll at physiological and liquid nitrogen temperatures. *Arch. Biochem. Biophys.* **95**, 521–525.

BRODY, S. S., G. NEWELL and T. CASTNER, 1960, Paramagnetic resonance of chlorophyll crystals and solutions. *J. Phys. Chem.* **64**, 554–557.

BRODY, S. S. and E. RABINOWITCH, 1957, Excitation lifetime of photosynthetic pigments *in vitro* and *in vivo*. *Science* **125**, 555.

BROWN, J. S., 1960, Factors influencing the proportion of forms of chlorophyll in algae. *Carnegie Inst. Washington Year Book* **59**, 330–333.

BROWN, P. K. and P. S. BROWN, 1958, Visual pigments of the octopus and cuttle fish. *Nature* **182**, 1288–1290.

BROWN, P. K. and G. WALD, 1963, Visual pigments in human and monkey retinas. *Nature*, **200**, 37–43.

BROWN, P. K. and G. WALD, 1964, Visual pigments in single rods and cones of the human retina. *Science* **144**, 45–52.

BRUNO, M. S. and D. KENNEDY, 1962, Spectral sensitivity of photoreceptor neurons in the sixth ganglion of the crayfish. *Comp. Biochem. Physiol.* **6**, 41–46.

BÜNNING, E., 1955, Weitere Untersuchungen über die Funktion gelber Pigmente beim Phototropismus der *Avena*-Koleoptile. *Zs. Bot* **43**, 167–174.

BÜNNING, E., 1956, Endogenous rhythms in plants. *Ann. Rev. Plant Physiol.* **7**, 71–90.

BÜNNING, E., 1964, The physiological clock. Springer-Verlag, Berlin, Göttingen, Heidelberg.

BÜNNING, E., I. DORN, G. SCHNEIDERHÖHN and I. THORNING, 1953, Zur Funktion von Lactoflavin und Carotin beim Phototropismus und bei lichtbedingten Wachstumsbeeinflussungen. *Ber. Deutsch. Bot. Ges.* **66**, 333–340.

BÜNNING, E. and H. ETZOLD, 1958, Über die Wirkung von polarisiertem Licht auf keimende Sporen von Pilzen, Moosen und Farnen. *Ber. Deutsch. Bot. Ges.* **71**, 304–306.

BÜNNING, E. and I. GÖSSEL, 1959, Ergänzende Versuche über die phototaktischen Aktionsspektren von *Euglena*. *Arch. Mikrobiol.* **32**, 319–321.

BÜNNING, E. and G. SCHNEIDERHÖHN, 1956, Über das Aktionsspektrum der phototaktischen Reaktionen von *Euglena*. *Arch. Mikrobiol.* **24**, 80–90.

BÜNNING, E. and M. TAZAWA, 1957, Über die negativ-phototaktische Reaktion von *Euglena*. *Arch. Mikrobiol.* **27**, 306–310.

BURGER, J. W., 1943, Some effects of colored illumination on the sexual activation of the male starling. *J. Exptl. Zool.* **94**, 161–168.

BURGER, J. W., 1949, A review of experimental investigations on seasonal reproduction in birds. *Wilson Bull.* **61**, 211–230.

BURKHARDT, D. and L. WENDLER, 1960, Ein direkter Beweis für die Fähigkeit einzelner Sehzellen des Insektenauges, die Schwingungsrichtung polarisierten Lichtes zu analysieren. *Zs. Vergl. Physiol.* **43**, 687–692.

BURKHOLDER, P. R. and E. S. JOHNSTON, 1937, Inactivation of plant growth substance by light. *Smithsonian Misc. Coll.* **95**, no. 20.

BURKHOLDER, P. R. and R. PRATT, 1936, Leaf movements of *Mimosa pudica* in relation to light. *Am. J, Bot.* **23**, 46–52.

BUTLER, W. L., 1961a, A far-red absorbing form of chlorophyll *in vivo*, *Arch. Biochem. Biophys.* **93**, 413–422.

BUTLER, W. L., 1961b, Some photochemical properties of phytochrome. *In*: B. Chr. Christensen and B. Buchmann, eds., Progress in Photobiology, Proc. 3rd Int. Congr. Photobiology, Elsevier Publ. Co., Amsterdam. pp. 569–571.

BUTLER, W. L. and R. J. DOWNS, 1960, Light and plant development. *Scientific American* **203**, 6, 56–63.

BUTLER, W. L. and K. H. NORRIS, 1960, The spectrophotometry of dense light-scattering material. *Arch. Biochem. Biophys.* **87**, 31–40.

BUTLER, W. L., K. H. NORRIS, H. W. SIEGELMANN and S. B. HENDRICKS, 1959, Detection, assay, and preliminary purification of the pigment controlling photoresponsive development of plants. *Proc. Natl. Acad. Sci.* **45**, 1703–1708.

CALVIN, M., 1961a, Quantum conversion in photosynthesis. *J. Theoret. Biol.* **1**, 258–287.

CALVIN, M., 1961b, Some photochemical and photophysical reactions of chlorophyll and its relatives. *In:* W. D. McElroy and B. Glass, eds., Light and Life. The Johns Hopkins Press, Baltimore. pp. 317–355.

CALVIN, M., 1962, The path of carbon in photosynthesis. *Angew. Chemie. Internatl. Edition* **1**, 65–75.

CAMA, H. R., P. D. DALVI, R. A. MORTON, M. K. SALAH, G. R. STEINBERG and A. L. STUBBS, 1952a, Studies in vitamin A. 19. Preparation and properties of retinene$_2$. *Biochem. J.* **52**, 535–540.

CAMA, H. R., P. D. DALVI, R. A. MORTON and M. K. SALAH, 1952b, Studies in vitamin A. 20. Some properties of retinene$_2$. *Biochem. J.* **52**, 540–542.

CARASSO, N., 1958, Ultra-structure des cellules visuelles de larves d'Amphibiens. *Compt. Rend.* **247**, 527–531.

CARIO, G. and J. FRANCK, 1923, Über sensibilisierte Fluoreszenz von Gasen. *Zs. Physik* **17**, 202–212.

CASPERS, H., 1951, Rhythmische Erscheinungen in der Fortpflanzung von *Clunio marinus* (Dipt. Chiron.) und das Problem der lunaren Periodizität bei Organismen. *Arch. Hydrobiol.* Suppl. **18**, 415–594.

CHADEFAUD, M. and L. PROVASOLI, 1938–1939, Une nouvelle Euglène graciloide: *Euglena gracilis* Klebs var. *urophora* n. var. *Arch. Zool.* **80**, 55–60.

CHASE, A. M., 1949, Studies on cell enzyme systems. I. The effect of ferricyanide on the reaction of *Cypridina* luciferin and luciferase and the combining weight of luciferin. *J. Cell. Comp. Physiol.* **33**, 113–121.

CHASE, A. M., J. H. BALL, C. E. CORNELIUS and R. J. LEDERMAN, 1961, *Cypridina* luciferin oxidation as a function of pH, and reduction of luciferin by ascorbic acid. *In:* W. D. McElroy and B. Glass, eds., Light and Life. The Johns Hopkins Press, Baltimore. pp. 258–261.

CHOLNOKY, L., C. GYÖRGYFY, E. NAGY and M. PÁNCZÉL, 1956, Function of carotenoids in chlorophyll-containing organs. *Nature* **178**, 410–411.

CHOLNOKY, L., J. SZABOLCS and E. NAGY, 1958, Untersuchungen über die Carotenoidfarbstoffe. IV. α-Kryptoxanthin. *Liebigs Ann. Chem.* **616**, 207–218.

CHOLODNY, N., 1927, Wuchshormone und Tropismen bei den Pflanzen. *Biol. Zentralbl.* **47**, 604–626.

CLAES, H., 1961, Energieübertragung von angeregtem Chlorophyll auf C_{40}-Polyene mit verschiedenen chromophoren Gruppen. *Zs. Naturforsch.* **16^b**, 445–454.

CLAYTON, R. K., 1953a, Studies in the phototaxis of *Rhodospirillum rubrum.* I. Action spectrum, growth in green light, and Weber law adherence. *Arch. Mikrobiol.* **19**, 107–124.

CLAYTON, R. K., 1953b, Studies in the phototaxis of *Rhodospirillum rubrum.* II. The relation between phototaxis and photosynthesis. *Arch. Mikrobiol.* **19**, 125–140.

CLAYTON, R. K., 1953c, Studies in the phototaxis of *Rhodospirillum rubrum.* III. Quantitative relations between stimulus and response. *Arch. Mikrobiol.* **19**, 141–165.

CLAYTON, R. K., 1958, On the interplay of environmental factors affecting taxis and motility in *Rhodospirillum rubrum. Arch. Mikrobiol.* **29**, 189–212.

CLAYTON, R. K., 1959, Phototaxis of purple bacteria. *In:* W. Ruhland, ed., Encyclopedia of Plant Physiology **17**, Pt. 1. Springer-Verlag, Berlin, Göttingen, Heidelberg. pp. 371–387.

CLAYTON, R. K., 1962, Primary reactions in bacterial photosynthesis. III. Reactions of carotenoids and cytochromes in illuminated bacterial chromatophores. *Photochem. Photobiol.* **1**, 313–323.

CLOUDSLEY-THOMPSON, J. L., 1961, Theoretical and Experimental Biology. I. Rhythmic activity in animal physiology and behaviour. Academic Press, New York, London.

COHEN, A. I., 1961, Some preliminary electron microscopic observations of the outer receptor segments of the retina of the Macaca rhesus. *In*: G. K. Smelser, ed., The Structure of the Eye. Academic Press, New York, London. pp. 151–158.

COHEN, R. Z. and T. W. GOODWIN, 1962, The effect of red and far-red light on carotenoid synthesis by etiolated mais seedlings. *Phytochemistry*, **1**, 67–72.

COLEMAN, J. W., A. S. HOLT and E. RABINOWITCH, 1957, Reversible photobleaching of chlorophyll *in vivo*. *In*: H. Gaffron, A. H. Brown, C. S. French, R. Livingston, E. I. Rabinowitch, B. L. Strehler, and N. E. Tolbert, eds., Research in Photosynthesis. Interscience Publishers, Inc., New York, Interscience Publishers, Ltd., London. pp. 68–71.

COLEMAN, J. W. and E. RABINOWITCH, 1960, Evidence of photoreduction of chlorophyll *in vivo*. *In*: L. J. Heidt, R. S. Livingston, E. Rabinowitch, and F. Daniels, eds., Photochemistry in the Liquid and Solid States. John Wiley and Sons, Inc., New York, London. pp. 87–92.

COLLINS, F. D., J. N. GREEN and R. A. MORTON, 1954, Studies in rhodopsin. 7. Regeneration of rhodopsin by comminuted ox retina. *Biochem. J.* **56**, 493–498.

COLLINS, F. D., R. M. LOVE and R. A. MORTON, 1952, Studies in rhodopsin. 4. Preparation of rhodopsin. *Biochem. J.* **51**, 292–298.

COLLINS, F. D. and R. A. MORTON, 1950a, Studies in rhodopsin. 2. Indicator yellow. *Biochem. J.* **47**, 10–18.

COLLINS, F. D. and R. A. MORTON, 1950b, Studies in rhodopsin. 3. Rhodopsin and transient orange. *Biochem. J.* **47**, 18–24.

COMMONER, B., 1961, Electron spin resonance studies of photosynthetic systems. *In:* W. D. McElroy and B. Glass, eds., Light and Life. The Johns Hopkins Press, Baltimore. pp. 356–377.

COMMONER, B., J. J. HEISE, B. B. LIPPINCOTT, R. E. NORBERG, J. V. PASSONNEAU and J. TOWNSEND, 1957, Biological activity of free radicals. *Science* **126**, 57–63.

COMMONER, B., J. J. HEISE and J. TOWNSEND, 1956, Light-induced paramagnetism in chloroplasts. *Proc. Natl. Acad. Sci.* **42**, 710–718.

CONANT, J. B., E. M. DIETZ, C. F. BAILEY and S. E. KAMERLING, 1931, Studies in the chlorophyll series. V. The structure of chlorophyll *a*. *J. Am. Chem. Soc.* **53**, 2382–2393.

CORMIER, M. J., 1960, Studies on the bioluminescence of *Renilla reniformis*. I. Requirements for luminescence in extracts and characteristics of the system. *Biochim. Biophys. Acta* **42**, 333–343.

CORMIER, M. J., 1962, Studies on the bioluminescence of *Renilla reniformis*. II. Requirement for 3′,5′-diphosphoadenosine in the luminescent reaction. *J. Biol. Chem.* **237**, 2032–2037.

CORMIER, M. J. and L. S. DURE, 1963, Studies on the bioluminescence of *Balanoglossus biminiensis* extracts. I. Requirement for hydrogen peroxide and characteristics of the system. *J. Biol. Chem.* **238**, 785–789.

CORMIER, M. J. and C. B. ECKROADE, 1962, Studies on the bioluminescence of *Renilla reniformis*. III. Some biochemical comparisons of the system to other *Renilla* species and determinations of the spectral energy distributions. *Biochim. Biophys. Acta* **64**, 340–344.

CORMIER, M. J. and B. L. STREHLER, 1953, The identification of KCF: requirement of long-chain aldehydes for bacterial extract luminescence. *J. Am. Chem. Soc.* **75**, 4864–4865.

CORMIER, M. J., J. R. TOTTER and H. H. ROSTORFER, 1956, Comparative studies on different bacterial luciferase preparations. *Arch. Biochem. Biophys.* **63**, 414–426.

CURRY, G. M. and H. E. GRUEN, 1959, Action spectra for the positive and negative phototropism of *Phycomyces* sporangiophores. *Proc. Natl. Acad. Sci.* **45**, 797–804.

CURRY, G. M. and H. E. GRUEN, 1961, Dose-response relationships at different wave lengths in phototropism of *Avena*. *In*: B. Chr. Christensen and B. Buchman, eds., Progress in Photobiology. Proc. 3rd Int. Congr. Photobiology. Elsevier Publ. Co., Amsterdam, London, New York, Princeton. pp. 155–157.

CURRY, G. M., K. V. THIMANN and P. M. RAY, 1956, The base curvature response of *Avena* seedlings to the ultraviolet. *Physiologia Plantarum* **9**, 429–440.

DARTNALL, H. J. A., 1948, Indicator yellow and retinene$_1$. *Nature* **162**, 222.

DARTNALL, H. J. A., 1952, Visual pigment 467, a photosensitive pigment present in tench retinae. *J. Physiol.* **116**, 257–289.

DARTNALL, H. J. A., 1957, The visual pigments. Methuen and Co., Ltd., London. Wiley and Sons, Inc., New York.

DARTNALL, H. J. A., 1962a, The identity and distribution of visual pigments in the animal kingdom. *In*: H. Davson, ed., The Eye. 2. Academic Press, New York, London. pp. 367–426.

DARTNALL, H. J. A. 1962b, The chemical structure and photochemistry of the visual pigments. *In*: H. Davson, ed., The Eye. 2. Academic Press, New York, London. pp. 427–471.

DARTNALL, H. J. A. and K. TANSLEY, 1963, Physiology of vision: retinal structure and visual pigments. *Ann. Rev. Physiol.* **25**, 433–458.

DAVENPORT, H. E., 1952, Cytochrome components in chloroplasts. *Nature*, **170**, 1112–1114.

DAVENPORT, H. E. and R. HILL, 1952, The preparation and some properties of cytochrome *f*. *Proc. Roy. Soc.*, B **139**, 327–345.

DAVSON, H., 1962, The Eye. 2. The visual process. Academic Press, New York, London.

DE LA MOTTE, I., 1963, Untersuchungen zur vergleichenden Physiologie der Lichtempfindlichkeit geblendeter Fische. *Naturwiss.* **50**, 363.

DE LINT, P. J. A. L. and C. J. P. SPRUIT, 1963, Phytochrome destruction following illumination of mesocotyls of *Zea Mais* L. *Meded. Landbouwhoogeschool Wageningen* **63**, 1–7.

DENTON, E. J., 1954, A method of easily observing the dichroism of the visual rods. *J. Physiol.* **124**, 16P–17P.

DE ROBERTIS, E. and A. LASANSKY, 1961, Ultrastructure and chemical organization of photoreceptors. *In*: G. K. Smelser, ed., The Structure of the Eye. Academic Press, New York, London. pp. 29–49.

DE SA, R., J. W. HASTINGS and A. E. VATTER, 1963, Luminescent "crystalline" particles: an organized subcellular bioluminescent system. *Science* **141**, 1269–1270.

DE VRIES, H., 1943, The quantum character of light and its bearing upon threshold of vision, the differential sensitivity and visual acuity of the eye. *Physica* **10**, 553–564.

DE WILDE, J., 1962, Photoperiodism in insects and mites. *Ann. Rev. Entomol.* **7**, 1–26.

DE WILDE, J. and D. STEGWEE, 1960, Two major effects of the corpus allatum in the adult Colorado beetle. *Arch. Néerl. Zool.* **13**, 278–289.

DONOVAN, B. T. and G. W. HARRIS, 1955, Neurohumoral mechanisms in reproduction. *British Med. Bull.* **11**, 93–97.

DODT, E. and V. ELENIUS, 1960, Change of threshold during dark adaptation measured with orange and blue light in cats and rabbits. *Experientia* **16**, 313–314.

DODT, E. and E. HEERD, 1962, Mode of action of pineal nerve fibers in frogs. *J. Neurophysiol.* **25**, 405–429.

DODT, E. and K. H. JESSEN, 1961, The duplex nature of the retina of the nocturnal gecko as reflected in the electroretinogram. *J. Gen. Physiol.* **44**, 1143–1158.

DOORENBOS, J. and S. J. WELLENSIEK, 1959, Photoperiodic control of floral induction. *Ann. Rev. Plant Physiol.* **10**, 147–184.

DRAPER, J. W., 1872, Researches in actino-chemistry. Memoir Second. On the distribution of chemical force in the spectrum. *Phil. Mag.* **44**, 4, 422–443.

DUKE-ELDER, S., 1958, System of Ophthalmology. I. The Eye in Evolution. H. Kimpton, Publ., London.

DURANTON, J., J.-M. GALMICHE and E. ROUX, 1958, Métabolisme des pigments chlorophylliens chez le Tabac. *Compt. Rend.* **246**, 992–995.

DURE, L. S. and M. J. CORMIER, 1963, Studies on the bioluminescence of *Balanoglossus biminiensis* extracts. II. Evidence for the peroxidase nature of balanoglossid luciferase. *J. Biol. Chem.* **238**, 790–793.

DUTTON, H. J., J. W. M. MANNING and B. M. DUGGAR, 1943, Chlorophyll fluorescence and energy transfer in the diatom *Nitzschia closterium*. *J. Phys. Chem.* **47**, 308–313.

DUYSENS, L. N. M., 1951, Transfer of light energy within the pigment systems present in photosynthesizing cells. *Nature* **168**, 548–550.

DUYSENS, L. N. M., 1952, Transfer of excitation energy in photosynthesis. Doctoral Thesis, State Univ. Utrecht.

DUYSENS, L. N. M., 1954a, Reversible changes in the absorption spectrum of *Chlorella* upon irradiation. *Science*, **120**, 353–354.

DUYSENS, L. N. M., 1954b, Reversible photo-oxidation of a cytochrome pigment in photosynthesizing *Rhodospirillum rubrum*. *Nature* **173**, 692–693.

DUYSENS, L. N. M., 1955, Role of cytochrome and pyridine nucleotide in algal photosynthesis. *Science* **121**, 210–211.

DUYSENS, L. N. M. and J. AMESZ, 1962, Function and identification of two photochemical systems in photosynthesis. *Biochim. Biophys. Acta* **64**, 243–260.

DUYSENS, L. N. M., J. AMESZ and B. M. KAMP, 1961, Two photochemical systems in photosynthesis. *Nature* **190**, 510–511.

DUYSENS, L. N. M. and G. SWEEP, 1957, Fluorescence spectrophotometry of pyridine nucleotides in photosynthesizing cells. *Biochim. Biophys. Acta* **25**, 13–16.

EAKIN, R. M., W. B. QYAY and J. A. WESTFALL, 1961, Cytochemical and cytological studies of the parietal eye of the lizard, *Sceloporus occidentalis*. *Zs. Zellforsch. Mikrosk. Anat.* **53**, 449–470.

EGLE, K., 1960, Chlorophyllase, *In*· W. Ruhland ed., Encyclopedia of Plant Physiology. **5**, Pt. 1. Springer-Verlag, Berlin, Göttingen, Heidelberg, pp. 387–393.

EIMHJELLEN, K. E., O. AASMUNDRUD and A. JENSEN, 1963, A new bacterial chlorophyll. *Biochem. Biophys. Res. Comm.* **10**, 232–236.

EINSTEIN, A., 1905, Über einen die Erzeugung und Verwandlung des Lichtes betreffenden heuristisches Gesichtspunkt. *Ann. Physik,* IV. Folge **17**, 132–148.

ELSDEN, S. R., M. D. KAMEN and L. P. VERNON, 1953, A new soluble cytochrome. *J. Am. Chem. Soc.* **75**, 6347–6348.

EMERSON, R., R. CHALMERS and C. CEDERSTRAND, 1957, Some factors influencing the long-wave limit of photosynthesis, *Proc. Natl. Acad. Sci.* **43**, 133–143.

EMERSON, R. and C. M. LEWIS, 1943, The dependence of the quantum yield of *Chlorella* photosynthesis on wave length of light. *Am. J. Bot.* **30**, 165–178.

EMERSON, R. and E. RABINOWITGH, 1960, Red drop and role of auxiliary pigments in photosynthesis. *Plant Physiol,* **35**, 477–485.

ENGELMANN, TH. W., 1888, Die Purpurbacterien und ihre Beziehungen zum Licht. *Bot. Ztg.* **46**, 661–720.

ENOCH, J. M., 1960, Waveguide modes: are they present and what is their possible role in the visual mechanism? *J. Opt. Soc. Am.* **50**, 1025–1026.

EVSTIGNEEV, V. B. and V. A. GRAVILOVA, 1953, *Compt. Rend.* (*Doklady*) *Acad. Sci. U.S.S.R.* **89**, 527. Ref. E. Rabinowitch, 1956.

EVSTIGNEEV, V. B., V. A. GRAVILOVA and A. A. KRASNOVKSY, 1950, *Compt. Rend.*(*Doklady*) *Acad. Sci. U.S.S.R.* **74**, 315. Ref. E. Rabinowitch, 1956.

EYRING, H., 1935, The activated complex in chemical reactions. *J. Chem. Phys.* **3**, 107–115.

FARNER, D. S., 1959, Photoperiodic control of annual gonadal cycles in birds. *In*: R. B. Withrow, ed., Photoperiodism and Related Phenomena in Plants and Animals. American Association for the Advancement of Science, Washington, D.C. pp. 717–750.

FARNER, D. S., 1961, Comparative physiology: photoperiodicity. *Ann. Rev. Physiol.* **23**, 71–96.

FERNÁNDEZ-MORÁN, H., 1961, The fine structure of vertebrate and invertebrate photoreceptors as revealed by low-temperature electron microscopy. *In*: G. K. Smelser, ed., The Structure of the Eye. Academic Press, New York, London. pp. 521–556.

FICKEN, G. E., R. B. JOHNS and R. P. LINSTEAD, 1956, Chlorophyll and related compounds. Part IV. The position of the extra hydrogens in chlorophyll. The oxidation of pyrophaeophorbide-*a*. *J. Am. Chem. Soc.* **68**, 2272–2280.

FISCHER, H., 1940, Fortschritte der Chlorophyllchemie. *Naturwiss.* **28**, 401–405.

FISCHER, H. and H. ORTH, 1937, Die Chemie des Pyrrols. **2**, Pt. 1. Akademische Verlagsgesellschaft, Leipzig.

FISCHER, H. and J. RIEDMAIR, 1933, Über die Aufspaltung von Chlorophyll *a* und seinen Derivaten durch Diazomethan. Kristallisiertes allomerisiertes Äthylphäophorbid *a*. *Liebigs Ann. Chem.* **506**, 107–123.

FISCHER, H. and A. STERN 1940, *In*: H. Fischer and H. Orth, Die Chemie des Pyrrols. **2**, Pt. 2. Akademische Verlagsgesellschaft, Leipzig.

FÖRSTER, TH., 1948, Zwischenmolekulare Energiewanderung und Fluoreszenz. *Ann. Physik* **2**, 55–65.

FÖRSTER, TH., 1949, Experimentelle und theoretische Untersuchung des zwischenmolekularen Übergangs von Elektronenanregungsenergie. *Zs. Naturforsch.* **4a**, 321–327.

FÖRSTER, TH., 1951, Fluoreszenz organischer Verbindungen. Vandenhoeck und Ruprecht, Göttingen.

FRANCK, J., 1958, Remarks on the long-wave-length limits of photosynthesis and chlorophyll fluorescence. *Proc. Natl. Acad. Sci.* **44**, 941–948.

FRANCK, J. and R. LIVINGSTON, 1949, Remarks on intra- and inter-molecular migration of excitation energy. *Rev. Modern Phys.* **21**, 505–509.

FRANCK, J. and E. RABINOWITCH, 1934, Some remarks about free radicals and the photochemistry of solutions. *Trans. Faraday Soc.* **30**, 120–131.

FRANCK, J. and E. TELLER, 1938, Migration and photochemical action of excitation energy in crystals. *J. Chem. Phys.* **6**, 861–872.

FRENCH, C. S., 1959, Various forms of chlorophyll *a* in plants. *In:* The Photochemical Apparatus. Its Structure and Function. *Brookhaven Symp. Biol.* **11**. Brookhaven National Laboratory, Upton. pp. 65–73.

FRENCH, C. S., 1960, The chlorophylls *in vivo* and *in vitro*. *In*: W. Ruhland, ed., Encyclopedia of Plant Physiology. **5**, Pt. 1. Springer-Verlag, Berlin, Göttingen, Heidelberg. pp. 252–297.

FRENCH, C. S., 1962, Relations between the two photochemical reactions of photosynthesis. *Carnegie Inst. Washington Year Book* **61**, 345–350.

FRENCH, C. S. and R. F. ELLIOT, 1958, The absorption spectra of chlorophylls in various algae. *Carnegie Instit. Washington Year Book* **57**, 278–286.

FRENCH, C. S. and V. K. YOUNG, 1952, The fluorescence spectra of red algae and the transfer of energy from phycoerythrin to phycocyanin and chlorophyll. *J. Gen. Physiol.* **35**, 873–890.

FRENCH, C. S. and V. K. YOUNG, 1956, The absorption, action, and fluorescence spectra of photosynthetic pigments in living cells and in solutions. *In*: A. Hollaender, ed., Radiation Biology. 3. McGraw Hill Co., New York. pp. 343–391.

FRENKEL, A. W., 1954, Light induced phosphorylation by cell-free preparations of photosynthetic bacteria. *J. Am. Chem. Soc.* **76**, 5568–5569.

FRENKEL, J., 1931a, On the transformation of light into heat in solids. I. *Phys. Rev.* **37**, 1, 17–44.

FRENKEL, J., 1931b, On the transformation of light into heat in solids. II. *Phys. Rev.* **37**, 2, 1276–1294.

FREY-WYSSLING, A., 1957, Macromolecules in cell structure. Harvard University Press, Cambridge, Mass.

FRUTON, J. S. and S. SIMMONDS, 1953, General Biochemistry. John Wiley and Sons, Inc., New York. Chapman and Hall, Ltd., London.

FUJIMORI, E. and R. LIVINGSTON, 1957, Interactions of chlorophyll in its triplet state with oxygen, carotene, etc. *Nature* **180**, 1036–1038.

FUJITA, Y. and A. HATTORI, 1960a, Formation of phycoerythrin in pre-illuminated cells of *Tolypothrix tenuis* with special reference to nitrogen metabolism. *Plant and Cell Physiol.* **1**, 281–292.

FUJITA, Y. and A. HATTORI, 1960b, Effect of chromatic lights on phycobilin formation in a blue-green alga, *Tolypothrix tenuis*. *Plant and Cell Physiol.* **1**, 293–303.

FULLER, R. C., J. A. BERGERON and I. C. ANDERSON, 1961, Relation of photosynthetic activity to carotenoid-bacteriochlorophyll interaction in *Chromatium*. *Arch. Biochem. Biophys.* **92**, 273–279.

FULLER. R. C., S. F. CONTI and D. B. MELLIN, 1963, The structure of the photosynthetic apparatus in the green and purple bacteria. *In*: H. Gest, A. San Pietro, L. P. Vernon, eds., Bacterial Photosynthesis. The Antioch Press, Yellow Spings, Ohio. pp. 71–87.

GAFFRON, H., 1933, Über den Mechanismus der Sauerstoffaktivierung durch belichtete Farbstoffe. *Biochem. Zs.* **264**, 251–271.

GAFFRON, H., 1940, Carbon dioxide reduction with molecular hydrogen in green algae. *Am. J. Bot.* **27**, 273-283.

GAFFRON, H., 1960, Energy storage. *In*: F. C. Steward, ed., Plant Physiology. Academic Press, New York, London.

GALSTON, A. W., 1949, Riboflavin-sensitized photooxidation of indoleacetic acid and related compounds. *Proc. Natl. Acad. Sci.* **35**, 10–17.

GALSTON, A. W., 1950, Phototropism. II. *Bot. Rev.* **16**, 361–378.

GALSTON, A. W., 1959a, Phototropism of stems, roots and coleoptiles. *In*: W. Ruhland, ed., Encyclopedia of Plant Physiology **17**, Pt. 1. Springer-Verlag, Berlin, Göttingen, Heidelberg. pp. 492–529.

GALSTON, A. W., 1959b, Studies on indoleacetic acid oxidase inhibitor and its relation to photomorphogenesis. *In*: R. B. Withrow, ed., Photoperiodism and Related Phenomena in Plants and Animals. American Association for the Advancement of Science, Washington, D.C. pp. 137–157.

GALSTON, A. W. and R. S. BAKER, 1949, Studies on the physiology of light action. II. The photodynamic action of riboflavin. *Am. J. Bot.* **36**, 773–780.

GAYDON, A. G., 1947, Dissociation energies and spectra of diatomic molecules. John Wiley and Sons, Inc., New York.

GENTILE, A. C. and R. M. KLEIN, 1955, The apparent necessity of indoleacetic acid for the growth of *Diplodia* (Fungi imperfecti). *Physiologia Plantarum* **8**, 291–299.

GERSMANN, H. R. and J. A. A. KETELAAR, 1958, Chemical studies on insecticides. VIII. Ultraviolet spectra and opposing resonance in phosphate esters. *Rec. Trav. Chim. Pays-Bas* **77**, 1018–1025.

GEST, H. and M. D. KAMEN, 1948, Studies on the phosphorus metabolism of green algae and purple bacteria in relation to photosynthesis. *J. Biol. Chem.* **176**, 299–318.

GEST, H. and M. D. KAMEN, 1961, The photosynthetic bacteria. *In*: W. Ruhland, ed., Encyclopedia of Plant Physiology. **5**, Pt. 2. Springer-Verlag, Berlin, Göttingen, Heidelberg. pp. 568–612.

GIBBS, S. P., 1960, The fine structure of *Euglena gracilis* with special reference to the chloroplasts and pyrenoids. *J. Ultrastruct. Res.* **4**, 127–148.

GIESBRECHT, P. and G. DREWS, 1962, Elektronenmikroskopische Untersuchungen über die Entwicklung der "Chromatophoren" von *Rhodospirillum molischianum* Giesberger. *Arch. Mikrobiol.* **43**, 152–161.

GING, N. S. and J. M. STURTEVANT, 1954, The heat of hydrolysis of inorganic pyrophosphate. *J. Am. Chem. Soc.* **76**, 2087–2091.

GLASSTONE, S., K. J. LAIDLER and H. EYRING, 1941, The Theory of Rate Processes. McGraw-Hill Book Co., Inc., New York.

GODNEV, T. N. and M. V. TERENTJEVA, 1953, *Compt. Rend.* (*Doklady*) *Acad. Sci. U.S.S.R.* **88**, 725. Ref. Rabinowitch, 1956.

GOEDHEER, J. C., 1957, Optical properties and *in vivo* orientation of photosynthetic pigments. Doctoral thesis. State University, Utrecht.

GOEDHEER, J. C., 1958, Investigations on bacteriochlorophyll in organic solutions. *Biochim. Biophys. Acta* **27**, 478–490.

GOEDHEER, J. C., 1962, Afterglow of chlorophyll *in vivo* and photosynthesis. *Biochim. Biophys. Acta* **64**, 294–308.

GOEDHEER, J. C., 1963a, An attempted concept of photosynthesis based on luminescence experiments. *In*: Colloques Internationaux du Centre National de la Recherche Scientifique, no. 119: La Photosynthèse. Centre National de la Recherche Scientifique, Paris. pp. 147–157.

GOEDHEER, J. C., 1963b, A cooperation of two pigment systems and respiration in photosynthetic luminescence. *Biochim. Biophys. Acta* **66**, 61–71.

GOEDHEER, J. C., G. H. HORREUS DE HAAS and P. SCHULLER, 1958, Oxidation-reduction potentials of different chlorophylls in methanol. *Biochim. Biophys. Acta* **28**, 278–283.

GOODWIN, T. W., 1952, The Comparative Biochemistry of the Carotenoids. Chapman and Hall, Ltd., London.

GOODWIN, T. W., 1956, Studies in carotenogenesis. XXII. The structure of echinenone. *Biochem. J.* **63**, 481–484.

GOODWIN, T. W., 1959, The biosynthesis and function of the carotenoid pigments. *Adv. Enzymol.* **21**, 295–368.

GOODWIN, T. W., 1960, Chemistry, biogenesis and physiology of the carotenoids. (Carotenoids associated with chlorophyll). *In*: W. Ruhland, ed., Encyclopedia of Plant Physiology **5**, Pt. 1. Springer-Verlag, Berlin, Göttingen, Heidelberg. pp. 394–443.

GOODWIN, T. W. and D. G. LAND, 1956, Studies in carotenogenesis. 20. Carotenoids of some species of *Chlorobium*. *Biochem. J.* **62**, 553–556.

GORDON, S. A. and K. SURREY, 1960, Red and far-red action on oxidative phosphorylation. *Radiation Research*, **12**, 325–339.

GÖSSEL, I., 1957, Über das Aktionsspektrum der Phototaxis chlorophyllfreier Euglenen und über die Absorption des Augenflecks. *Arch. Mikrobiol.* **27**, 288–305.

GOVINDJEE, C. CEDERSTRAND and E. RABINOWITCH, 1961, Existence of absorption bands at 730–740 and 750–760 millimicrons in algae of different divisions. *Science* **134**, 391–392.

GOVINDJEE and E. RABINOWITCH, 1960, Two forms of chlorophyll *a in vivo* with distinct photochemical functions. *Science* **132**, 355–356.

GOVINDJEE, E. RABINOWITCH and J. B. THOMAS, 1960, Inhibition of photosynthesis in certain algae by extreme red light. *Biophys. J.* **1**, 91–97.

GOVINDJEE, R., GOVINDJEE and G. HOCH, 1962, The Emerson enhancement effect in TPN-photoreduction by spinach chloroplasts. *Biochem. Biophys. Res. Comm.* **9**, 222–225.

GOVINDJEE, R., J. B. THOMAS and E. RABINOWITCH, 1960, "Second Emerson effect" in the Hill reaction of *Chlorella* cells with quinone as oxidant. *Science* **132**, 421.

GRANICK, S., 1948a, Protoporphyrin 9 as a precursor of chlorophyll. *J. Biol. Chem.* **172**, 717–727.

GRANICK, S., 1948b, Magnesium protoporphyrin as a precursor of chlorophyll in *Chlorella*. *J. Biol. Chem.* **175**, 333–342.

GRANICK, S., 1949, The pheoporphyrin nature of chlorophyll *c*. *J. Biol. Chem.* **179**, 505.

GRANICK, S., 1951, Biosynthesis of chlorophyll and related pigments. *Ann. Rev. Plant Physiol.* **2**, 115–144.

GRAY, C. H., 1953, The Bile Pigments. Methuen, London. Wiley and Sons, Inc., New York.

GRAY, C. H. and D. C. NICHOLSON, 1958, The chemistry of the bile pigments. The structure of stercobilin and d-urobilin. *J. Chem. Soc.* **1958**, 3085–3099.

GREEN, A. A. and W. D. MCELROY, 1956, Crystalline firefly luciferase. *Biochim. Biophys. Acta* **20**, 170–176.

GRIFFITHS, M., W. R. SISTROM, G. COHEN-BAZIRE and R. Y. STANIER, 1955, Function of carotenoids in photosynthesis. *Nature* **176**, 1211–1215.

HAIG, C., 1934, The spectral sensibility of *Avena*. *Proc. Natl. Acad. Sci.* **20**, 476–479.

HALLDAL, P., 1957, Importance of calcium and magnesium ions in phototaxis of motile green algae. *Nature* **179**, 215–216.

HALLDAL, P., 1958a, Pigment formation and growth in blue-green algae in crossed gradients of light intensity and temperature. *Physiologia Plantarum* **11**, 401–420.

HALLDAL, P., 1958b, Action spectra of phototaxis and related problems in Volvocales, Ulva-gametes and Dinophyceae. *Physiologia Plantarum* **11**, 118–153.

HALLDAL, P., 1959, Factors affecting light response in phototactic algae. *Physiologia Plantarum* **12**, 742–752.

HALLDAL, P., 1960, Action spectra of induced phototactic response changes in *Platymonas*. *Physiologia Plantarum* **13**, 726–735.

HALLDAL, P., 1961a, Ultraviolet action spectra of positive and negative phototaxis in *Platymonas subcordiformis*. *Physiologia Plantarum* **14**, 133–139.

HALLDAL, P., 1961b, Action spectra of phototaxis in unicellular algae. *In*: B. Chr. Christensen and B. Buchmann, eds., Progress in Photobiology. Proc. 3rd Int. Congr. Photobiol. Elsevier Publishing Co., Amsterdam. pp. 121–126.

HANEDA, Y., F. H. JOHNSON, Y. MASUDA, Y. SAIGA, O. SHIMOMURA, H.-C. SIE, N. SUGIYAMA and I. TAKATSUKI, 1961, Crystalline luciferin from live *Cypridina*. *J. Cell. Comp. Physiol.* **57**, 55–62.

HANKE, W. and H. GIERSBERG, 1963, Hormone. *Fortschr. Zool.* **16**, 1–57.

HANSON, E. A., 1937, Notes on some physical properties of chlorophyll films. *Proc. Kon. Akad. Wet. Amsterdam* **40**, 281–285.

HANSON, E. A., 1938, Some properties of the chlorophyll in relation to its biological function. Doctoral thesis. State University, Leiden.

HARBURY, H. A., K. F. LaNOUE, P. A. LOACH and R. M. AMICK, 1959, Molecular interaction of isoalloxazine derivatives. II. *Proc. Natl. Acad. Sci.* **45**, 1708–1717.

HARRINGTON, JR., R. W., 1959, Photoperiodism in fishes in relation to the annual sexual cycle. *In*: R. B. Withrow, ed., Photoperiodism and Related Phenomena in Plants and Animals. The American Association for the Advancement of Science, Washington, D.C. pp. 561–667.

HARVEY, E. N., 1940, Living Light. Princeton University Press, Princeton.

HARVEY, E. N., 1952, Bioluminescence. Academic Press, Inc., New York.

HARVEY, E. N., 1955, Survey of luminous organisms: problems and prospects. *In*: F. H. Johnson, ed., The Luminescence of Biological Systems. The American Association for the Advancement of Science, Washington, D.C. pp. 1–24.

HASTING, J. W., 1964, Personal communication.

HASTINGS, J. W. and Q. H. GIBSON, 1963, Intermediates in the bioluminescent oxidation of reduced flavin mononucleotide. *J. Biol. Chem.* **238**, 2537–2554.

HASTINGS, J. W., J. SPUDICH and G. MALNIC, 1963, The influence of aldehyde chain length upon relative quantum yield of the bioluminescent reaction of *Achromobacter fischeri*. *J. Biol. Chem.* **238**, 3100–3105.

HASTINGS, J. W. and B. M. SWEENEY, 1957, The luminescent reaction in extracts of the marine dinoflagellate, *Gonyaulax polyedra*. *J. Cell. Comp. Physiol.* **49**, 209–225.

HASTINGS, J. W. and B. M. SWEENEY, 1960. The action spectrum for shifting the phase of the rhythm of luminescence in *Gonyaulax polyedra*. *J. Gen. Physiol.* **43**, 697–706.

HAUPT, W., 1959a, Die Chloroplastendrehung bei *Mougeotia*. I. Mitteilung. Über den quantitativen und qualitativen Lichtbedarf der Schwachlichtbewegung. *Planta* **53**, 484–501.

HAUPT, W., 1959b, Chloroplastenbewegung. *In*: W. Ruhland, ed., Encyclopedia of Plant Physiology. **17**, Pt. 1. Springer-Verlag, Berlin, Göttingen, Heidelberg. pp. 278–317.

HAUPT, W., 1959c, Die Phototaxis der Algen. *In*: W. Ruhland, ed., Encyclopedia of Plant Physiology. **17**, Pt. 1. Springer-Verlag, Berlin, Göttingen, Heidelberg. pp. 318–370.

HAUPT, W., 1959d, Photodinese. *In*: W. Ruhland, ed., Encyclopedia of Plant Physiology. **17**, Pt. 1. Springer-Verlag, Berlin. Göttingen, Heidelberg. pp. 388–398.

HAUPT, W., 1960, Die Chloroplastendrehung bei *Mougeotia*. II. Mitteilung. Die Induktion der Schwachlichtbewegung durch linear polarisiertes Licht. *Planta* **55**, 465–479.

HAUPT, W., 1962, Über die Lokalisierung des Phytochroms in der *Mougeotia*-Zelle. *Vortr. Gesamtgeb. Bot., N.F.* **1**, 116–121.

HAUPT, W. and G. BOCK, 1962, Die Chloroplastendrehung bei *Mougeotia*. IV. Die Orientierung der Phytochrom-Moleküle im Cytoplasma. *Planta* **59**, 38–48.

HAUPT, W. and E. SCHÖNBOHM, 1962, Das Wirkungsspektrum der "negativen Phototaxis" des *Mougeotia*-Chloroplasten. *Naturwiss.* **49**, 42.

HAUPT, W. and I. SCHÖNFELD, 1962, Über das Wirkungsspektrum der "negativen Phototaxis" der *Vaucheria*-Chloroplasten. *Ber. Deutsch. Bot. Ges.* **75**, 14–23.

HAUPT, W. and R. RHIELE, 1961, Chloroplastenbewegung bei *Mesotaenium*. *Planta* **56**, 388–401.

HAXO, F. and L. R. BLINKS, 1950, Photosynthetic action spectra of marine algae. *J. Gen. Physiol.* **33**, 389–421.

HAXO, F. T. and C. O'HEOCHA, 1960, Chromoproteins of algae. *In*: W. Ruhland, ed., Encyclopedia of Plant Physiology. **5**, Pt. 1. Springer-Verlag, Berlin, Göttingen, Heidelberg. pp. 497–510.

HAXO, F., C. O'HEOCHA and P. NORRIS, 1955, Comparative studies of chromatographically separated phycoerythrins and phycocyanins. *Arch. Biochem. Biophys.* **54**, 162–173.

HAXO, F. T. and B. M. SWEENEY, 1955, Bioluminescence in *Gonyaulax polyedra*. *In*: F. H. Johnson, ed., The Luminescence of Biological Systems. The American Association for the Advancement of Science, Washington, D.C. pp. 415–420.

HECHT, S., 1942, The chemistry of visual substances. *Ann. Rev. Biochem.* **11**, 465–496.

HECHT, S., S. SHLEAR and M. H. PIRENNE, 1942, Energy, quanta, and vision. *J. Gen. Physiol.* **25**, 819–840.

HEILBRONN, I. M. and B. LYTHGOE, 1936, The chemistry of the algae. Part II. The carotenoid pigments of *Oscillatoria rubrescens*. *J. Chem. Soc.* **1936**, 1376–1380.

HELLER, W. R. and A. MARCUS, 1951, A note on the propagation of excitation in an idealized crystal. *Phys. Rev.* **84**, 809–813.

HENDERSON, N. E., 1963, Influence of light and temperature on the reproductive cycle of the eastern brook trout, *Salvelinus fontinalis* (Mitchill). *J. Fish. Res. Bd. Canada* **20**, 859–897.

HENDRICKS, S. B., H. A. BORTHWICK and R. J. DOWNS, 1956, Pigment conversion in the formative responses of plants to radiation. *Proc. Natl. Acad. Sci.* **42**, 19–26.

HENDRICKS, S. B., W. L. BUTLER and H. W. SIEGELMAN, 1962, A reversible photoreaction regulating plant growth. *J. Phys. Chem.* **66**, 2550–2555.

HENDRICKS, S. B., E. H. TOOLE, V. K. TOOLE and H. A. BORTHWICK, 1960, Photocontrol of plant development by simultaneous excitations of two interconvertible pigments. III. Control of seed germination and axis elongation. *Bot. Gaz.* **121**, 1–8.

HILL, R., 1954, The cytochrome *b* component of chloroplasts. *Nature* **174**, 501.

HILL, R., 1956, The cytochrome components and chlorophyll in relation to the carbon cycle of Calvin. *In*: C. Liébecq, ed., Proc. 3rd Int. Congr. Biochem., Brussels 1955 Academic Press, New York. pp. 225–227.

HILL, R. and F. BENDALL, 1960, Function of the two cytochrome components in chloroplasts: a working hypothesis. *Nature* **186**, 136–137.

HILL, R. and W. D. BONNER JR., 1961, The nature and possible function of chloroplast cytochromes. *In*: W. D. McElroy and B. Glass, eds., Light and Life. The Johns Hopkins Press, Baltimore. pp. 424–435.

HILL, R. and R. SCARISBRICK, 1951, The hematin compounds of leaves. *New Phytologist* **50**, 98–111.

HILL, R. and C. P. WHITTINGHAM, 1955, Photosynthesis. Methuen and Co., Ltd., London. John Wiley and Sons, Inc., New York.

HILL, T. L. and M. F. MORALES, 1951, On "high energy phosphate bonds" of biochemical interest. *J. Am. Chem. Soc.* **73**, 1656–1660.

HIRATA, Y., O. SHIMOMURA and S. EGUCHI, 1959, The structure of *Cypridina* luciferin. *Tetrahedron Letters*, **5**, 4–9.

HOFFMANN-BERLING, H., 1954, Adenosintriphosphat als Betriebsstoff von Zellbewegungen. *Biochim. Biophys. Acta* **14**, 182–194.

HOFFMANN-BERLING, H., 1955, Geisselmodelle und Adenosintriphosphat (ATP.) *Biochim. Biophys. Acta* **16**, 146–154.

HOLT, A. S., 1958, The phase test intermediate and the allomerization of chlorophyll *a*. *Can. J. Biochem. Physiol.* **36**, 439–456.

HOLT, A. S., 1961, Further evidence of the relation between 2-desvinyl-2-formyl-chlorophyll *a* and chlorophyll *d*. *Can. J. Bot.* **39**, 327–331.

HOLT, A. S. and D. W. HUGHES, 1961, Studies of Chlorobium chlorophylls. III. Chlorobium chlorophyll (650). *J. Am. Chem. Soc.* **83**, 499.

HOLT, A. S. and E. E. JACOBS, 1954a, Spectroscopy of plant pigments. I. Ethyl chlorophyllides *a* and *b* and their pheophorbides. *Am. J. Bot.* **41**, 710–717.

HOLT, A. S. and E. E. JACOBS, 1954b, Spectroscopy of plant pigments. II. Methylbacteriochlorophyllide and bacteriochlorophyll. *Am. J. Bot.* **41**, 718–722.

HOLT, A. S. and E. E. JACOBS, 1955, Infrared absorption spectra of chlorophylls and derivatives. *Plant Physiol.* **30**, 553–559.

HOLT, A. S. and H. V. MORLEY, 1959, A proposed structure for chlorophyll *d*. *Can J. Chem.* **37**, 507–514.

HOLT, A. S. and H. V. MORLEY, 1960, Chlorobium chlorophyll. *J. Am. Chem. Soc.* **82**, 500.

HUBBARD, R., 1954, The molecular weight of rhodopsin and the nature of the rhodopsin-digitonin complex. *J. Gen. Physiol.* **37**, 381–399.

HUBBARD, R., 1959, The thermal stability of rhodopsin and opsin. *J. Gen. Physiol.* **42**, 259–280.

HUBBARD, R., P. K. BROWN and A. KROPF, 1959, Action of light on visual pigments. Vertebrate lumi- and metarhodopsins. *Nature* **183**, 442–446.

HUBBARD, R. and A. KROPF, 1958, The action of light on rhodopsin. *Proc. Natl. Acad. Sci.* **44**, 130–139.

HUBBARD, R. and A. KROPF, 1959, Molecular aspects of visual excitation. *Ann. New York Acad. Sci.* **81**, 388–398.

HUBBARD, R. and R. C. C. ST. GEORGE, 1958, The rhodopsin system of the squid. *J. Gen. Physiol.* **41**, 501–528.

HUBBARD, R. and G. WALD, 1951, The mechanism of rhodopsin synthesis. *Proc. Natl. Acad. Sci.* **37**, 69–79.

HUBBARD, R. and G. WALD, 1953, *Cis-trans* isomers of vitamin A and retinene in the rhodopsin system. *J. Gen. Physiol.* **36**, 269–315.

HUBERT, B., 1935, The physical state of chlorophyll in the living plastid. *Rec. Trav. Bot. Néerl.* **32**, 323–390.

HUGHES, D. W. and A. S. HOLT, 1961, Studies of chlorobium chlorophylls. IV. Preparative liquid-liquid partition chromatography of porphyrins and chlorophyll derivatives and its use to resolve chlorobium pheophorbide (650) into six components. *Can. J. Chem.* **40**, 171–176.

HUISINGA, B., 1964, Personal communication.

HURVICH, L. M. and D. JAMESON, 1961, An opponent-process theory of color vision. *In*: R. C. Teevan and R. C. Birney, eds., Color Vision. D. Van Nostrand Co., Inc., Princeton, Toronto, London, New York. pp. 113–137.

INGRAM, D. J. E., 1958, Free Radicals as studied by Electron Spin Resonance. Butterworths Scientific Publications, London.

INHOFFEN, H. H., F. BOHLMANN and G. RUMMERT, 1951, Synthesen in der Carotenoid-Reihe. XVIII. Über die Stereo-isomerisierung des 9,9′-mono-*cis*-β-Carotins. *Liebig's Ann. Chem.* **571**, 75–83.

INMAN, O. L. and A. F. BLAKESLEE, 1938, New or modified chlorophylls resulting from a recessive pale mutation in *Datura*. *Science* **87**, 428–429.

JACOBS, E. E., A. S. HOLT, R. KROMHOUT and E. RABINOWITCH, 1957, Spectroscopic properties of crystals and monolayers of chlorophyll and related compounds. *Arch. Biochem. Biophys.* **72**, 495–511.

JACOBS, E. E., A. E. VATTER and A. S. HOLT, 1954, Crystalline chlorophyll and bacteriochlorophyll. *Arch. Biochem. Biophys.* **53**, 228–238.

JAFFE, L. F., 1958, Tropistic responses of zygotes of the Fucaceae to polarized light. *Exptl. Cell Res.* **15**, 282–299.

JAFFE, L. and H. ETZOLD, 1962, Orientation and locus of tropic photoreceptor molecules in spores of *Botrytis* and *Osmunda*. *J. Cell Biol.* **13**, 13–31.

JAGENDORF, A. T., 1956, Oxidation and reduction of pyridine nucleotides by purified chloroplasts. *Arch. Biochem. Biophys.* **62**, 141–150.

JAGENDORF, A. T., 1962, Biochemistry of energy transformations during photosynthesis. *Survey Biol. Progr.* **4**, 181–344.

JAROSCH, R., 1957, Zur Mechanik der Protoplasmafibrillenbewegung. *Biochim. Biophys. Acta* **25**. 204–205.

JEFFREY, S. W., 1963, Purification and properties of chlorophyll *c* from *Sargassum flavicans*. *Biochem. J.* **86**, 313–318.

JOHNSON, F. H., 1955, The Luminescence of Biological Systems. The American Association for the Advancement of Science, Washington, D.C.

JOHNSON, F. H., 1959, Kinetics of luminescence in *Chaetopterus* slime, and the influence of certain factors thereon. *J. Cell. Comp. Physiol.* **53**, 259–278.

JOHNSON, F. H., H. EYRING and M. J. POLISSAR, 1964, The Kinetic Basis of Molecular Biology. John Wiley and Sons, Inc., New York. Chapman and Hill, Ltd., London.

JOHNSTON, E. S., 1934, Phototropic sensitivity in relation to wave length. *Smithsonian Misc. Coll.* **92**, no. 11.

KAISSLING, K.-E. 1962, Die phototropische Reaktion der Zoide von *Bugula avicularia* L. *Zs. Vergl. Physiol.*, **46**, 541–594.

KALCKAR, H., 1941, The nature of energetic coupling in biological syntheses. *Chem. Revs.* **28**, 71–178.

KAMEN, M. D., 1956, Hematin compounds in the metabolism of photosynthetic tissues. *In*: O. H. Gaebler, ed., Enzymes: units of biological structure and function. Academic Press, Inc., New York. pp. 483–498.

KAMEN, M. D., 1961a, Comments on the function of haem proteins as related to primary photochemical processes in photosynthesis. *In*: W. D. McElroy and G. Glass, eds., Light and Life. The Johns Hopkins Press, Baltimore. pp. 483–488.

KAMEN, M. D., 1961b, Haem protein content and function in relation to structure and early photochemical processes in bacterial chromatophores. *In*: T. W. Goodwin and O. Lindberg, eds., Biological Structure and Function. **2**. Academic Press, London, New York. pp. 277–294.

KAMEN, M. D., 1963, On bacterial "cytochromoids". *Acta Chem. Scand.* **17**, S41–S46.

KAMEN, M. D. and R. G. BARTSCH, 1961, The atypical haemoprotein of purple photosynthetic bacteria. *In*: Haematin Enzymes. Pergamon Press, Oxford, London, New York, Paris. pp. 419–432.

KAMIYA, N., 1960, Physics and chemistry of protoplasmic streaming. *Ann. Rev. Plant Physiol.* **11**, 323–340.

KANDELER, R., 1962, Physikalische und chemische Grundlagen der Lebensprozesse (Strahlenbiologie). *Fortschr. Bot.* **25**, 201–211.

KARRER, P., W. FATZER, M. FAVARGER and E. JUCKER, 1943, Die Antheridienfarbstoffe von *Chara*-Arten (Armleuchtergewächse). *Helvetica Chim. Acta* **26**, 2121–2122.

KARRER, P. and E. JUCKER, 1945, Partialsynthesen des Flavoxanthins, Chrysanthemaxanthins, Antheraxanthins, Violaxanthins, Mutatoxanthins und Auroxanthins. *Helvetica Chim. Acta* **28**, 300–315.

KARRER, P. and E. JUCKER, 1948, Carotenoide. Verlag Birkhäuser, Basel.

KARRER, P. and H. KOENIG, 1940, Carotenoide der Purpurbakterien. V. Über Rhodoviolascin. *Helvetica Chim. Acta* **23**, 460–463.

KARRER, P. and J. RUTSCHMANN, 1944, Beitrag zur Kenntnis der Carotenoide aus *Oscillatoria rubescens*. *Helvetica Chim. Acta*, **27**, 1691–1695.

KARRER, P. and U. SOLMSSEN, 1935, Pflanzenfarbstoffe. LXIII. Zur Kenntnis der Oxydationsprodukte der Carotine. Das Carotenoid der *Thiocystis*-Bakterien. *Helvetica Chim. Acta* **18**, 25–27.

KARRER, P. and U. SOLMSSEN, 1935a, Die Carotenoide der Purpurbakterien. I. *Helvetica Chim. Acta* **18**, 1306–1315.

KARRER, P. and E. WÜRGLER, 1943, Absorptionsspektren einiger Carotenoide. *Helvetica Chim. Acta* **26**, 116–121.

KASHA. M., 1950, Characterization of electronic transitions in complex molecules. *Disc. Faraday Soc.* **9**, 14–19.

KASHA, M., 1959, Relation between exciton bands and conduction bands in molecular lamellar systems. *Rev. Modern Phys.* **31**, 162–169.

KASHA, M., 1961, The nature and significance of n → π* transitions. *In:* W. D. McElroy and B. Glass, eds., Light and Life. The Johns Hopkins Press, Baltimore. pp. 31–68.

KATO, M., 1959, Light effect on the production of diapause eggs in the silkworm, *Bombyx mori. Annotationes Zool. Japon.* **32**, 174–178.

KATZ, E. and E. C. WASSINK, 1939, Infrared absorption spectra of chlorophyllous pigments in living cells and extra-cellular states. *Enzymologia* **7**, 97–112.

KATZ, J. J., M. R. THOMAS, H. L. CRESPI and H. H. STRAIN, 1961, Evidence for exchangeable hydrogen in chlorophyll. *J. Am. Chem. Soc.* **83**, 4180–4182.

KATZ, J. J., M. R. THOMAS and H. H. STRAIN, 1962, Site of exchangeable hydrogen in chlorophyll *a* from proton magnetic resonance measurements on deuterio-chlorophyll *a. J. Am. Chem. Soc.* **85**, 3587.

KENNEDY, D., 1963, Physiology of photoreceptor neurons in the abdominal nerve cord of the crayfish. *J. Gen. Physiol.* **46**, 551–572.

KETELAAR, J. A. A., 1953, Chemical Constitution. Elsevier Publ. Co., Amsterdam, Houston, New York, London.

KETELAAR, J. A. A. and H. R. GERSMANN, 1959, Chemical studies on insecticides. IX. The infra-red absorption spectra of phosphorus acid esters. *Rec. Trav. Chim. Pays-Bas* **78**, 190–198.

KINCAID, R. R., 1935, The effect of certain environmental factors on germination of Florida cigar wrapper tobacco seeds. *Florida Agr. Expt. Sta. Bull.* No. 277.

KITÔ, Y., M. ISHIGAMI and T. YOSHIZAWA, 1961, On the labile intermediate of rhodopsin as demonstrated by low temperature illumination. *Biochim. Biophys. Acta* **48**, 287–298.

KOK, B., 1956, On the reversible absorption change at 705 mμ in photosynthetic organisms. *Biochim. Biophys. Acta* **22**, 399–401.

KOK, B., 1961, Partial purification and determination of oxidation reduction potential of the photosynthetic chlorophyll complex absorbing at 700 mμ. *Biochim. Biophys. Acta* **48**, 527–533.

KOK, B. and H. BEINERT, 1962, The light induced EPR signal of photocatalyst P700. II. Two light effects. *Biochem. Biophys. Res. Comm.* **9**, 349–354.

KOK, B. and G. HOCH, 1961, Spectral changes in photosynthesis. *In*: W. D. McElroy and B. Glass, eds., Light and Life. The Johns Hopkins Press, Baltimore. pp. 397–416.

KOMEN, J. G., 1956, Observations on the infrared absorption spectrum of bacteriochlorophyll. *Biochim. Biophys. Acta* **22**, 9–15.

KOSKI, V. M. and J. H. C. SMITH, 1948, The isolation and spectral absorption properties of protochlorophyll from etiolated barley seedlings. *J. Am. Chem. Soc.* **70**, 3558–3562.

KRASNOVSKY, A. A., 1948, *Compt. Rend.* (*Doklady*) *Acad. Sci. U.S.S.R.* **60**, 421. Ref. E. Rabinowitch, 1956.

KRANOVSKY, A. A., 1960, The primary processes of photosynthesis in plants. *Ann. Rev. Plant Physiol.* **11**, 363–410.

KRASNOVSKY, A. A. and G. P. BRIN, 1949, *Compt. Rend. (Doklady) Acad. Sci. U.S.S.R.* **67**, 325. Ref. E. Rabinowitch, 1956.

KRASNOVSKY, A. A., V. B. EVSTIGNEEV, G. P. BRIN and V. A. GRAVILOVA, 1952, *Compt. Rend. (Doklady) Acad. Sci. U.S.S.R.* **82**, 947. Ref. E. Rabinowitch, 1956.

KRASNOVSKY, A. A. and L. M. KOSOBUTSKAJA, 1952, *Doklady Akad. Nauk. S.S.S.R.* **85**, 177. Ref. K. Shibata, 1957.

KRASNOVSKY, A. A. and L. M. KOSOBUTSKAJA, 1955, *Doklady Akad. Nauk. S.S.S.R.* **104**, 440–443. Ref. M. B. Allen, C. S. French and J. S. Brown, 1960.

KRASNOVSKY, A. A., L. M. VOROB'EVA and E. V. PAKASHINA, 1957, *Fiziol. Rastenii Akad.*

Nauk. S.S.S.R. **4**, 124–133. Ref. M. B. Allen, C. S. French and J. S. Brown, 1960.

KRASNOVSKY, A. A. and K. K. VOYNOVSKAYA, 1951, *Compt. Rend. (Doklady) Acad. Sci. U.S.S.R.* **81**, 879. Ref. E. Rabinowitch, 1956.

KROPF, A. and R. HUBBARD, 1958, The mechanism of bleaching rhodopsin. *Ann. New York Acad. Sci.* **74**, 266–280.

KÜHN, A., 1929, Phototropismus und Phototaxis der Tiere. *In*: A. Bethe, G. Embden, G. von Bergmann and A. Ellinger, eds., Handbuch der normale und pathologische Physiologie. **12**. Springer-Verlag, Berlin. pp. 17–35.

KUHN, R. and H. BROCKMANN, 1933, γ-Carotin (Über das Vitamin des Wachstums, IV. Mitteil.). *Ber. Deutsch. Chem. Ges.* **66**, 407–410.

KUHN, R. and CH. GRUNDMANN, 1933, Über Kryptoxanthin, ein Xanthophyll der Formel $C_{40}H_{56}O$ (Über das Vitamin des Wachstums, V. Mitteil.). *Ber. Deutsch. Chem. Ges.* **66**, 1746–1750.

KÜHNE, W., 1879, Chemische Vorgänge in der Netzhaut. *In*: L. Hermann, ed., Handbuch der Physiologie. **3**, Pt. 3. Vogel Verlag, Leipzig. pp. 235–342.

KUPKE, D. W. and C. S. FRENCH, 1960, Relationship of chlorophyll to protein and lipoids; molecular and colloidal solutions, chlorophyll units. *In*: W. Ruhland, ed., Encyclopedia of Plant Physiology. **5**, Pt. 1. Springer-Verlag, Berlin, Göttingen, Heidelberg. pp. 298–322.

KUTYRIN, V. M., 1960, *Fiziologia Rastenii,* **7**, 133. Ref. J. J. Katz *et al.*, 1961.

LABOURIAU, L. G. and A. W. GALSTON, 1955, Phototropism in carotene-free plant organs. *Plant Physiol.* **30**, xxii.

LAIDLER, K. J., 1955, The Chemical Kinetics of Excited States. Clarendon Press, Oxford.

LANGE, S., 1928, Die Verteilung der Lichtempfindlichkeit in der Spitze der Haferkoleoptile. *Jahrb. Wiss. Bot.* **67**, 1–51.

LAVOREL, J., 1957, Effect of energy migration on fluorescence in dye solutions. *J. Phys. Chem.* **61**, 864–869.

LAVOREL, J., 1961, Mécanismes de collection des quanta et d'action photochimique dans la photosynthèse. Mécanique ondulatoire et biologie moléculaire. *In*: Ed. Rev. Optique, Paris. pp. 139–156.

LEMBERG, R., 1928, Die Chromoproteide der Rotalgen. I. *Liebig's Ann. Chem.* **461**, 46–89.

LEMBERG, R., 1929, Pigmente der Rotalgen. *Naturwiss.* **17**, 541.

LEMBERG, R., 1930, Chromoproteide der Rotalgen. II. Spaltung mit Pepsin and Säuren. Isolierung eines Pyrrolfarbstoffs. *Liebig's Ann. Chem.* **477**, 195–245.

LEMBERG, R. and J. W. LEGGE, 1949, Hematin Compounds and Bile Pigments. Their Constitution, Metabolism and Function. Interscience Publ., Inc., New York. Interscience Publ., London.

LEVITT, L. S., 1953, Photosynthesis as a photoelectric phenomenon. *Science* **118**, 696–697.

LEYON, H., 1956, The structure of chloroplasts. *Svensk Kem. Tidskr.* **68**, 70–89.

LINKS, J., 1955, I. Een hypothese over het mechanisme van de (phobo-)chemotaxis. II. De carotenoïden, steroïden en vetzuren van *Polytoma uvella.* (With a summary in English). Doctoral thesis. State University, Leiden.

LINSCHITZ, H., 1960, Studies on the photochemistry of rhodopsin and chlorophyll. *Radiation Research* Suppl. **2**, 182–185.

LINSCHITZ, H., 1961, Chemiluminescence in porphyrin-catalyzed decomposition of peroxides. *In*: W. D. McElroy and B. Glass, eds., Light and Life. The Johns Hopkins Press, Baltimore. pp. 173–182.

LINSCHITZ, H. and J. RENNERT, 1952, Reversible photobleaching of chlorophyll in rigid solvents. *Nature* **169**, 193–194.

LINSCHITZ, H. and K. SARKANEN, 1958, The absorption spectra and decay kinetics of the metastable states of chlorophyll *a* and *b*. *J. Am. Chem. Soc.* **80**, 4826–4832.

LIPMANN, F., 1941, Metabolic generation and utilization of phosphate bond energy. *Adv. Enzymol.*, **1**, 99–162.

LIVERMAN, J. L. and J. BONNER, 1953, The interaction of auxin and light in the growth responses of plants. *Proc. Natl. Acad. Sci.* **39**, 905–916.

LIVINGSTON, R., 1941, The reversible bleaching of chlorophyll. *J. Phys. Chem.* **45**, 1312–1320.

LIVINGSTON, R., 1954, Preliminary study of a metastable form of chlorophyll in fluid solutions. *J. Am. Chem. Soc.* **77**, 2179–2182.

LIVINGSTON, R., 1960, The photochemistry of chlorophyll. *In*: W. Ruhland, ed., Encyclopedia of Plant Physiology. **5**, Pt. 1. Springer-Verlag, Berlin, Göttingen, Heidelberg. pp. 830–883.

LIVINGSTON, R. and A. C. P. PUGH, 1960, Role of the triplet state in the photoreduction of chlorophyll. *Nature* **186**, 969–970.

LIVINGSTON, R. and V. A. RYAN, 1953, The phototropy of chlorophyll in fluid solutions. *J. Am. Chem. Soc.* **75**, 2176–2181.

LOCKHART, J. A., 1962, Physiology of light and gibberellin action on internode elongation. *Plant Physiol.* **37**, Suppl. xxxvii.

LONGUETT-HIGGINS, H. C., C. W. RECTOR and J. R. PLATT, 1950, Molecular orbital calculations on porphine and tetrahydroporphine. *J. Chem. Phys.* **18**, 1174–1181.

LOSADA, M., A. V. TREBST and D. I. ARNON, 1960, Photosynthesis by isolated chloroplasts. XI. CO_2 assimilation in a reconstituted chloroplast system. *J. Biol. Chem.* **235**, 832–839.

LOSADA, M., F. R. WHATLEY and D. I. ARNON, 1961, Separation of two light reactions in non-cyclic photo-phosphorylation of green plants. *Nature* **190**, 606–610.

LUBIMENKO, V., 1927, Les pigments des plastes et leur transformation dans les tissues vivants de la plante. *Rev. Gén. Bot.* **39**, 619–637.

LUMRY, R. and J. D. SPIKES, 1960, Collection and utilization of energy in photosynthesis. *In:* Radiation Research, Suppl. 2, Academic Press, Inc. U. S. A. pp. 539–577.

LUMRY, R., J. D. SPIKES and H. EYRING, 1954, Photosynthesis. *Ann. Rev. Plant Physiol.* **5**, 271–340.

LUNTZ, A., 1931, Untersuchungen über die Phototaxis. I. Mitteilung. Die absoluten Schwellenwerte und die relative Wirksamkeit von Spektralfarben bei grünen und farblosen Einzelligen. *Zs. Vergl. Physiol.* **14**, 69–92.

LUNTZ, A., 1932, Untersuchungen über die Phototaxis. III. Mitteilung. Die Umkehr der Reaktionsrichtung bei starken Lichtintensitäten und ihre Bedeutung für eine allgemeine Theorie der photischen Reizwirkung. *Zs. Vergl. Physiol.* **16**, 204–217.

LYTHGOE, R. J., 1937, The absorption spectra of visual purple and of indicator yellow. *J. Physiol.* **89**, 331–358.

LYTHGOE, R. J. and J. P. QUILLIAM, 1938, The relation between transient orange to visual purple and indicator yellow. *J. Physiol.* **94**, 399–410.

MAHLER, H. R., 1954, Studies on the fatty acid oxidizing system of animal tissues. IV. The prosthetic group of butyryl coenzyme A dehydrogenase. *J. Biol. Chem.* **206**, 13–26.

MANNING, W. M. and H. H. STRAIN, 1943, Chlorophyll *d*, a green pigment of red algae. *J. Biol. Chem.* **151**, 1–19.

MANTEN, A., 1948, Phototaxis, phototropism, and photosynthesis in purple bacteria and blue-green algae. Doctoral thesis. State University, Utrecht.

MARCUS, A., 1960, Photocontrol of formation of red kidney bean leaf triphosphopyridine nucleotide linked triosephosphate dehydrogenase. *Plant Physiol.* **35**, 126–128.

MARGOLIASH, E., 1955, Position and reactivity of the histidine residues in cytochrome c. *Nature* **175**, 293–295.

MARKS, W. B., W. H. DOBELLE and E. F. MACNICHOL, Jr., 1964, Visual pigments of single primate cones. *Science* **143**, 1181–1183.

MARRIOTT, F. H. C., 1962, Colour vision: theories. *In*: H. Davson, ed., The Eye. Academic Press, New York, London. pp. 299–320.

MARSHALL, F. H. A. and F. P. BOWDEN, 1934, The effect of irradiation with different wave-lengths on the oestrus cycle of the ferret, with remarks on factors controlling sexual periodicity. *J. Exptl. Biol.* **11**, 409–422.

MAST, S. O., 1926, Reaction to light in *Volvox*, with special reference to the process of orientation. *Zs. Vergl. Physiol.* **4**, 637–658.

MAST, S. O., 1928, Structure and function of the eye-spot in unicellular and colonial organisms. *Arch. Protistenk.* **60**, 197–220.

MATTHEWS, G. V. T., 1955, An investigation of the "chronometer" factor in bird navigation. *J. Exptl. Biol.* **32**, 39–59.

MATTHEWS, R. G., R. HUBBARD, P. K. BROWN and G. WALD, 1963, Tautomeric forms of metarhodopsin. *J. Gen. Physiol.* **47**, 215–240.

MCCONNELL, D. G. and D. G. SCARPELLI, 1963, Rhodopsin: an enzyme. *Science* **139**, 848.

MCELROY, W. D., 1947, The energy source for bioluminescence in an isolated system. *Proc. Natl. Acad. Sci* **33**, 342–345.

MCELROY, W. D. and A. A. GREEN, 1955, Enzymatic properties of bacterial luciferase. *Arch. Biochem. Biophys.* **56**, 240–255.

MCELROY, W. D. and A. GREEN, 1956, Function of adenosine triphosphate in the activation of luciferin. *Arch. Biochem. Biophys.* **64**, 257–271.

MCELROY, W. D., J. W. HASTINGS, V. SONNENFELD and J. COULOMBRE, 1953, The requirement of riboflavin phosphate for bacterial luminescence. *Science* **118**, 385–386.

MCELROY, W. D. and H. H. SELIGER, 1961, Mechanisms of bioluminescent reactions. *In*: W. D. McElroy and B. Glass, eds., Light and Life. The Johns Hopkins Press, Baltimore. pp. 219–257.

MCELROY, W. D. and H. H. SELIGER, 1963, The chemistry of light emission. *Adv. Enzymol.* **25**, 119–166.

MCELROY, W. D. and B. L. STREHLER, 1954, Bioluminescence. *Bacteriol. Rev.* **18**, 177–194.

MCLEAN, J. D., 1956, The structure of the plant cell. Doctoral thesis. University of Sydney.

MENKE, W., 1962, Structure and chemistry of plastids. *Ann. Rev. Plant Physiol.* **13**, 27–44.

MER, C. L., 1957, A re-examination of the supposed effect of riboflavin on growth. *Plant Physiol.* **32**, 175–185.

MERCER, F., 1960, The submicroscopic structure of the cell. *Ann. Rev. Plant Physiol.* **11**, 1–24.

MERCER, F. V., A. J. HODGE, A. B. HOPE and J. D. MCLEAN, 1955, The structure and swelling properties of *Nitella* chloroplasts. *Austral. J. Biol. Sci.* **8**, 1–18.

METZNER, P., 1922, Über den Farbstoff der grünen Bakterien. *Ber. Deutsch. Bot. Ges.* **40**, 125–129.

MILLS, K. S. and A. R. SCHRANK, 1954, Electrical and curvature responses of the *Avena* coleoptile to unilateral ultraviolet irradiation. *J. Cell. Comp. Physiol.* **43**, 39–55.

MILNE, L. J. and M. J. MILNE, 1956, Invertebrate photoreceptors. *In*: A. Hollaender, ed., Radiation Biology. **3**. McGraw-Hill Book Co., Inc., New York, Toronto, London. pp. 621–692.

MOHR, H., 1956, Die Abhängigkeit des Protonemawachstums und der Protonemapolarität bei Farnen vom Licht. *Planta* **47**, 127–158.

MOHR, H., 1957, Der Einfluss monochromatischer Strahlung auf das Längenwachstum des Hypokotyls und auf die Anthocyanbildung bei Keimlingen von *Sinapis alba* L. (= *Brassica alba* Boiss.). *Planta* **49**, 389–405.

MOHR, H., 1962, Primary effects of light on growth. *Ann. Rev. Plant Physiol.* **13**, 465–488.

MOHR, H. and M. WEHRUNG, 1960, Die Steuerung des Hypokotylswachstums bei den Keimlingen von *Lactuca sativa* L. durch sichtbare Strahlung. *Planta* **55**, 438–450.

MOLISCH, H., 1896, Eine neue mikrochemische Reaction auf Chlorophyll. *Ber. Deutsch. Bot. Ges.* **14**, 16–18.

MORAW, R. and H. T. WITT, 1961a, Über eine photochemische Reaktion der Photosynthese. IV. Mitteilung. *Zs. Phys. Chem. N.F.* **29**, 1–12.

MORAW, R. and H. T. WITT, 1961b, Zusammenhang zwischen Zellstruktur, Energiewanderung und Chlorophyllreaktion. Die π-π^*-Triplettzustande des Chlorophylls in Pflanzenzellen. VI. Mitteilung. *Zs. Phys. Chem. N.F.* **29**. 25–42.

MORTON, R. A. and G. A. J. PITT, 1955, Studies on rhodopsin. 9. pH and the hydrolysis of indicator yellow. *Biochem. J.* **59**. 128–134.

MOYER, L. S. and M. M. FISHMAN, 1943, The chlorophyll-protein complex. II. Species relationships in certain legumes as shown by electric mobility curves. *Bot. Gaz.* **104**, 449–454.

MÜHLETHALER, K., 1960, Die Struktur der Grana- und Stromalamellen in Chloroplasten. *Zs. Wiss. Mikroskop. und Mikroskop. Technik* **64**, 444–452.

MÜLLER, A. and H. T. WITT, 1961, Trapped primary product of photosynthesis in green plants. *Nature* **189**, 944–945.

MUNZ, F. W., 1958, Photosensitive pigments from the retinae of certain deep-sea fishes. *J. Physiol.* **140**, 220–235.

MYERS, J. and C. S. FRENCH 1960, Relationships between time course, chromatic transients, and enhancement phenomena of photosynthesis. *Plant Physiol.* **35**, 963–969.

MYERS, O. E., 1962, Spectral sensitivity of visual receptor cells. *Nature* **193**, 449–451.

NAKAYAMA, S., H. A. BORTHWICK and S. B. HENDRICKS 1960, Failure of photoreversible control of flowering in *Pharbitis nil*. *Bot. Gaz.* **121**, 237–243.

NAYLOR, A. W., 1961, The photoperiodic control of plant behavior. *In*: W. Ruhland, ed., Encyclopedia of Plant Physiology. **16**. Springer-Verlag, Berlin, Göttingen, Heidelberg. pp. 331–389.

NEEDHAM, D. M., 1952, Adenosine triphosphate and the structural proteins in relation to muscle contraction. *Adv. Enzymol.* **13**, 151–197.

NEILANDS, J. B. and P. K. STUMPF, 1958, Outlines of Enzyme Chemistry. John Wiley and Sons, Inc., New York. Chapman and Hall, London.

NIKLOWITZ, W. and G. DREWS, 1955, Zur elektronenmikroskopischen Darstellung der Feinstruktur von *Rhodospirillum rubrum*. *Arch. Mikrobiol.* **23**, 123–129.

NIKLOWITZ, W. and G. DREWS, 1956, Beiträge zur Cytologie der Blaualgen. I. Untersuchungen zur Substruktur von *Phormidium uncinatum* Gom. *Arch. Mikrobiol.* **24**, 134–146.

NISHIMURA, M. and K. TAKAMATSU, 1957, A carotene-protein complex isolated from green leaves. *Nature* **180**, 699–700.

NISHIMURA, M. and K. TAKAMATSU, 1960, Studies on a carotene-protein complex isolated from green leaves. *Plant Cell Physiol.* **1**, 305–309.

NULTSCH, W., 1956, Studien über die Phototaxis der Diatomeen. *Arch. Protistenk.* **101**, 1–68.

NULTSCH, W., 1962a, Der Einfluss des Lichtes auf die Bewegung der Cyanophyceen. III. Mitteilung. Photophobotaxis von *Phormidium uncinatum*. *Planta* **58**, 647–663.

NULTSCH, W., 1962b, Phototaktische Aktionsspektren von Cyanophyceen. *Ber. Deutsch. Bot. Ges.* **75**, 443–453.

NULTSCH, W., 1962c, Der Einfluss des Lichtes auf die Bewegung der Cyanophyceen. II. Mitteilung. Photokinesis bei *Phormidium autumnale*. *Planta* **57**, 613–523.

OESPER, P., 1950, Sources of the high energy content in energy-rich phosphates. *Arch. Biochem. Biophys.* **27**, 255–270.

OESPER, P., 1951, The chemistry and thermodynamics of phosphate bonds. *In*: W. D. McElroy and B. Glass, eds., Phosphorus Metabolism. I. The Johns Hopkins Press, Baltimore, pp. 523–536.

O'HEOCHA, C., 1958, Comparative biochemical studies of the phycobilins. *Arch. Biochem. Biophys.* **73**, 207–219.

O'HEOCHA, C., 1960, Chemical studies of phycoerythrins and phycocyanins. *In*: M. B. Allen, ed., Comparative Biochemistry of Photoreactive Systems. Academic Press, New York, London. pp. 181–203.

O'HEOCHA, C. and F. T. HAXO, 1960, Some atypical algal chromoproteins. *Biochim. Biophys. Acta* **41**, 516–520.

OKSCHE, A. and M. VON HARNACK, 1963, Elektronenmikroskopische Untersuchungen am Stirnorgan von Anuren (zur Frage der Lichtrezeptoren). *Zs. Zellforsch. Mikrosk. Anat.* **59**, 239–288.

OLSON, J. M. and C. A. ROMANO, 1962, A new chlorophyll from green bacteria. *Biochim. Biophys. Acta* **59**, 726–728.

OPPENOORTH, W. F. F. J., 1941, On the role of auxin in phototropism and light-growth-reactions of *Avena*-coleoptiles. *Rec. Trav. Bot. Néerl.* **38**, 287–372.

PACKER, L., 1962, Light scattering changes correlated with photosynthetic phosphorylation in chloroplast fragments. *Biochem. Biophys. Res. Comm.* **9**, 355–360.

PAGE, R. M., 1962, Light and the asexual reproduction of *Pilobolus*. *Science* **138**, 1238–1245.

PARDI, L. and F. PAPI, 1961, Kinetic and tactic responses. *In*: T. H. Waterman, ed., The Physiology of Crustacea. **2**. Academic Press, New York, London. pp. 365–399.

PARK, R. B. and N. G. PON, 1961, Correlation of structure with function in *Spinacea oleracea* chloroplasts. *J. Mol. Biol.* **3**, 1–10.

PARKER, M. W. and H. A. BORTHWICK, 1950, Influence of light on plant growth. *Ann. Rev. Plant Physiol.* **1**, 43–58.

PARKER, M. W., S. B. HENDRICKS, H. A. BORTHWICK and F. W. WENT, 1949, Spectral sensitivities for leaf and stem growth of etiolated pea seedlings and their similarity to action spectra for photoperiodism. *Am. J. Bot.* **36**, 194–204.

PAUL, K.-G., 1951, The porphyrin component of cytochrome c and its linkage to the protein. *Acta Chem. Scand.* **5**, 389–405.

PEIERLS, R., 1932, Theorie der Absorptionsspektren fester Körper. *Ann. Physik.* [5. Folge] **13**, 905–952.

PERRIN, F., 1932, Théorie quantique des transferts d'activation entre molécules de même espèce. Cas des solutions fluorescentes. *Ann. Phys.* (Paris) **17**, 283–314.

PIRENNE, M. H., 1962a, Absolute thresholds and quantum effects. *In*: H. Davson, ed., The Eye. **2**. Academic Press, New York, London. pp. 123–140.

PIRENNE, M. H., 1962b, Quantum fluctuations at the absolute threshold. *In*: H. Davson, ed., The Eye. **2**. Academic Press, New York, London. pp. 141–158.

PIRENNE, M. H., 1962c, Rods and cones. *In*: H. Davson, ed., The Eye. **2**. Academic Press, New York, London. pp. 13–29.

PITT, G. A. J., F. D. COLLINS, R. A. MORTON and P. STOK, 1955, Studies on rhodopsin. 8. Retinylidenemethylamine, an indicator yellow analogue. *Biochem. J.* **59**, 122–128.

PLATT, J. R., 1956, Electronic structure and excitation of polyenes and porphyrins. *In*: A. Hollaender, ed., Radiation Biology. **3**, McGraw-Hill Book Co., Inc., New York, Toronto, London. pp. 71–123.

POLYAK, S. L., 1941, The Retina. The University of Chicago Press, Chicago.

PORRET, D. and E. RABINOWITCH, 1937, Reversible bleaching of chlorophyll. *Nature* **140**, 321–322.

PRICE, W. C. and R. W. G. WYCKOFF, 1938, The ultracentrifugation of the proteins of cucumber viruses 3 and 4. *Nature* **141**, 685–686.

PULLMAN, B. and A. PULLMAN, 1960, Electronic structure of energy-rich phosphates. *Radiation Research, Suppl.* **2**. 160–181.

PULLMAN, B. and A. PULLMAN, 1963, Quantum Biochemistry. Interscience Publ., New York, London.

QUAY, W. B., 1961, Reduction of mammalian pineal weight and lipid during continuous light. *Gen. Comp. Endocrinol.* **1**, 211–217.

QUAY, W. B., 1963a, Circadian rhythm in rat pineal serotonin and its modifications by estrous cycle and photoperiod. *Gen. Comp. Endocrinol.* **3**, 473–479.

QUAY, W. B., 1963b, Cytologic and metabolic parameters of pineal inhibition by continuous light in the rat (*Rattus norvegicus*). *Zs. Zellforsch.* **60**, 479–490.

RABINOWITCH, E. I., 1945, Photosynthesis and Related Processes. **1**. Interscience Publ., Inc., New York.

RABINOWITCH, E. I., 1951, Photosynthesis and Related Processes. **2**. Pt. 1. Interscience Publ., Inc., New York.

RABINOWITCH, E. I., 1956, Photosynthesis and Related Processes. **2**. Pt. 2. Interscience Publ., Inc., New York.

RABINOWITCH, E., 1957, Photosynthesis and energy transfer. *J. Phys. Chem.* **61**, 870–878.

RABINOWITCH, E., 1958, La Photosynthèse. Gauthier-Villars, Paris.

RABINOWITCH, E., 1959a, Primary photochemical and photophysical processes in photosynthesis. *Disc. Faraday Soc.* **27**, 161–172.

RABINOWITCH, E., 1959b, Primary photochemical and photophysical processes in photosynthesis. *Plant Physiol.* **34**, 213–218.

RABINOWITCH, E., GOVINDJEE and J. B. THOMAS, 1960, Inhibition of photosynthesis in some algae by extreme-red light. *Science* **132**, 422.

RABINOWITCH, E. and J. WEISS, 1937, Reversible oxidation of chlorophyll. *Proc. Roy. Soc. London, A*, **162**, 251–267.

RADDING, C. M. and G. WALD, 1956a, Acid-base properties of rhodopsin and opsin. *J. Gen. Physiol.* **39**, 909–922.

RADDING, C. M. and G. WALD, 1956b, The stability of rhodopsin and opsin. Effects of pH and aging. *J. Gen. Physiol.* **39**, 923–933.

REID, C., 1957, Excited States in Chemistry and Biology. Butterworths Scientific Publications, London.

REINERT, J., 1953, Über die Wirkung von Riboflavin und Carotin beim Phototropismus von *Avena*koleoptilen und bei anderen pflanzlichen Lichtreizreaktionen. *Zs. Bot.* **41**, 103–122.

REINERT, J., 1959, Phototropism and phototaxis. *Ann. Rev. Plant Physiol.* **10**, 441–458.

RIVAS, L. R., 1953, The pineal apparatus of tunas and related scombrid fishes as a possible light receptor controlling phototactic movements. *Bull. Marine Sci. Gulf Caribbean* **3**, 168–180.

ROBERTS, D. W. A. and H. J. PERKINS, 1962, Chlorophyll biosynthesis and turnover in wheat leaves. *Biochim. Biophys. Acta* **58**, 499–506.

ROBINSON, G. W., 1961, Electronic excited states of simple molecules. *In*: W. D. McElroy and B. Glass, eds., Light and Life. The Johns Hopkins Press, Baltimore. pp. 11–30.

RODRIGO, F. A., 1955, Experiments concerning the state of chlorophyll in the plant. Doctoral thesis. State University, Utrecht.

ROSENBERG, J. L., 1957, Photochemistry of chlorophyll. *Ann. Rev. Plant Physiol.* **8**, 115–136.

RUBEN, S., 1943, Photosynthesis and phosphorylation. *J. Am. Chem. Soc.* **65**, 279–282.

RUBINSTEIN, D. and E. RABINOWITCH, 1963, Fluorescence and absorption changes in *Chlorella* exposed to strong light: the red band. *Science* **142**, 681–682.

RUCH, F., 1957, Dichroismus und Difluoreszenz der Chloroplasten. *Exptl. Cell Res.* Suppl. **4**, 58–63.

RUMBERG, B., A. MÜLLER and H. T. WITT, 1962, New results about the mechanism of photosynthesis. *Nature* **194**, 854–856.

RUSHTON, W. A. H., 1959, Visual pigments in man and animals and their relation to seeing. *Progr. Biophys. and Biophys. Chem.* **9**, 240–283.

RUSHTON, W. A. H., 1961, The chemical basis of colour vision. *New Scient.* **10**, 374–377.

SAGER, R. and G. E. PALADE, 1957, Structure and development of the chloroplast in *Chlamydomonas*. I. The normal green cell. *J. Biophys. Biochem. Cytol* **3**, 463–488.

SALISBURY, F. B., 1961, Photoperiodism and the flowering process. *Ann. Rev. Plant Physiol.* **12**, 293–326.

SANDS, R. H., 1960, EPR spectroscopy. *In*: NMR and EPR Spectroscopy. Pergamon Press, Oxford, London, New York, Paris. pp. 44–55.

SAPOZHNIKOV, D. I. and N. V. BAZANOVA, 1958, *Doklady Akad. Nauk. S.S.S.R. Bot. Sci. Sect.* **120**, 162–164. Ref. J. M. Anderson, U. Blass and M. Calvin, 1960.

SAPOZHNIKOV, D. I., T. A. KRASOVSKAJA and A. N. MAEVSKAYA, 1957, *Doklady Akad. Nauk. S.S.S.R. Bot. Sci. Sect.* **113**, 74–76. Ref. J. M. Anderson, U. Blass and M. Calvin, 1960.

SAPOZHNIKOV, D. I. and Y. B. LOPATKIN, 1950, *Doklady Akad. Nauk. S.S.S.R.* **72**, 413. Ref. T. W. Goodwin, 1952.

SAUER, F., 1957, Die Sternenorientierung nächtlich ziehender Grasmücken (*Sylvia atricapilla, borin* und *curruca*). *Zs. Tierpsychol.* **14**, 29–70.

SAUER, K. and M. CALVIN, 1962, Molecular orientation in quantasomes. I. Electric dichroism and electric birefringence of quantasomes from spinach chloroplasts. *J. Mol. Biol.* **4**, 451–466.

SCHACHMAN, H. K., A. B. PARDEE and R. Y. STANIER, 1952, Studies on the macromolecular organization of microbial cells. *Arch. Biochem. Biophys.* **38**, 245–260.

SCHEIBE, G., 1937a, Über die Veränderlichkeit der Absorptionsspektren in Lösungen und die Nebenvalenzen als ihre Ursache. *Zs. Angew. Chem.* **50**, 212–219.

SCHEIBE, G., 1937b, Über den Mechanismus der Sensibilisierung photochemischer Reaktionen der Farbstoffe, insbesondere der Assimilation. *Naturwiss.* **25**, 795.

SCHEIBE, G., L. KANDLER and H. ECKER, 1937, Polymerization und polymere Adsorption als Ursache neuartiger Absorptionsbanden von organischen Farbstoffen. *Naturwiss.* **25**, 75.

SCHEIBE, G., A. MARELS and H. ECKER, 1937, Über reversibele Polymerisation als Ursache neuartiger Absorptionsbanden (III). *Naturwiss.* **25**, 474–475.

SCHMIDT, W. J., 1938, Polarizationsoptische Analyse eines Eiweiss-Lipoid-Systems, erläutert am Aussenglied der Sehzellen. *Kolloid. Zs.* **85**, 137–148.

SCHRANK, A. R., 1950, Plant tropisms. *Ann. Rev. Plant Physiol.* **1**, 59–74.

SCHULTZE, M., 1866, Zur Anatomie und Physiologie der Retina. *Arch. Mikr. Anat.* **2**, 175–286.

SCHWEIKERDT, H., 1928, Untersuchungen über Photodinese bei Vallisneria spiralis. *Jahrb. Wiss. Bot.* **68**, 79–134.

SELIGER, H. H., 1962, Direct action of light in naturally pigmented muscle fibers. 1. Action spectrum for contraction in eel iris sphincter. *J. Gen. Physiol.* **46**, 333–342.

SELIGER, H. H. and W. D. MCELROY, 1959, Quantum yield in the oxidation of firefly luciferin. *Biochem. Biophys. Res. Comm.* **1**, 21–24.

SELIGER, H. H. and W. D. MCELROY, 1960, Spectral emission and quantum yield of firefly bioluminescence. *Arch. Biochem. Biophys.* **88**, 136–141.

SELIGER, H. H. and W. D. MCELROY, 1960a, Pathways of energy transfer in bioluminescence. *Radiation Research*, Suppl. **2**, 528–538.

SELIGER, H. H. and W. D. MCELROY, 1962, Chemiluminescence of firefly luciferin without enzyme. *Science* **138**, 683–685.

SELIGER, H. H., W. D. MCELROY, E. H. WHITE and G. F. FIELD, 1961, Stereospecificity and firefly bioluminescence. A comparison of natural and synthetic luciferins. *Proc. Natl. Acad. Sci.* **47**, 1129–1134.

SENN, G., 1908, Die Gestalts- und Lageveränderung der Pflanzenchromatophoren. W. Engelmann, Leipzig.

SEYBOLD, A. and K. EGLE, 1938, Zur Kenntnis des Protochlorophylls. II. *Planta* **29**, 119–128.

SHIBATA, K., 1957, Spectroscopic studies on chlorophyll formation in intact leaves. *J. Biochem.* (Tokyo) **44**, 147–173.

SHIMOMURA, O., T. GOTO and Y. HIRATA, 1957, Crystalline *Cypridina* luciferin. *Bull. Chem. Soc. Japan* **30**, 929–933.

SHIMOMURA, O., F. H. JOHNSON and Y. SAIGA, 1961, Purification and properties of *Cypridina* luciferase. *J. Cell. Comp. Physiol.* **58**, 113–123.

SHIMOMURA, O., F. H. JOHNSON and Y. SAIGA, 1962, Extraction, purification and properties of aequorin, a bioluminescent protein from the luminous hydromedusan *Aequorea*. *J. Cell. Comp. Physiol.* **59**, 223–240.

SHIMOMURA, O., F. H. JOHNSON and Y. SAIGA, 1963a, Partial purification of the *Odontosyllis* luminescent system. *J. Cell. Comp. Physiol.* **61**, 275–292.

SHIMOMURA, O., F. H. JOHNSON and Y. SAIGA, 1963b, Further data on the bioluminescent protein, aequorin. *J. Cell. Comp. Physiol.* **62**, 1–8.

SHIMOMURA, O., F. H. JOHNSON and Y. SAIGA, 1963c, Extraction and properties of halistaurin, a bioluminescent protein from the hydromedusan *Halistaura*. *J. Cell. Comp. Physiol.* **62**, 9–16.

SHLYK, A. A., 1956, Tagged atom method of studying the biosynthesis of chlorophyll. Translation U. S. Atomic Energy Commission AEC-tr-3541. Tech. Inf. Serv. Extension, Oak Ridge.

SHNEOUR, E. A. and M. CALVIN, 1962, Isotopic oxygen incorporation in xanthophylls of *Spinacea oleracea* quantasomes. *Nature* **196**, 439–441.

SHROPSHIRE, W., 1963, Photoresponses of the fungus, *Phycomyces*. *Physiol. Rev.* **43**, 38–67.

SHROPSHIRE, W. and R. B. WITHROW, 1958, Action spectrum of phototropic tip-curvature of *Avena*. *Plant Physiol.* **33**, 360–365.

SIE, E. H.-C., W. D. MCELROY, F. H. JOHNSON and Y. HANEDA, 1961, Spectroscopy of the *Apogon* luminescent system and of its cross reaction with the *Cypridina* system. *Arch. Biochem. Biophys.* **93**, 286–291.

SIEGELMAN, H. W., E. M. FIRER, W. L. BUTLER and S. B. HENDRICKS, 1962, Phytochrome from corn and barley seedlings. *Plant Physiol.* **37**, Suppl. xxvii.

SIEGELMAN, H. W. and S. B. HENDRICKS, 1957, Photocontrol of anthocyanin formation in turnip and red cabbage seedlings. *Plant Physiol.* **32**, 393–398.

SIEGELMAN, H. W. and S. B. HENDRICKS, 1958, Photocontrol of anthocyanin synthesis in apple skin. *Plant Physiol.* **33**, 185–190.

SISLER, E. C. and W. H. KLEIN, 1961, Effect of red and far-red irradiation on nucleotide phosphate and adenosine triphosphate levels in dark-grown bean and *Avena* seedlings. *Physiologia Plantarum.* **14**, 115–123.

SJÖSTRAND, F. S., 1961, Electron microscopy of the retina. *In*: G. K. Smelser, ed., The Structure of the Eye. Academic Press, New York, London. pp. 1–28.

SMITH, E. L. and E. G. PICKELS, 1941, The effect of detergents on the chlorophyll-protein compound of spinach as studied in the ultracentrifuge. *J. Gen. Physiol.* **24**, 753–764.

SMITH, J. H. C., 1960, Protochlorophyll transformations. *In*: M. B. Allen, ed., Comparative Biochemistry of Photoreactive Systems. Academic Press, New York, London. pp. 257–277.

SMITH, J. H. C. and A. BENITEZ, 1953, The protochlorophyll-chlorophyll transformation: The nature of protochlorophyll in leaves. *Carnegie Inst. Washington Year Book* **52**, 149–153.

SMITH, J. H. C. and A. BENITEZ, 1954, Absorption spectra of chlorophylls. *Carnegie Inst. Washington Year Book* **53**, 168–172.

SMITH, J. H. C., L. J. DURHAM and C. F. WURSTER, 1959, Formation and bleaching of chlorophyll in albino corn seedlings. *Plant Physiol.* **34**, 340–345.

SMITH, J. H. C. and C. S. FRENCH, 1963, The major and accessory pigments in photosynthesis. *Ann. Rev. Plant Physiol.* **14**, 181–224.

SMITH, J. H. C. and V. M. K. YOUNG, 1956, Chlorophyll formation and accumulation in plants. *In*: A. Hollaender, ed., Radiation Biology. **3**. McGraw-Hill Book Co., Inc., New York, Toronto, London. pp. 393–442.

SMITH, L. and B. CHANCE, 1958, Cytochromes in plants. *Ann. Rev. Plant Physiol.* **9**, 449–482.

SMITH, L. and J. RAMIREZ, 1959, Reactions of pigments of photosynthetic bacteria following illumination or oxygenation. *In*: The Photochemical Apparatus. Its Structure and Function. Brookhaven Symp. Biol. **11**. Brookhaven National Laboratory, Upton. pp. 310–315.

SOGO, P. B., N. G. PON and M. CALVIN, 1957, Photo spin resonance in chlorophyll-containing plant material. *Proc. Natl. Acad. Sci.* **43**, 387–393.

SOGO, P. B. and B. M. TOLBERT, 1957, Nuclear and electron paramagnetic resonance and its application to biology. *Adv. Biol. Med. Phys.* **5**, 1–35.

SPOEHR, H. A., 1926, Photosynthesis. Chemical Catalog Co., Inc., New York.

SPRUIT-VAN DER BURG, A., 1950, Emission spectra of luminous bacteria. *Biochim. Biophys. Acta* **5**, 175–178.

STANIER, R. Y., 1959, Formation and function of the photosynthetic pigment system in purple bacteria. *In*: The Photochemical Apparatus. Its Structure and Function. Brookhaven National Laboratory, Upton. pp. 43–51.

STANIER, R. Y., 1960, On the existence of two chlorophylls in green bacteria. *In*: M. B. Allen, ed., Comparative Biochemistry of Photoreactive Systems. Academic Press, New York, London. pp. 69–72.

STANIER, R. Y. and J. H. C. SMITH 1959, Protochlorophyll from a purple bacterium. *Carnegie Inst. Washington Year Book* **58**, 336–338.

STANIER, R. Y. and J. H. C. SMITH, 1960, The chlorophylls of green bacteria. *Biochim. Biophys. Acta* **41**, 478–484.

STEWART, W. S. and F. W. WENT, 1939, Light stability of auxin in *Avena* coleoptiles. *Bot. Gaz.* **101**, 706–714.

STEYN, W., 1960, Observations on the ultrastructure of the pineal eye. *J. Roy. Microsc. Soc.*, Ser. III **79**, 47–58.

STILES, W., 1925, Photosynthesis. Longmans, Green and Co., London, New York, Toronto, Bombay, Calcutta, Madras.

STOCKHAMMER, K., 1959, Die Orientierung nach der Schwingungsrichtung linear polarisierten Lichtes und ihre sinnesphysiologischen Grundlagen. *Ergebn. Biol.* **21**, 23–56.

STOLL, A. and E. WIEDEMANN, 1938, Chlorophyll. *Fortschr. Chem. Organ. Naturstoffe* **1**, 159–254.

STOREY, W. H., C. M. MONITA and D. G. CADENA, 1962, Kinetics and oxygen requirements of a light-induced electron spin resonance signal from spinach chloroplasts. *Nature* **195**, 963–965.

STRAIN, H. H., 1938, Leaf xanthophylls. Carnegie Inst. Publ. no. 490, 1–147.

STRAIN, H. H., 1944, Chloroplast pigments. *Ann. Rev. Biochem.* **13**, 591–610.

STRAIN, H. H., 1949, Functions and properties of the chloroplast pigments. *In*: J. Franck and W. E. Loomis, eds., Photosynthesis in Plants. Iowa State College Press, Ames. pp. 133–178.

STRAIN, H. H., 1951, The pigments of algae. *In*: G. M. Smith, ed., Manual of Phycology. Chronica Botanica Co., Waltham. pp. 243–262.

STRAIN, H. H., 1954, Leaf xanthophylls: the action of acids on violaxanthin, violeoxanthin, taraxanthin and tareoxanthin. *Arch. Biochem. Biophys.* **48**, 458–468.

STRAIN, H. H. and W. M. MANNING, 1942a, Chlorofucine (chlorophyll γ), a green pigment of diatoms and brown algae. *J. Biol. Chem.* **144**, 625–636.

STRAIN, H. H. and W. M. MANNING, 1942b, Isomerization of chlorophylls *a* and *b*. *J. Biol. Chem.* **146**, 275–276.

STRAIN, H. H. and W. M. MANNING, 1943, A unique polyene pigment of the marine diatom *Navicula torquatum*. *J. Am. Chem. Soc.* **65**, 2258–2259.

STRAIN, H. H., W. M. MANNING and G. HARDIN, 1944, Xanthophylls and carotenes of diatoms, brown algae, dinoflagellates, and sea anemones. *Biol. Bull.* **86**, 169–191.

STREHLER, B. L., 1953, Luminescence in cell-free extracts of luminous bacteria and its activation by DPN. *J. Am. Chem. Soc.* **75**, 1264.

STREHLER, B. L., 1955, Factors and biochemistry of bacterial luminescence. *In*: F. H. Johnson, ed., The Luminescence of Biological Systems. American Association for the Advancement of Science, Washington, D.C. pp. 209–240.

STREHLER, B. L. and M. J. CORMIER, 1953, Factors affecting the luminescence of cell-free extracts of the luminous bacterium, *Achromobacter fischeri*. *Arch. Biochem. Biophys.* **47**, 16–33.

STRUGGER, S., 1956, Elektronenmikroskopische Beobachtungen an den Chloroplasten von *Chlorophytum comosum*. *Ber. Deutsch. Bot. Ges.* **69**, 177.

STRUGGER, S. and M. LOSADA-VILLASANTE, 1955/56, Die Plastiden in den albicaten Geweben der Blätter einer mediovariegaten Form von *Chlorophytum comosum*. *Protoplasma* **45**, 540–551.

SVEDBERG, T. and I.-B. ERIKSSON, 1932, The molecular weights of phycocyanin and of phycoerythrin. III. *J. Am. Chem. Soc.* **54**, 3998–4010.

SWEENEY, B. M., F. T. HAXO and J. W. HASTINGS, 1959, Action spectra for two effects of light on luminescence in *Gonyaulax polyedra*. *J. Gen. Physiol.*, **43**, 285–299.

TAGAKI, M., 1963, Studies on the ultra-violet spectral displacements of cattle rhodopsin. *Biochim. Biophys. Acta* **66**, 328–340.

TANADA, T., 1951, Photosynthetic efficiency of carotenoid pigments in *Navicula minima*. *Am. J. Bot.* **38**, 276–283.

TEEVAN, R. C. and R. C. BIRNEY, 1961, Color Vision. D. Van Nostrand Co., Inc., Princeton, Toronto, London, New York.

TERPSTA, W., 1958, The interaction of luciferase, flavin mono-nucleotide and long-chain aldehydes in the light reaction catalyzed by preparations of luminous bacteria. *Biochim. Biophys. Acta* **28**, 159–168.

TERPSTRA, W., 1960, On the role of long-chain aldehydes in the light reaction in *Photobacterium phosphoreum* enzyme preparations. *Biochim. Biophys. Acta* **41**, 55–67.

TERPSTRA, W., 1962, Evidence for the presence of an unknown factor, active in the light reaction, in preparations of *Photobacterium phosphoreum*. *Biochim. Biophys. Acta* **60**, 580–590.

TERPSTRA, W., 1963, Investigations on the identity of the light-emitting molecule in *Photobacterium phosphoreum*. *Biochim. Biophys. Acta* **75**, 355–364.

TERPSTRA, W., 1964, Personal communication.

TERPSTRA, W. and H. G. VAN EIJK, 1961, Ion sensitivity of the light reaction catalyzed by enzyme preparations from *Photobacterium phosphoreum*. *Biochim. Biophys. Acta* **51**, 473–481.

TERPSTRA, W. and C. L. M. STEENBERGEN, 1964, Influence of some inhibiting and activating substances on the light reaction *in vitro* of *Photobacterium phosphoreum*. *Biochim. Biophys. Acta* **88**, 267–277.

THIMANN, K. V. and G. M. CURRY, 1960, Phototropism and phototaxis. *In*: M. Florkin and H. S. Mason, eds., Comparative Biochemistry. I. Sources of Free Energy. Academic Press, Inc., New York, London. pp. 243–309.

THIMANN, K. V. and G. M. CURRY, 1961, Phototropism. *In*: W. D. McElroy and B. Glass, eds., Light and Life. The Johns Hopkins Press, Baltimore, pp. 646–670.

THOMAS, J. B., 1939, Electric control of polarity in plants. *Rec. Trav. Bot. Néerl.* **36**, 374–437.

THOMAS, J. B., 1950, On the rôle of the carotenoids in photosynthesis in *Rhodospirillum rubrum*. *Biochim. Biophys. Acta* **5**, 186–196.

THOMAS, J. B., 1958, The chloroplast as the photoreceptive mechanism in photosynthesis. *In*: Transactions of the Conference on the Use of Solar Energy. The Scientific Basis. IV. The University of Arizona Press, Tucson. pp. 130–134.

THOMAS, J. B., 1960, Chloroplast structure. *In*: W. Ruhland, ed., Encyclopedia of Plant Physiology. **5**, Pt. 1. Springer-Verlag, Berlin, Göttingen, Heidelberg. pp. 511–565.

THOMAS, J. B., 1962, Structure of the red absorption band of chlorophyll *a* in *Aspidistra elatior*. *Biochim. Biophys. Acta* **59**, 202–210.

THOMAS, J. B., 1963, Shape of the red absorption band of chlorophyll *a* in algae lacking chlorophyll *b*. *In*: Colloques Internationaux du Centre National de la Recherche Scientifique, no. 119: La Photosynthèse. Centre National de la Recherche Scientifique, Paris. pp. 287–297.

THOMAS, J. B., O. H. BLAAUW and L. N. M. DUYSENS, 1953, On the relation between size and photochemical activity of fragments of spinach grana. *Biochim. Biophys. Acta* **10**, 230–240.

THOMAS, J. B., F. J. M. DAEMEN and A. SCHAAP, 1958, Transfert d'énergie et structure du chloroplaste. *J. Chim. Phys.* **55**, 934–941.

THOMAS, J. B. and GOVINDJEE, 1960, Changes in quantum yield of photosynthesis in the red alga *Porphyridium cruentum* caused by stepwise reduction in the intensity of light preferentially absorbed by the phycobilins. *Biophys. J.* **1**, 63–72.

THOMAS, J. B. and GOVINDJEE, 1961, On the long-wave decline of the quantum yield of photosynthesis in the red alga *Porphyridium cruentum*. *In*: W. D. McElroy and B. Glass, eds., Light and Life. The Johns Hopkins Press, Baltimore. pp. 475–478.

THOMAS, J. B. and J. F. W. NUBOER, 1959, Fluorescence induction phenomena in granular and lamellate chloroplasts. *J. Phys. Chem.* **63**, 39–44.

THORNING, I., 1955, Untersuchungen über die Lichtwachstumsreaktionen dekapitierter *Avena*koleoptilen. *Zs. Bot.* **43**, 175–179.

TIBBS, J., 1957, The nature of algal and related flagella. *Biochim. Biophys. Acta* **23**, 275–288.

TISCHER, J., 1939, Über die Polyenpigmente der Blaualge *Aphanizomenon flos-aquae*. II. (Carotenoide der Süsswasseralgen, VII Teil). *Zs. Physiol. Chem.* **260**, 257–271.

TOBIAS, J. M., 1951, Qualitative observations on visible changes in single frog, squid and other axones subjected to electrical polarization. Implications for excitation and conduction. *J. Cell. Comp. Physiol.* **37**, 91–105.

TOLLIN, G., P. B. SOGO and M. CALVIN, 1958, Energy transfer in ordered and unordered photochemical systems. *Ann. New York Acad. Sci.* **74**, 310–328.

TOLMACH, L. J., 1951, Effects of triphosphopyridine nucleotide upon oxygen evolution and carbon dioxide fixation by illuminated chloroplasts. *Nature* **167**, 946–948.

TOMITA, G. and E. RABINOWITCH, 1962, Excitation energy transfer between pigments in photosynthetic cells. *Biophys. J.* **2**, 483–499.

TOTTER, J. R. and M. J. CORMIER, 1955, The relation of bacterial luciferase to alternative pathways of dihydroflavin mononucleotide oxidation. *J. Biol. Chem.* **216**, 801–811.

TREHARNE, R. W., T. E. BROWN, H. C. EYSTER and H. A. TANNER, 1960, Electron spin resonance studies of manganese in *Chlorella pyrenoidosa. Biochem. Biophys. Res. Comm.* **3**, 119–122.

TRUDINGER, P. A., 1956, Fixation of carbon dioxide by extracts of the strict autotroph *Thiobacillus denitrificans. Biochem. J.* **64**, 274–286.

TRURNIT, H. J. and G. COLMANO, 1958, Chloroplast studies. I. Absorption spectra of chlorophyll monolayers at liquid interfaces. *Biochim. Biophys. Acta* **30**, 434–447.

TSUJI, F. I. and R. SOWINSKI, 1961, Purification and molecular weight of *Cypridina* luciferase. *J. Cell. Comp. Physiol.* **58**, 125–130.

VAN DE KAMER, J. C., 1964, Histological structure and cytology of the pineal organ in fishes, amphibians and reptiles. Proc. Int. Round Table Conf. on the Epiphysis cerebri, Amsterdam. (in the press).

VAN DER LEK, B. 1962, Personal communication.

VAN DER VELDEN, H. A., 1944, Over het aantal lichtquanta dat noodig is voor een lichtprikkel bij het menschelijk oog. *Physica.* **11**, 179–189.

VAN DER VELDEN, H. A., 1946, The number of quanta necessary for the perception of light of the human eye. *Ophthalmologica* **111**, 321–331.

VAN DER WEY, H. G., 1929, Über die phototropische Reaktion von *Pilobolus. Proc. Kon. Ned. Akad. Wet.*, **32**, 65–77.

VAN NIEL, C. B., 1941, The bacterial photosyntheses and their importance for the general problem of photosynthesis. *Adv. Enzymol.* **1**, 263–328.

VAN OVERBEEK, J., 1933, Wuchsstoff, Lichtwachstumsreaktion und Phototropismus bei *Raphanus. Rec. Trav. Bot. Néerl.* **30**, 537–626.

VATTER, A. E. and R. S. WOLFE, 1958, The structure of photosynthetic bacteria. *J. Bacteriol.* **75**, 480–488.

VAVILOV, S. I., 1950, Mikrostruktura Sveta. *Acad. Sci. U.S.S.R.*, (Moscow-Leningrad). Ref. E. Rabinowitch, 1956.

VERNON, L. P. and M. D. KAMEN, 1954, Hematin compounds in photosynthetic bacteria. *J. Biol. Chem.* **211**, 643–662.

VIRGIN, H. I., 1949, The relation between the viscosity of the cytoplasm, the plasma flow, and the motive force. An experimental study. *Physiologia Plantarum* **2**, 157–163.

VIRGIN, H. I., 1951, The effect of light on the protoplasmic viscosity. *Physiologia Plantarum* **4**, 255–357.

VIRGIN, H. I., 1952, An action spectrum for the light induced changes in the viscosity of plant protoplasm. *Physiologia Plantarum* **5**, 575–582.

VIRGIN, H. I., 1954, Further studies of the action spectrum for light-induced changes in the protoplasmic viscosity of *Helodea densa. Physiologia Plantarum* **7**, 343–353.

VISHNIAC, W., 1960, Chemical participation of chlorophyll in photosynthesis. *In*: M. B. Allen, ed., Comparative Biochemistry of Photoreactive Systems. Academic Press, New York, London. pp. 377–386.

VISHNIAC, W., B. L. HORECKER and S. OCHOA, 1957, Enzymic aspects of photosynthesis. *Adv. Enzymol.* **19**, 1–77.

VISHNIAC, W. and S. OCHOA, 1951, Photochemical reduction of pyridine nucleotides by spinach grana and coupled carbon dioxide fixation. *Nature* **167**, 768–769.

VON FRISCH, K., M. LINDAUER and K. DAUMER,1960, Über die Wahrnehmung des polarisierten Lichtes durch das Bienenauge. *Experientia* **16**, 289–302.

VON GUTTENBERG, H. and L. KRÖPELIN, 1948, Über den Einfluss des Heteroauxins auf das Laminargelenk von *Phaseolus coccineus*. *Planta* **35**, 257–280.

VON WETTSTEIN, D., 1957, Chlorophyll-Letale und der submikroskopische Formwechsel der Plastiden. *Exptl. Cell Res.* **12**, 427–506.

VOROB'EVA, L. M. and A. A. KRASNOVSKY, 1956, *Biokhimiya* **21**, 126–136. Ref. M. B. Allen *et al.*, 1960.

WALD, G., 1935, Carotenoids and the visual cycle. *J. Gen. Physiol.* **19**, 351–371.

WALD, G., 1936, Pigments of the retina. I. The bull frog. *J. Gen. Physiol.* **19**, 781–795.

WALD, G., 1937, Pigments of the retina. II. Sea robin, sea bass and scup. *J. Gen. Physiol.* **20**, 45–56.

WALD, G., 1938, On rhodopsin in solution. *J. Gen. Physiol.* **21**, 795–832.

WALD, G., 1942, The visual system and vitamins A of the sea lamprey. *J. Gen. Physiol.* **25**, 331–336.

WALD, G., 1951, The chemistry of rod vision. *Science* **113**, 287–291.

WALD, G., 1953a, The biochemistry of vision. *Ann. Rev. Biochem.* **22**, 497–526.

WALD, G., 1953b, Vision. *Fed. Proc.* **12**, 606–611.

WALD, G., 1956, The biochemistry of visual excitation. *In*: O. Gaebler, ed., Enzymes: Units of Biological Structure and Function. Academic Press, Inc., New York. pp. 355–367.

WALD, G., 1959, The photoreceptor process in vision. *In*: J. Field, H. W. Magoun and V. E. Hall, eds., Handbook of Physiology. Sect. 1. Neurophysiology. **1**. The American Physiological Society, Washington, D. C. pp. 671–692.

WALD, G., 1961a, The molecular organization of visual systems. *In*: W. D. McElroy and B. Glass, eds., Light and Life. The Johns Hopkins Press, Baltimore. pp. 724–749.

WALD, G., 1961b, General discussion of retinal structure in relation to the visual process. *In*: G. K. Smelser, ed., The Structure of the Eye. Academic Press, New York, London. pp. 101–115.

WALD, G. and P. K. BROWN, 1952, The role of sulfhydryl groups in the bleaching and synthesis of rhodopsin. *J. Gen. Physiol.* **35**, 797–821.

WALD, G. and P. K. BROWN, 1954, The molar extinction of rhodopsin. *J. Gen. Physiol.* **37**, 189–200.

WALD, G., P. K. BROWN and I. R. GIBBONS, 1963, The problem of visual excitation. *J. Opt. Soc. Am.* **53**, 20–35.

WALD, G., P. K. BROWN and P. H. SMITH, 1952, Iodopsin. *Fed. Proc.*, **11**, 304–305.

WALD, G., P. K. BROWN and P. H. SMITH, 1953, Cyanopsin, a new pigment of cone vision. *Science* **118**, 505–508.

WALD, G., P. K. BROWN and P. H. SMITH, 1955, Iodopsin. *J. Gen. Physiol.* **38**, 623–681.

WALD, G., J. DURELL and R. C. C. ST. GEORGE, 1950, The light reaction in the bleaching of rhodopsin. *Science* **111**, 179–181.

WALD, G. and H. ZUSSMAN, 1937, Carotenoids of the chicken retina. *Nature* **140**, 197.

WALRAVEN, P. L., 1962, On the mechanisms of colour vision. Doctoral thesis. State University, Utrecht.

WARBURG, E., 1920, Quantentheoretische Grundlagen der Photochemie. *Zs. Electr. Chem.* **26**, 54–59.

WASSINK, E. C., 1948, Observations on the luminescence in fungi, I, including a critical review of the species mentioned as luminescent in literature. *Rec. Trav. Bot. Néerl.* **41**, 150–211.

WASSINK, E. C., E. KATZ and R. DORRESTEIN, 1939, Infrared absorption spectra of various strains of purple bacteria. *Enzymologia* **7**, 113–129.

WASSINK, E. C. and J. A. H. KERSTEN, 1946, Observations sur le spectre d'absorption et sur le role des caroténoides dans la photosynthèse des diatomées. *Enzymologia* **12**, 3–32.

WASSINK, E. C. and G. H. M. KRONENBERG, 1962, Strongly carotenoid-deficient *Chromatium*-strain *D* cells with "normal" bacteriochlorophyll absorption peaks in the 800–850 mμ region. *Nature* **194**, 553–554.

WASSINK, E. C., J. E. TJIA and J. F. G. M. WINTERMANS, 1949, Phosphate-exchanges in purple sulphur bacteria in connection with photosynthesis. *Proc. Kon. Ned. Akad. Wet.* **52**, 412–422.

WAYGOOD, E. R. and G. A. MACLACHLAN, 1956, The effect of catalase, riboflavin and light on the oxidation of indoleacetic acid. *Physiologia Plantarum* **9**, 607–617.

WEALE, R. A., 1958, Retinal summation and human visual thresholds. *Nature* **181**, 154–156.

WEBER, H. H., 1958, The Motility of Muscle and Cells. Harvard University Press, Cambridge Mass.

WEIGL, J. W. and R. LIVINGSTON, 1952a, An attempt to detect hydrogen-deuterium exchange between chlorophyll and water. *J. Am. Chem. Soc.* **74**, 4160–4162.

WEIGL, J. W. and R. LIVINGSTON, 1952b, Concerning hydrogen transfer in a reaction sensitized by chlorophyll. *J. Am. Chem. Soc.* **74**, 4211–4212.

WEIGL, J. W. and R. LIVINGSTON, 1953, Infrared spectra of chlorophyll and related compounds. *J. Am. Chem. Soc.* **75**, 2173–2176.

WEIR, J. H., F. I. TSUJI and A. M. CHASE, 1955, The isoelectric point of *Cypridina* luciferase. *Arch. Biochem. Biophys.* **56**, 235–239.

WELLER, A., 1954, The visible absorption spectra of the phase test intermediates of chlorophyll-*a* and -*b*. *J. Am. Chem. Soc.* **76**, 5819–5821.

WENT, F. W., 1928, Wuchsstoff und Wachstum. *Rec. Trav. Bot. Néerl.* **25**, 1–116.

WENT, F. W., 1956, Phototropism. *In*: A. Hollaender, ed., Radiation Biology. McGraw-Hill Book Co., Inc., New York, Toronto, London. pp. 463–478.

WERTZ, J. E., 1955, Nuclear and electronic spin magnetic resonance. *Chem. Rev.* **55**, 829–955.

WEST, W., 1956, Technique of Organic Chemistry, A. Weissberger, ed., Vol. IX. Chemical Applications of Spectroscopy. Interscience Publ., Inc., New York, London.

WHITE, E. H., F. MCCAPRA, G. F. FIELD and W. D. MCELROY, 1961, The structure and synthesis of firefly luciferin. *J. Am. Chem. Soc.* **83**, 2402–2403.

WILDMAN, S. G., T. HONGLADAROM and S. I. HONDA, 1962, Chloroplasts and mitochondria in living plant cells: cinephotomicrographic studies. *Science* **138**, 434–435.

WILLSTÄTTER, R. and W. MIEG, 1907, Untersuchungen über Chlorophyll. IV. Über die gelben Begleiter des Chlorophylls. *Liebig's Ann. Chem.* **355**, 1–28.

WILLSTÄTTER, R. and A. STOLL, 1913, Untersuchungen über das Chlorophyll. Springer-Verlag, Berlin.

WILLSTÄTTER, R. and A. STOLL, 1918, Untersuchungen über die Assimilation der Kohlensäure. Springer-Verlag, Berlin.

WITT, H. T. and R. MORAW, 1959a, Untersuchungen über die Primärvorgänge bei der Photosynthese. I. Mitteilung. *Zs. Phys. Chem., N.F.* **20**, 253–282.

WITT, H. T. and R. MORAW, 1959b, Untersuchungen über die Primärvorgänge bei der Photosynthese. II. Mitteilung. *Zs. Phys. Chem., N.F.* **20**, 283–298.

WITT, H. T., R. MORAW, A. MÜLLER, B. RUMBERG and G. ZIEGER, 1960, Kinetische Untersuchungen über die Primärvorgänge der Photosynthese. *Zs. Elektrochem.* **64**, 181–187.

WITT, H. T. and A. MÜLLER, 1959c, Quantitative Untersuchungen über die Primärvorgänge der Photosynthese an isolierten Chloroplasten. III. Mitteilung. *Zs. Phys. Chem., N.F.* **21**, 1–23.

WITT, H. T., A. MÜLLER and B. RUMBERG, 1961a, Experimental evidence for the mechanism of photosynthesis. *Nature* **191**, 194–195.

WITT, H. T., A. MÜLLER and B. RUMBERG, 1961b, Oxidized cytochrome and chlorophyll in photosynthesis. *Nature* **192**, 967–969.

WOHL, K., 1937, Zur Theorie der Assimilation. V. Gesamtübersicht. *Zs. Phys. Chem.* **37**, 209–230.

WOLFSON, A., 1959, Role of light in the progressive phase of the photoperiodic responses of migratory birds. *Biol. Bull.* **117**, 601–610.

WOLKEN, J. J., 1961a, A structural model for a retinal rod. *In*: G. K. Smelser, ed., The Structure of the Eye. Academic Press, New York, London. pp. 173–191.

WOLKEN, J. J., 1961b, *Euglena*. An Experimental Organism for Biochemical and Biophysical Studies. The Rutgers University Press, New Brunswick.

WOLKEN, J. J., 1961c, The photoreceptor structures. *Int. Rev. Cytol.* **11**, 195–218.

WOLKEN, J. J., 1962, Photoreceptor structures: their molecular organization for energy transfer. *J. Theoret. Biol.* **3**, 192–208.

WOLKEN, J. J., 1963, Structure and molecular organization of retinal photoreceptors. *J. Opt. Soc. Am.* **53**, 1–19.

WOLKEN, J. J. and F. A. SCHWERTZ, 1953, Chlorophyll monolayers in chloroplasts. *J. Gen. Physiol.* **37**, 111–120.

WOLKEN, J. J. and E. SHIN, 1958, Photomotion in *Euglena gracilis*. I. Photokinesis. II. Phototaxis. *J. Protozool.* **5**, 39–46.

WULFF, V. J., R. G. ADAMS, H. LINSCHITZ and D. KENNEDY, 1958, The behavior of flash-illuminated rhodopsin in solution. *A. M. A. Arch. Ophthal.* **60**, 695–701.

WYNNE-JONES, W. F. K. and H. EYRING, 1935, The absolute rate of reactions in condensed phases. *J. Chem. Phys.* **3**, 492–502.

YAMAMOTO, H. Y., T. O. M. NAKAYAMA and C. O. CHICHESTER, 1962, Studies on the light and dark interconversions of leaf xanthophylls. *Arch. Biochem. Biophys.* **97**, 168–173.

YOSHIZAWA, T., Y. KITO and M. ISHIGAMI, 1960, Studies on the metastable states in the rhodopsin cycle. *Biochim. Biophys. Acta* **43**, 329–334.

YOSHIZAWA, T. and G. WALD, 1963, Pre-lumirhodopsin and the bleaching of visual pigments. *Nature* **197**, 1279–1286.

ZSCHEILE, F. P., J. W. WHITE, Jr., B. W. BEADLE and J. R. ROACH, 1942, The preparation and absorption spectra of five pure carotenoid pigments. *Plant Physiol.* **17**, 331–346.

ZURZYCKI, J., 1951, The influence of temperature on the protoplasmic streaming in *Elodea densa* Casp. *Acta Soc. Bot. Polon.* **21**, 241–264.

ZURZYCKI, J., 1960, Studies on the centrifugation of chloroplasts in *Lemna trisulca*. *Acta Soc. Bot. Polon.* **29**, 385–393.

ZURZYCKI, J., 1962a, The action spectrum for the light dependent movements of chloroplasts in *Lemna trisulca* L. *Acta Soc. Bot. Polon.* **31**, 489–538.

ZURZYCKI, J., 1962b, The mechanism of the movements of plastids. *In*: W. Ruhland, ed., Encyclopedia of Plant Physiology. **17**, Pt. 2. Springer-Verlag, Berlin, Göttingen, Heidelberg. pp. 940–978.

ZURZYCKI, J. and A. ZURZYCKA, 1955, Influence of some catalyst poisons on phototactic movements of chloroplasts. *Acta Soc. Bot. Polon.* **24**, 663–674.

Abbreviations

AMP — adenosine monophosphate
ADP — adenosine diphosphate
ATP — adenosine triphosphate
CoA — coenzyme A
DPA — 3′,5′-diphosphoadenosine
ESR — electron spin resonance
FMN — flavin mononucleotide
$FMNH_2$ — flavin mononucleotide, reduced form
IAA — indoleacetic acid
NAD — nicotinamide adenine dinucleotide. Formerly: DPN, diphosphopyridine nucleotide
$NADH_2$ — nicotinamide adenine dinucleotide, reduced form. Formerly: $DPNH_2$
NADP — nicotinamide adenine dinucleotide phosphate. Formerly: TPN, triphosphopyridine nucleotide
$NADPH_2$ — nicotinamide adenine dinucleotide phosphate, reduced form. Formerly: $TPNH_2$
NAD(P) — NAD or NADP
$NAD(P)H_2$ — $NADH_2$ or $NADPH_2$
PP — inorganic pyrophosphate
RHP — Rhodospirillum haem protein

Index

D

Q

R

S

T

U

V

W

X

Z